S250 Science in Context
Science: Level 2

The Open University

TOPIC 6
Genetic manipulation

Prepared for the Course Team by John Baxter and Jeff Thomas
with David Bard and Barbara Brockbank

This publication forms part of the Open University course S250 *Science in Context*. Details of this and other Open University courses can be obtained from the Student Registration and Enquiry Service, The Open University, PO Box 197, Milton Keynes, MK7 6BJ, United Kingdom: tel. +44 (0)870 333 4340, email general-enquiries@open.ac.uk

Alternatively, you may visit the Open University website at http://www.open.ac.uk where you can learn more about the wide range of courses and packs offered at all levels by The Open University.

To purchase a selection of Open University course materials visit http://www.ouw.co.uk, or contact Open University Worldwide, Michael Young Building, Walton Hall, Milton Keynes MK7 6AA, United Kingdom for a brochure. tel. +44 (0)1908 858785; fax +44 (0)1908 858787; email ouwenq@open.ac.uk

The Open University
Walton Hall, Milton Keynes
MK7 6AA

First published 2006. Second edition 2007.

Edited and designed by The Open University.

Typeset by The Open University.

Printed and bound in the United Kingdom by Halstan Printing Group, Amersham.

ISBN 978 0 7492 1891 1

2.1

The S250 Course Team

Andrew J. Ball (*Author, Topic 2*)
John Baxter (*Author, Topic 6*)
Steve Best (*Media Developer*)
Kate Bradshaw (*Multimedia Producer*)
Audrey Brown (*Associate Lecturer and Critical Reader*)
Mike Bullivant (*Course Manager*)
James Davies (*Media Project Manager*)
Steve Drury (*Author, Topic 3*)
Lydia Eaton (*Media Assistant*)
Chris Edwards (*Course Manager*)
Mike Gillman (*Author, Topic 4*)
Debbie Gingell (*Course Assistant*)
Sara Hack (*Media Developer*)
Sarah Hofton (*Media Developer*)
Martin Keeling (*Media Assistant*)
Richard Holliman (*Course Themes and Author, Topic 1*)
Jason Jarratt (*Media Developer*)
Simon P. Kelley (*Author, Topic 2*)
Nigel Mason (*Topic 7*)
Margaret McManus (*Media Assistant*)
Elaine McPherson (*Course Manager*)
Pat Murphy (*Course Team Chair and Author, Topic 1*)
Judith Pickering (*Media Project Manager*)
William Rawes (*Media Developer*)
Shelagh Ross (*Author, Topic 7*)
Sam Smidt (*Author, Topic 7*)
Valda Stevens (*Learning Outcomes and Assessment*)
Margaret Swithenby (*Media Developer*)
Jeff Thomas (*Author, Topics 6 and 7*)
Pamela Wardell (*Media Developer*)
Kiki Warr (*Author, Topic 5*)

The Course Team would like to thank the following for their particular contributions: Benny Peiser (*Liverpool John Moores University; Author, Topic 2*), David Bard (*Associate Lecturer; Author, Topic 6*) and Barbara Brockbank (*Associate Lecturer; Author, Topic 6 and Critical Reader*).

Dr Jon Turney (*University College London and Imperial College London*) was External Assessor for the course. The External Assessors for individual topics were: Professor John Mann (*Queen's University, Belfast*); Professor John McArthur (*University College London*); Dr Richard Reece (*University of Manchester*); Dr Rosalind M. Ridley (*University of Cambridge*); Dr Duncan Steel (*Macquarie University, Australia*); Dr David Viner (*University of East Anglia*) and Professor Mark Welland FRS (*University of Cambridge*).

Contents

Chapter 1

Introduction

The title of this topic tells you that our attention is focused on genes and the ways in which they can be manipulated. Two reasons come to mind about why genetic manipulation is worth studying as a subject. First, the science that underlies the topic is inherently fascinating and informative. Second, our present-day capacity to manipulate genes raises a great number of social questions about how this new technology can be used wisely and productively by society at large. Studying this topic should help you come to (and challenge) informed and defensible points of view about a range of contentious issues, as you think through some of the society-wide dilemmas and personal choices that this new knowledge poses.

What does the term 'genetic manipulation' encompass? In simple terms, it refers to a series of techniques that can be used to transfer genes from one organism to another, to produce one or more genetically modified organisms (GMOs). The examples are many and wide-ranging.

- A well established procedure with a medical application is the modification of bacteria (i.e. prokaryotes) so that they produce human insulin.
- In the field of agriculture, a bacterial gene that confers resistance to several species of insects has been transferred into cotton plants. These plants then have an inbuilt resistance to pests and don't require the same degree of spraying with insecticides.
- In the field of medicine, 'healthy' genes can be introduced into human cells, with the intention of negating the effects of faulty genes, such as the one responsible for cystic fibrosis.

You'll read more about each of these examples (and a good many more besides) later in the topic.

Genetic manipulation is currently a very active and well funded field of research, in part because the area is of such great commercial significance to drug companies and agrochemical manufacturers. You'll appreciate that with such a fast-moving field, with new techniques and revelations constantly emerging, it would be impractical to provide an entirely up-to-date account. Many of the technicalities of precisely how genes are identified, isolated and transferred would require a level of explanation and constant updating beyond what is possible here. Our intention is more to provide you with the basic vocabulary of the field of genetic manipulation and the important background to present-day predicaments. We'll therefore spend some time looking at early findings and past controversies that have helped shape current thinking, especially in relation to the course themes.

The topic begins in Chapter 2 with an opportunity to refresh your memory of some of the basics of genetics. You will be reminded of the structure of genes and of the architecture of DNA. Of particular interest will be how genes are **expressed**, i.e. how they exert their effects (initially via the production of messenger RNA), and how they are structured and what happens when faults arise (via mutation) in DNA structure, which can be the trigger for a number of genetic diseases. Chapter 2 may well contain some information that is new to you, on how genes and other 'chunks' of DNA are put together to form the mass of genetic information that comprises an organism's **genome**. In Chapter 3, you're introduced to some of the basic 'tools of the trade' that are used for the manipulation of genes, by considering how a particular human gene (that responsible for insulin production) can be 'engineered', using bacteria, in order to produce significant amounts of pure insulin.

Much of what we cover in Chapters 2 and 3 relates to the human genome, but we then look at the genetic manipulation of plants (Chapters 4 and 5) and of non-human animals (Chapter 6). Rather than go through the approach in advance here, the story line will unfold once you reach those chapters. No doubt, you'll be encountering some familiar topics, in part because of their prominence in the news media, notably TV and newsprint. Take the controversial subject of genetically modified crops, for example. Its high-profile status reflects its newsworthiness, as evident from a wide range of *communication* 'events' that range from newspaper articles to the public pronouncements of scientists. Some critics hold the view that any potential benefits from GM crops are outweighed by what are claimed to be *risks* of uncertain magnitude – to human health perhaps, or to wildlife. Some have claimed that manipulation of crops is one part of a broader movement to alter what is 'natural', i.e. free of scientific interference. From this perspective, the development of GM crops and the consumption of their products by the public raise *ethical issues*, which pose choices as to the right way for society to proceed and how to accommodate the conflicting beliefs of different groups. In the face of varying opinions and pressure, the UK Government has attempted to adopt a type of *decision making* that seeks to balance public disquiet and commercial ambitions.

You can see how GM crops (and other applications of genetic manipulation) raise many issues of importance to the major themes of S250. Much the same logic has helped shape the latter part of the topic (Chapter 7), looking at a particular medical application of gene manipulation – gene therapy. The topic ends with Chapter 8, which draws together some key ideas from what's gone before.

Refreshment

Chapter 2

How to use this chapter

Your study of genetic manipulation will be a lot easier if we first refresh your memory of the basic vocabulary concerned with genes, proteins, messenger RNA (i.e. mRNA), mutation, DNA and the genome. What follows provides you with the key information you'll need about these and related matters before you move on to the later chapters of the topic. The more you absorb of this chapter, the firmer will be your grasp of what comes later.

At least some of what follows will be familiar, because it is, by and large, a concise summary of Level 1 information. Towards the end (Section 2.3) there's more by way of new information, building on the ground covered already. If your recollection of previous study is good, a quick read-through of Sections 2.1 and 2.2 should be enough to bring you up to speed. If you have not studied much biology before, or if you find you've forgotten much of what you knew, you will need to spend time working through these basic topics more thoroughly. A good indicator of your existing knowledge will come from tacking Questions 2.1–2.5 (at the end of this chapter). If you do find your recollection on some points is hazy, having the sources to hand that you first used to study these topics will be useful – especially the diagrams – for quick reference. The appropriate Level 1 Open University material is supplied on the S250 DVD. If you are very short of time or less interested in these areas of biology, you might choose not to spend much time on this chapter, but in this case, your understanding of later parts of this book is likely to be less well grounded.

2.1 The structure and function of DNA and of genes

1 In the simplest of terms, a gene is the unit of inheritance for a given characteristic. The great majority of genes exist in a range of different versions. For example, as you'll see in Section 7.3, the gene associated with cystic fibrosis (CF) can occur in a healthy and a whole range of 'faulty' versions. Geneticists refer to the different forms of a particular gene as **alleles**.

2 The genes of animals and plants most often occur in pairs, one on each of a pair of chromosomes. In humans, each of the 22 pairs of matching (or **homologous**) chromosomes is called an **autosome**, in contrast to the single pair of sex chromosomes, typically XX in females and XY in males. The human Y chromosome carries relatively few genes; the X chromosome carries more, though most of them are not involved in the determination of sex. Although the X and Y chromosomes are a great interest to geneticists, this topic will focus on the manipulation of autosomal genes.

3 Some genes can exert their effects only when both members of the pair are exactly the same version – in other words, a pair of identical alleles, representing the **homozygous** situation. An allele of that type is termed **recessive**. The allele responsible for CF is one example and, given the

gene's location on a non-sex chromosome (number 7, in fact), it is termed autosomal recessive; only those individuals who receive a 'double dose' of this faulty version of the gene (one from their mother and one from their father) will develop the disease. By contrast, a **dominant** allele produces a particular characteristic (such as eye colour) even in the **heterozygous** situation of a different allele being present as the other member of the pair. For example, inheriting the allele termed *BRCA1* can make a female more susceptible to some forms of breast and ovarian cancer. Inheriting just one *BRCA1* allele (whether from the father or mother) is sufficient to increase susceptibility, revealing this to be an autosomal dominant allele.

■ Can there be more than two versions (i.e. alleles) of a particular gene?

■ Yes. You may recall the genetic basis of the ABO blood group system in humans (see Box 1.6 of Topic 1), where three alleles of the particular gene occur. The two alleles each of us possesses determine our blood group, i.e. A, B, AB or O. Also you may have noticed an earlier references to a 'whole range of faulty versions' of the gene responsible for CF, of which more soon.

4 The notion of 'one gene, one characteristic' has a misleading simplicity; it is now evident that a single characteristic is often influenced by a variety of different genes, often widely dispersed on chromosomes. In most cases, a complex interaction between these genes – indeed, the particular alleles that are present – will determine a particular character. This has a bearing on the feasibility of genetic manipulation. Far more may be involved in modifying a particular characteristic than simply transferring a single gene from organism A to organism B. You'll be aware that environmental factors have a profound influence too; referring again to CF, two individuals might inherit the same combination of the faulty alleles but the disease might be expressed differently in the two individuals. The notion that nearly every aspect of human or animal biology is fundamentally shaped by genes – and often by no more than a single gene – is termed **genetic determinism**. This misleading sentiment lies behind many overblown claims – from newspaper headlines or from the laboratories of excited researchers – of the discovery of 'genes for' such complex characteristics as intelligence or sexual inclination.

5 You'll be aware that eukaryotic organisms – plants, animals and fungi – have complex genes, termed **split genes**. The DNA sequences within split genes contain some sections (called intervening sections, or **introns**) that do not contribute to the mature mRNA that forms the template for protein production. Introns therefore comprise the non-protein-coding portions of genes, in contrast to **exons**, which are the protein-coding DNA sequences within split genes. (The process of 'cutting-out' and resealing the sections of the mRNA that are initially produced from a gene by the process of **transcription** is called **mRNA splicing**, a process that results in the formation of mature mRNA.) The far right column of Table 2.1 shows that for a number of human genes – especially those of a substantial size – the percentage of the DNA that comprises exons can be very small.

■ Can you think of an easy means of remembering the difference between exons and introns – by using a mnemonic perhaps?

- Introns are so named because they are intervening sections, whereas exons are those parts of DNA that are expressed. Another aide mémoire is that introns are confined within the nucleus, whereas the product of the exons (as mature mRNA) is exported from the nucleus into the cytoplasm.

- What fate awaits mature RNA within the cytoplasm?

- After it leaves the nucleus, the information within a particular mature mRNA is subject to **translation**, in that it becomes the template for the production of a sequence of linked amino acids, i.e. a polypeptide chain or protein.

Table 2.1 Size and structure of some human genes. Gene sizes are given in thousands of base pairs, i.e. kilobase pairs (kbp). The number of exons is shown in column 3 and the percentage of the gene that is represented by these exons is given in the final column.

Gene	Gene size/kbp	Number of exons	% exon DNA
insulin	1.4	3	33
β-globin	1.6	3	38
serum albumin	18	14	12
blood clotting factor VIII	186	26	3
CFTR (cystic fibrosis)*	230	27	2.4
dystrophin (muscular dystrophy)*	2400	79	0.6

* These genes are named according to the disease associated with mutated forms (alleles) of the genes.

DNA structure and replication

You're probably already familiar with DNA structure from previous study, and Box 1.3 of Topic 1 was a further reminder. Look at Figure 2.1 to familiarise yourself with the important features. Remember that four bases (A, adenine; T, thymine; C, cytosine; and G, guanine) make up the inner component of this helical macromolecule (Figure 2.1c). The faithful pairing of these bases (in DNA, A only with T and C only with G), maintained by the hydrogen bonding shown in Figure 2.1d, ensures that the two sugar–phosphate backbones of the 'double helix' are closely associated. For each turn of the double helix, there are about 10 base pairs linking the two backbones together, though, for clarity, fewer are shown in Figure 2.1d. As you can see, DNA, like other biological macromolecules, is a polymer and comprises monomer units called **nucleotides**. When DNA is heated, the (weak) hydrogen bonds between the paired bases are broken allowing the two (polymer) strands to separate. With more drastic (e.g. chemical) treatment, the sugar–phosphate backbone of the two DNA strands would be broken, releasing the individual nucleotides; Figure 2.1a and b shows a single such nucleotide (adenine nucleotide). Each DNA nucleotide comprises three components; a sugar (deoxyribose), a phosphate group and one or other of the four characteristic bases.

- Does DNA break down into the individual constituent nucleotides during the process of replication?

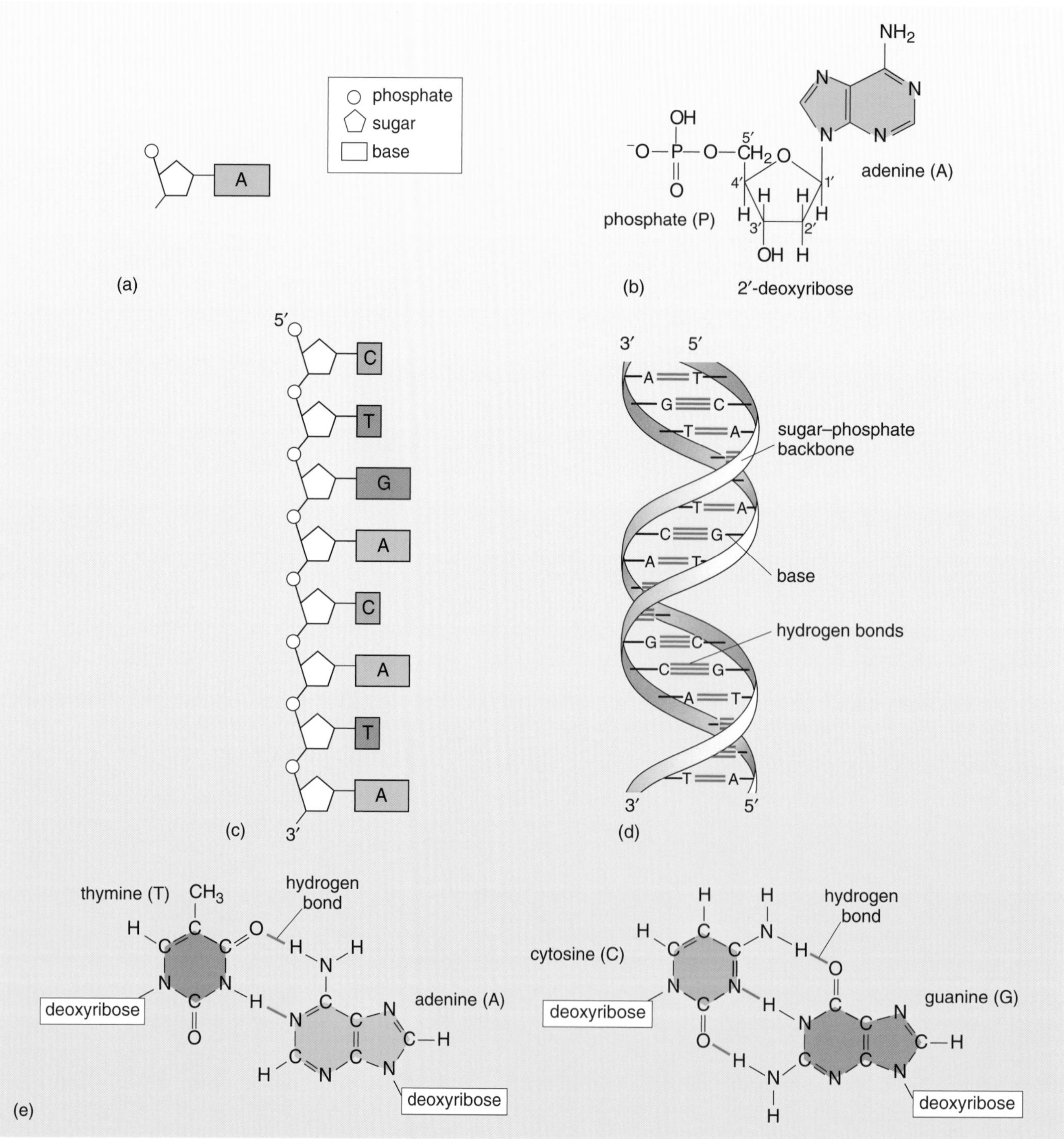

Figure 2.1 The structure of DNA and its components. (a) Simplified representation of a nucleotide, in this case adenine nucleotide. (b) Detailed structure of adenine nucleotide. (c) Simplified representation of a chain of linked nucleotides. (d) The double-helical structure of DNA, showing hydrogen bonding between the bases of the two strands. (Note that the two DNA strands run in opposite directions; one end of each strand is known as the 5′ end, because the phosphate group is attached to the 5′ carbon of the deoxyribose sugar. The other end of that strand is the 3′ end, with a hydroxyl (OH) group attached to carbon 3′ of the sugar.) (e) shows the chemical details of base pairing between T and A, and between C and G. The bases adenine (A) and guanine (G) are both purine bases; the smaller thymine (T) and cytosine (C) bases are pyrimidine bases.

- No it doesn't. Replication begins with the unwinding and separation of the two sugar–phosphate strands, as the hydrogen bonds between matching base pairs are broken. But the stronger (covalent) bonds that hold sugar and phosphate components together (Figure 2.1c) remain, so the two backbones unwind intact, exposing the bases on each strand.

Each single DNA strand now becomes a template upon which a new nucleotide sequence is constructed. Individual deoxynucleotides line up opposite the newly exposed bases, finding their appropriate 'partner' according to the base pairing rules. The enzyme **DNA polymerase** binds to the free strand and moves along it, catalysing the formation of the sugar–phosphate backbone. In this way, two double-stranded DNA molecules are produced, each identical to the original parent molecule. The genetic information encoded within the sequence of the four bases is faithfully replicated, though as you'll see in Section 2.2, mistakes can happen if the 'wrong' nucleotide becomes inserted.

Transcription, translation and the genetic code

The information contained within a DNA sequence (or gene) specifies the order of amino acids in a particular protein. However, in eukaryotes, protein synthesis occurs in the cytoplasm and DNA never leaves the nucleus. The information is conveyed out of the nucleus by an intermediary molecule, appropriately termed messenger RNA (mRNA), synthesised by the process of transcription. This outward communication of information has been likened to the photocopying of an article from a reference book that cannot be removed from a library. Like DNA, mRNA is a polymer of nucleotides, but the sugar component is different (it is ribose, as opposed to the deoxyribose component of DNA). mRNA is generally single-stranded; furthermore, three of the bases it contains will be familiar to you (G, guanine, C, cytosine and A, adenine) but you may also recall that the fourth is distinct; thymine (present in DNA) is replaced by uracil (U).

Like DNA replication, the transcription of DNA involves unwinding of the double helix, but here just one of the strands becomes the template for the formation of mRNA – hence this is known as the template strand. A length of mRNA is built up through the activity of the enzyme **RNA polymerase**, which links free ribonucleotides together. This enzyme initiates transcription by becoming attached to the DNA at a specific site, generally located just 'upstream' of the particular gene. As Figure 2.2 indicates, such a site is called a

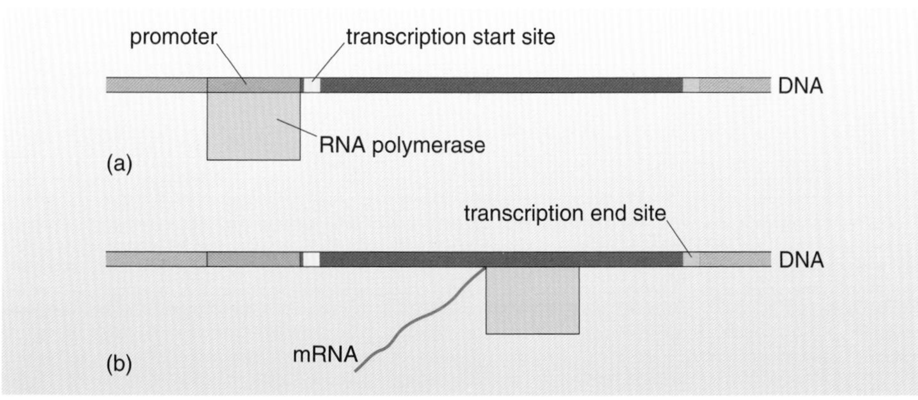

Figure 2.2 The process of transcription. (a) RNA polymerase binds to the promoter. (b) The RNA polymerase works its way along the adjacent protein-coding gene, joining nucleotide to nucleotide, to form mRNA as it does so.

promoter; the binding of RNA polymerase to it 'promotes' the subsequent transcription of the adjacent gene. (The so-called 'transcription start site' is generally a little downstream from the site at which RNA polymerase becomes bound.) A particular promoter therefore needs to be 'recognised' by RNA polymerase, otherwise transcription of the adjacent gene is unlikely.

Promoters for any particular gene may differ between species, so the RNA polymerase of one species may not recognise promoters of another species. The more different the species, the less likely a foreign promoter will be recognised. Without this recognition there will be no transcription, no mRNA and no polypeptide product (i.e. there will be no expression of this gene). So where a particular gene is being transferred from one organism to another, it's important (as Chapter 3 will emphasise) that the 'foreign' gene has an adjacent promoter of a type that is compatible with (i.e. is recognised by) the RNA polymerase of the host cell. Ease of transfer is also linked with the size of genes; Table 2.1 gives you an idea of the variability of gene size, with size expressed as thousands of base pairs (kbp).

A key point about transcription is that it is not a continuous process; it is highly regulated. In fact, only a modest proportion of the genes within any one cell type are active, largely because only those relatively few are transcribed. For example, the genes responsible for the manufacture of the substances that comprise bone are active (i.e. are expressed) in the cells that make up the skeleton; the genes responsible for producing haemoglobin remain inactive (or repressed) in nervous tissue. However, in juvenile cells on the way to becoming red blood cells, genes that trigger haemoglobin production become switched on. But individual promoters are far more than simple 'on' or 'off' switches; they have been likened more to microcomputers, as they integrate a large number of signals, some emanating from distant genes in the same cell and some originating from other cells. The factors that determine whether a particular gene is expressed or not are therefore complex and not fully understood. Influences on transcription are very important, but control at the next steps in the process are significant too.

Let's now think a bit more about mRNA structure.

■ Suppose the base sequence in the template strand of a section of DNA is GTGACATACT. Applying the pairing rules you're familiar with, and bearing in mind how RNA and DNA differ, predict the sequence of mRNA that would be transcribed from this portion of DNA.

■ CACUGUAUGA. Identifying the first three bases of mRNA (CAC...) is easy enough, since they follow the DNA pairing rules but remember that the counterpart of T within DNA is U in RNA, which explains why the fourth base, for example, in the mRNA sequence is U.

You may know something already about the process of translation, where the information within the mRNA (i.e. the particular base sequence) is translated into a specific sequence of amino acids in a polypeptide chain.

The process involves other forms of RNA, notably the different types of transfer RNAs (tRNAs), each no larger than about 90 nucleotides. What is fascinating is how the 'four-letter' language of base sequences (as in DNA and mRNA) is translated into the '20-letter' language of polypeptides, the 20 'letters' being different amino acids.

Figure 2.3 reminds you how translation works, a process that occurs at ribosomes. Figure 2.3a shows that particular tRNAs have already 'picked up' specific amino acids – in this case in (a), methionine (Met) and proline (Pro). The coding system at work here uses groups of three consecutive bases within mRNA, as shown in Figure 2.3a. Each triplet is called a **codon**, a term that you may recall from Level 1; six such distinct codons are shown in Figure 2.3a. A particular codon, say AUG, will match, i.e. form hydrogen bonds with, a particular anticodon (UAC) located on the 'arm' of a particular tRNA 'charged', in this example, with the amino acid methionine. Indeed, the base sequence AUG is generally a 'start codon', so the tRNA with a UAC anticodon and carrying the amino acid methionine, is normally the first to attach at the ribosome, allowing translation to begin. Figure 2.3b shows that once the first tRNA has bound to its codon, a second tRNA soon follows, to bring in another amino acid, such as proline, which can then link (via a strong

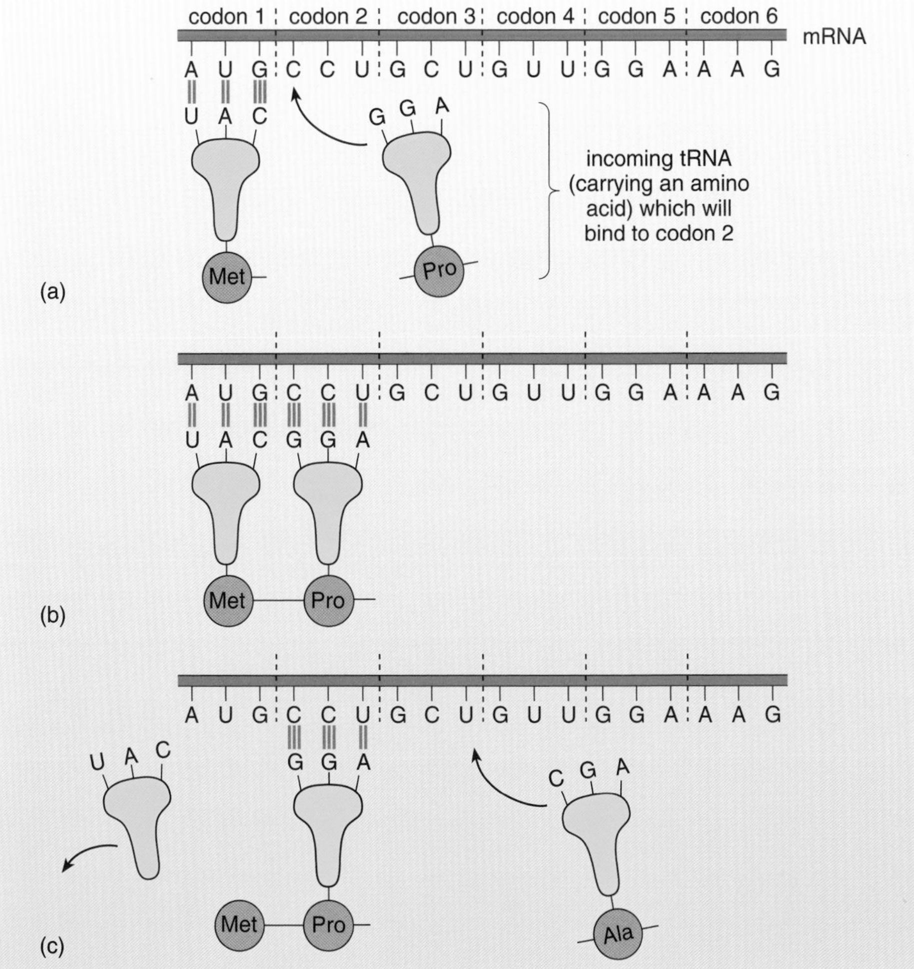

Figure 2.3 A simplified representation of translation. (a) One tRNA molecule is already bound to mRNA and a second is about to bind alongside it. (b) Two tRNA molecules are now bound to the mRNA and the two amino acids they are carrying, methionine (Met) and proline (Pro), are linked together. (c) The first tRNA molecule is now released (as will others be after delivery of their attached amino acids) and a third, carrying alanine (Ala), is about to bind.

covalent bond) with methionine, to begin the progressive build-up (i.e. synthesis) of a polypeptide chain. As the ribosome moves along the mRNA, the successively 'discharged' tRNA molecules move away. In this way, amino acids become linked together in the specific order determined by the mRNA base sequence.

The relationship between the 64 possible different codons of mRNA (i.e. the four bases in all possible triplet combinations) and their matching anticodons (in tRNAs which are linked to specific amino acids) comprises the **genetic code**, which, with a few inexplicable exceptions, is common to all living organisms. Figure 2.3 includes a few examples.

■ What amino acids do the mRNA codons CCU and GCU code for?

■ Proline and alanine respectively.

The details of the complete code needn't concern us here, but three aspects are worth reminding you of. First, some amino acids are coded for by more than one codon; for example, proline is coded for by any one of CCU, CCC, CCA and CCG. Second, three of the codons do not code for an amino acid but act as stop signals, bringing polypeptide synthesis to an end; UAA is one such codon. Third, because the genetic code is almost universal, mRNA produced by an introduced foreign gene can generally be 'read' by the ribosomal machinery of a unrelated host species into which the gene has been transferred.

Activity 2.1

Allow 15 minutes

Figure 2.4 is a diagram reproduced from the 2003 Government publication called *Our Inheritance, Our Future: Realising the Potential of Genetics in the NHS*. This diagram aims to communicate to those who know little about the subject what a gene is and how it functions.

Look critically at the diagram and write down how accurate you think it is and how well it gets across the important points. There is one piece of labelling that is misleading – can you spot it? Is the parallel that is drawn between a gene and DNA and a sound recording on an audiocassette a helpful one?

What's been outlined so far are the key processes that comprise gene expression, i.e. transcription and translation. There are often further steps beyond translation before a functional protein is produced, technically termed **post-translational modification**, which you met in Topic 1 (Box 1.5). We'll return to the significance of post-translational modification of newly synthesised proteins later in the topic.

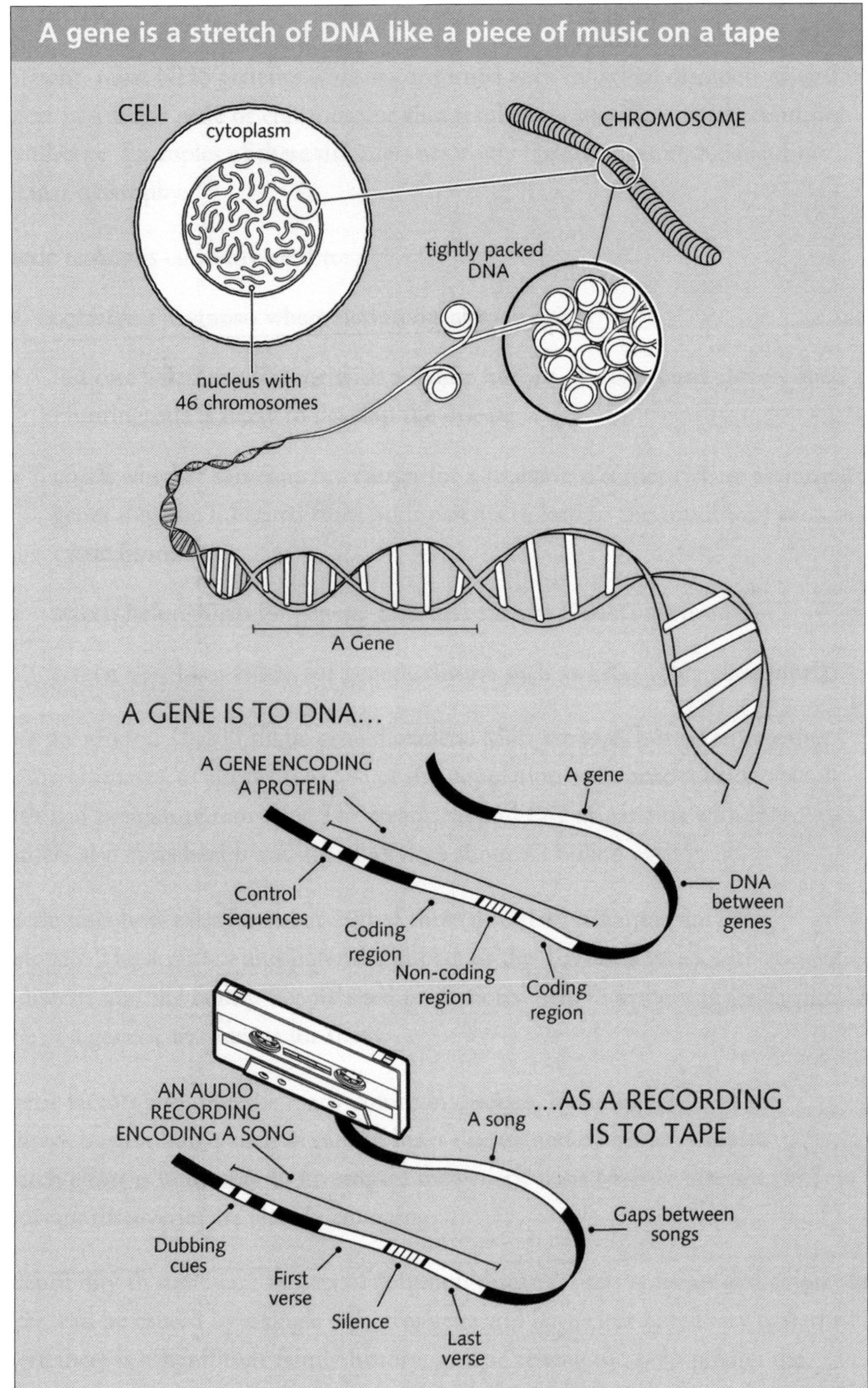

Figure 2.4 A diagram reproduced from a Government publication, to convey the analogy between the genes and music on an audiocassette.

2.2 DNA errors and repair; mutations

As before, this section quickly runs through what may well be familiar material, in order to remind you of key points for later sections.

First, in broad terms, a mutation is a change in the amount, arrangement or structure of the DNA of an organism. Such alterations might be of a 'large-scale' type, at the level of the chromosome, or at a much smaller scale, at the level of the gene, which often means changes in particular nucleotides. One type of the former (a **chromosomal mutation**) is characterised by the presence of an additional chromosome; for example, individuals who have three copies of chromosome 21, rather than two, display Down's syndrome. Sometimes, a particular part of a chromosome, consisting of many thousand of base pairs, might be duplicated further along the same chromosome. Other types of chromosomal mutations involve the deletion of a chunk of chromosome or the inversion of a segment of chromosome, i.e. the segment is turned around by 180 degrees.

Sometimes a chunk becomes detached from one chromosome and inserts into another, which is often not the homologous chromosome (i.e. not the matching chromosome of the pair). You can appreciate that all such large-scale changes can have significant effects. Genes may be lost or they may be over- or underexpressed. Even when no chromosome material is lost, an effect may well be evident; perhaps a gene is broken into two parts. The activity of some genes seems to be affected by their *position* on their chromosomes, a point well worth bearing in mind for later in the topic.

In terms of mutations at the level of the gene/DNA, some arise during the process of DNA replication, in which case they are called **replication errors**. They come about because DNA polymerase sometimes inserts the wrong nucleotide, perhaps an A opposite G rather than a C, i.e. a **base substitution** occurs. Such mismatches are generally repaired by the **DNA mismatch repair system**. A DNA mismatch distorts the geometry of the DNA double helix, and this distortion is recognised by the DNA mismatch repair enzymes, which then remove the newly synthesised length of faulty DNA. Into the gap to be repaired comes DNA polymerase, which 'proofreads' as it synthesises anew. The ends of the repair are sealed back with the help of the enzyme **DNA ligase**, which catalyses the formation of a strong bond to reconnect the sugar–phosphate backbone.

In addition to replication errors, changes in any base pair of DNA can be caused by chemical modification of a base – a form of DNA damage. This can occur spontaneously or by the effects of radiation. Ultraviolet light, X-rays and gamma (γ)-rays can cause mutations (i.e. they are mutagenic), as can high-energy particles such as α and β particles. Caffeine, some food preservatives and pesticides have the same potential, i.e. are chemical mutagens, at high enough doses.

Figure 2.5 shows some of the range of possible outcomes of what is called a point mutation, where a single DNA nucleotide changes in each strand. Figure 2.5a represents the normal, unmutated DNA section, where the nucleotides AGT will give rise during transcription to the codon UCA within a length of mature mRNA. The amino acid that corresponds to UCA is serine (abbreviated to Ser) and it is this amino acid that will become located in that particular position within the polypeptide chain that is emerging.

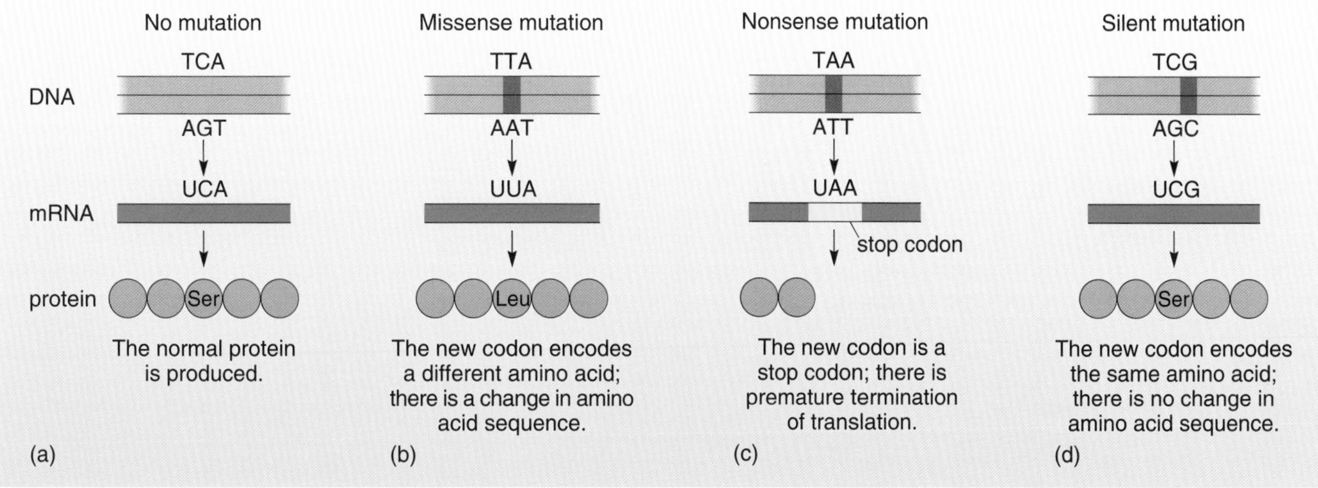
No mutation
Missense mutation
Nonsense mutation
Silent mutation
DNA
TCA
AGT
TTA
AAT
TAA
ATT
TCG
AGC
mRNA
UCA
UUA
UAA
UCG
stop codon
protein
Ser
Leu
Ser
The normal protein is produced.
The new codon encodes a different amino acid; there is a change in amino acid sequence.
The new codon is a stop codon; there is premature termination of translation.
The new codon encodes the same amino acid; there is no change in amino acid sequence.
(a)
(b)
(c)
(d)

Figure 2.5 The effects of different forms of point mutation in a particular DNA triplet (AGT) on the protein product.

■ Study Figure 2.5b–d; they show different types of point mutations, called respectively, **missense**, **nonsense** and **silent mutations**. Why do you think they are so called?

■ In (b), the 'sense' of particular codon is changed; whereas AGT corresponds to Ser, AAT corresponds to the amino acid leucine (Leu), so a protein will still be produced, but with a different amino acid at one position in the chain, so its conformation, and therefore its functional properties, may well be different. (You were introduced to the link between protein conformation and behaviour in Topic 1.) In (c), translation comes to a premature end because of the presence of a stop codon, UAA. The protein produced is not a 'sensible' one – it is a truncated version of the normal product of the gene. In (d), codon UCG codes for serine, just like the original triplet UCA, so although a mutation has occurred, there will be no effect on the protein produced; it is 'silent' in that there is no evidence of that mutational event.

■ For the mutations shown in (b) and (c), would the outcome be the same if they occurred within *introns* of a eukaryotic split gene?

■ No; in each case, the mutations are likely to prove silent, because the sections of mRNA containing the base substitution would be 'spliced out' during the formation of the mature mRNA (Section 2.1, point 5).

mRNA only involve exons

Suppose a base sequence within a coding section of a eukaryotic gene mutated by virtue of the *deletion* of a single nucleotide. For example, let's assume that the base sequence within a DNA template strand changes as follows, with the deleted base shown in bold:

from AGT **A**GT AGT AAT ACG CCC, etc.

to AGT GTA GTA ATA CGC CC…

(You'll appreciate that the base sequence is spaced out in threes in this way for your convenience; in reality, the bases form a continuous sequence.)

The original mRNA sequence will be UCA UCA UCA UUA UGC GGG. After the mutation the codon sequence reads UCA CAU CAU UAU GCG, etc. The original base sequence codes for the amino acid sequence:

serine-serine-serine-leucine-cysteine-glycine, etc.

The effect of the base deletion will be to produce mRNA which is translated into:

serine-histidine-histidine-tyrosine-alanine, etc.

In this instance, a single base deletion (a common form of gene mutation) not only changes the codon at the site of the mutation but all subsequent codons are altered too. The effect is likely to alter most (if not all) of the amino acids coded for following the mutation site, with a very different protein product emerging from translation. Deletions (or insertions) of bases that alter the protein encoded in this profound way are termed **frameshift mutations**, because they change the way triplet groups are read, or more technically, they change ('shift' along) the reading 'frame' that is applied.

Changes in DNA of the types mentioned are extraordinarily frequent. By far the majority are patched up by the extremely efficient repair systems. Only those mutations that occur in particular locations and escape the DNA repair mechanism are likely to influence the functionality of the genome, for better or (more commonly) for worse. The fact that mutations are so commonplace explains why individuals differ so much with respect to their DNA sequences. Mutations affecting a single base (and therefore its base pair as well) are sufficiently commonplace to account for a very large fraction of the variation due to human genetic differences.

One form of gene mutation worth highlighting now is **expanding trinucleotide repeats (ETRs)**. In fact, the DNA of humans is full of adjacent trinucleotide repeats, which vary in number between individuals. In some genetic diseases, the number of repeats increases substantially. Huntington's disease is one example, where the number of CAG repeats increases from below 34 copies found in most of the population, to between 40 and 100 copies found in individuals with Huntington's disease. This occurs within a gene that encodes a protein expressed in the brain. Although uncertainty continues about the way such a gene mutation leads to the neurodegeneration that is typical of this disease, the greater the number of repeats, the earlier the onset of the disease symptoms. It is uncertain why ETRs come about, but some drastic hiccup in the machinery of DNA replication is the most likely cause. (The most popular theories hypothesize 'stuttering' mechanisms involving attachment and reattachment of replication enzymes in regions of repeated triplets.)

2.3 Genome organisation at the DNA level

This final section of preparatory study looks at the way genetic material is organised and introduces you to some of the complexity of how genes work, again as a prelude to thinking about some of the problems of how genes might be transferred from one organism to another. Most of the ground it covers may well be familiar to you from previous studies but a modest amount of what may be new information is presented.

The term genome is a collective term for all the DNA of an organism. One point of obvious interest is the size of genomes in different organisms, measured in numbers of base pairs. Table 2.2 provides some data from a few representative species.

Table 2.2 Genome size in some organisms.

Organism	Genome size/Mbp*
Escherichia coli (bacterium)	4.7
Saccharomyces cerevisiae (yeast)	12.5
Drosophila melanogaster (fruit-fly)	170
Homo sapiens (human)	3100
Mus musculus (mouse)	2700
Nicotiana tabacum (tobacco)	4800
Triticum aestivum (wheat)	17 000

* Genome sizes are given in megabase pairs (Mbp). (1 Mbp = 10^6 base pairs.)

Most of the genome is located within the nucleus, but particular organelles, notably mitochondria and chloroplasts (in plants), also contain DNA (and therefore replicate), though these non-nuclear genomes are not of great concern here. Bacterial genomes are of interest to us however, for reasons to be explained in Chapter 3.

■ Bacterial (and viral) genomes are sometimes said to be very 'efficient' in their use of DNA for encoding their genes. What grounds are there for saying so?

■ Bacterial genomes are comparatively small – perhaps a few million base pairs. Table 2.2 gives the data for *Escherichia coli*. Nearly all the DNA (which is much more simply structured than in eukaryotes) codes for protein. The processes of transcription and translation occur in close proximity and one follows on from the other very swiftly, without the complications of mRNA splicing that we've already talked of. This seems a very efficient use of a modestly sized genome.

The bacterial genome is economical in one further respect; genes with related function are generally grouped together in units called **operons**, where individual genes are sometimes separated by no more than one or two nucleotides. One example is the *lac* operon in *Escherichia coli*, responsible for the production of three enzymes that control the metabolic utilisation by *E. coli* of the sugar lactose. Activation of the single promoter linked with this operon prompts transcription of one long mRNA molecule, from which the different enzymes are translated. Figure 2.6 is a simplified representation of the *lac* operon. To the right are the three *lac* genes (*lacZ*, *lacY* and *lacA*) that code for enzymes involved in metabolising lactose; their names are given in the diagram, but their precise roles needn't concern us. The promoter region (P) is just upstream of these genes. Incidentally, the binding of RNA polymerase to this promoter can be blocked by the (protein) product of another gene further upstream, called a repressor gene (Figure 2.6). What happens is that the repressor protein binds at a site immediately adjacent to the promoter, called O, so preventing the production of *lac* mRNA. The key point therefore is that a cluster of genes, with related functions, come under the influence of a single control region.

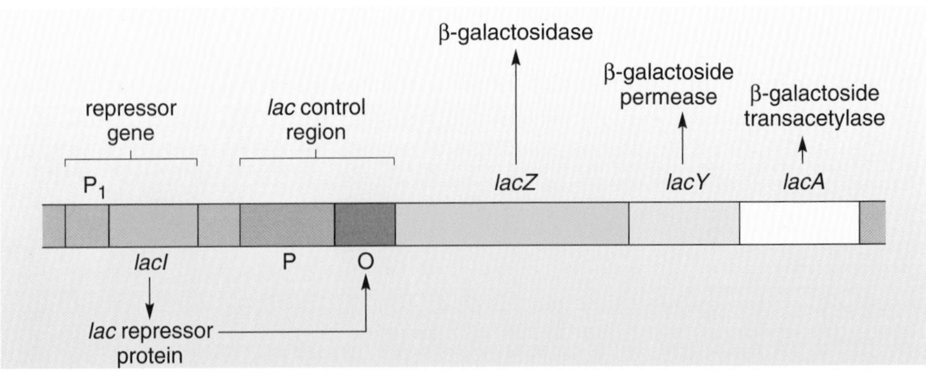

Figure 2.6 The *lac* operon in the bacterium *E. coli*, much simplified. P is the promoter region and O is the region where the *lac* repressor binds in a way that prevents binding of RNA polymerase. (The repressor gene, *lacI*, has its own promoter, P_1.) O and P comprise the control region of the *lac* operon.

Contrast this neatness with the genomes of eukaryotes, which have the introns and exons that characterise split genes and where mRNA splicing within the nucleus intervenes between transcription and translation. Furthermore the form in which DNA is organised in the human genome is extraordinary and complex. As we now know almost the entire DNA sequence of the human genome, we have a complete picture of how it is made up. From this we can see that the human genome (like those of other mammals) consists of DNA sequences that are in some cases present in just one copy, whereas others are present as many thousands or millions of copies. In order to describe the human genome in more detail, I'll follow one of the simpler classifications of DNA types, as generally applied to the human genome, but you should be aware that nomenclature in this area can vary significantly, in part because of the variety of types of DNA now subject to analysis.

Single (or very low) copy DNA

About 45% of the total human DNA can be classed as single (or very low) copy DNA. This includes all the DNA present in just one or two copies per genome, i.e. as unique genes, of the type shown in Table 2.1, plus many sequences that are present just a few times, including a number of genes whose primary role is to control the expression of other genes. But what is remarkable is that protein-coding sequences account for just a small fraction of this DNA type – a little over 1% of the total human genome, though the incompleteness of our present-day knowledge means that estimates of the precise amount vary amongst different researchers. Far more of the genome comprises introns (which, as Table 2.1 revealed, can form a very sizeable fraction of a gene) plus the **'spacer'** (or intergenic) **DNA** between genes, much of which, as far as we know, has no apparent function – or at least not one that seems to depend on the base sequence.

■ It's possible to compare the base sequences in spacer DNA in related organisms, to see what differences occur over evolutionary time. It appears that these sections change much more rapidly over these extended periods of time than do sequences within the coding sections of genes. Why do you think this is?

■ As you saw from Figure 2.5, changes within coding regions can have drastic effects, likely to be disadvantageous to the organism. This may well reduce an organisms 'fitness'; there would be such strong selection pressure against such mutations that the unchanged sequence would tend to be strongly conserved from one generation to the other. But within the spacer DNA, mutations would be likely to affect an organism's fitness much less obviously; remember that the function of such sequences (though unknown) seems not to depend on base sequence. The selection pressure against such changes is lower, with the resulting variability evident today.

■ Thinking just of the coding sequences in single (or very low) copy DNA, would all such DNA encode for *proteins* of one type or another?

▒ Much of it would, but not all. You'll recall an earlier mention of tRNAs, vital to translation, and you may already know of the most abundant type of RNA – ribosomal RNA (or rRNA) – that (together with proteins) make up the ribosomes, the cellular structures upon which translation occurs. All such types of RNAs are end-products of gene expression, not coding for proteins.

It is estimated that only 25–50% of the protein-coding sequences in the genome are present as 'unique' copies; about half or more are members of families of genes, which have identical or similar nucleotide sequences. Many are likely to have arisen in our ancestry through the duplication of genes, which then diverged via successive mutations. About 5% of the human genome appears to have arisen through duplication of large segments of DNA, some containing one or two genes, others carrying more. This over-provision of genes offers an explanation of why some genes can be lost over evolutionary time, seemingly with no ill effect. So-called **pseudogenes** have DNA sequences that are similar to functional genes, but have ceased functioning, generally as a result of the accumulation of frameshift and nonsense mutations over their evolutionary history.

It is worth emphasising once again how very little of the human genome codes for proteins. As Figure 2.7 shows, the spacer (intergenic) DNA and the introns comprise the great majority of the remaining single/low copy DNA. The remainder, about 55%, is DNA that is repetitive to varying degrees, which we'll look at in more detail shortly.

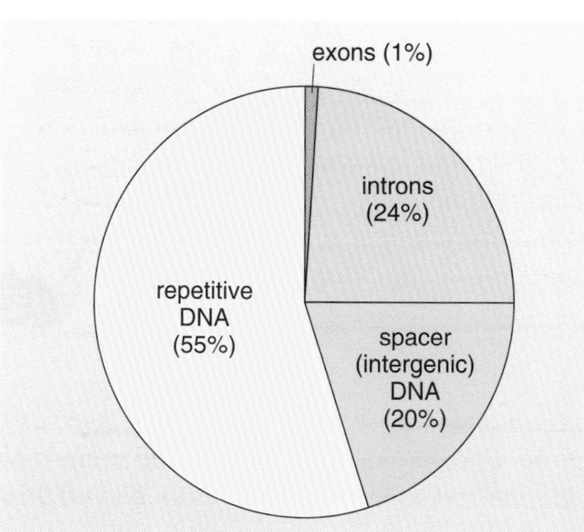

Figure 2.7 The make-up of the human genome. In all, genes occupy about 25% of the human genome, but only a very small fraction (about 1%) of the genome comprises protein-coding sequences; 24% comprises introns. Spacer DNA comprises about 20%, while about 55% is repetitive DNA.

But first, what of the total *number* of genes evident within the human genome? You'll have heard of the Human Genome Mapping Project, now complete, at least in a draft form. This huge international initiative set out to sequence the 3000 million base pairs that comprise the human genome and to map the entire array of genes. One of the most surprising findings is that the data suggested a total gene count of about 30 000–35 000 in total – a great deal fewer than was anticipated. Prior to this finding, estimates of gene number were closer to 100 000. In June 2003, the estimate was downgraded further to an even more modest 20 000–25 000. Gene counts are available for other organisms for which genome projects have been completed (Table 2.3).

Table 2.3 Gene counts for some organisms for which genome projects have been completed.

Common name	Scientific name	Number of genes
yeast	*Saccharomyces cerevisiae*	6144
roundworm	*Caenorhabditis elegans*	18 266
fruit-fly	*Drosophila melanogaster*	13 338
thale cress	*Arabidopsis thaliana*	25 706
rice	*Oryza sativa*	37 544

The precise numbers aren't important – and indeed will change to some degree as analyses become more refined – but the scale of the differences are. What is implied is that the level of complexity of organisms is not entirely accounted for by differences in the number of genes. If it were, how could we explain the fact that humans have very approximately the same number of genes as the two plant species in the list? Part of the explanation is that some genes are 'smarter' than many others – a point we'll return to later.

Moderately repetitive DNA

Between 25 and 40% of mammalian DNA consists of sequences that are typically somewhere between 150 and 300 bp in length and can be repeated from about 50 to several thousands of times. Some of the human rRNA genes are repeated 150–200 times, each repeat adjacent to the next. This repetition may be linked to the fact that large amounts of rRNA may be needed at times of intense cellular activity, on a scale that only multiple gene copies can supply. Not all repeats are so clustered together; some are dispersed throughout the genome and vary greatly in size, perhaps up to 8 kb long. One intriguing fragment, called *Alu* and found only in primates, is about 200 bp long and is repeated many thousands of times in the human genome, to the point where it corresponds to about 10% of the genome. Some longer repeats of this type encode a form of the enzyme **reverse transcriptase** that is related to that found in viruses. (Viruses will be mentioned throughout this topic and Box 2.1 provides some important background information.)

Many of the moderately repetitive DNA sequences are termed transposons – 'rogue elements' that seem to have been present in mammalian genomes for many millions of years, copying themselves and 'jumping' around the genome. When they insert into a functional gene, the gene is likely to become disabled. In the mouse, where an estimated 3000 mobile units of this type exist, their activity may account for 10% of all mutations. In some eukaryotes, more than half the genome consists of transposons and geneticists have little idea why this should be so. Some transposons seem to have the capacity to act on the mRNA produced from functional genes, reverse transcribing the mRNA into DNA, in which case they are called **retrotransposons**. If they act on mature mRNA, the DNA produced (via reverse transcriptase activity) contains only that fraction coded by the exons. The result is a slightly altered gene, which may become randomly inserted. It is thought likely that as many as 300 functional genes in the human genome arose during our evolution in just this way. It is not surprising that many genomes have evolved mechanisms geared towards keeping such fragments away from key areas of the genome. The overall picture that emerges from all this is of a dynamic genome in eukaryotes, changing in ways that are unpredictable and complex.

Box 2.1 Some background on viruses

Viruses have a genetic make-up fundamentally different from that of both prokaryotes and eukaryotes. Some, for example **retroviruses**, do not contain DNA. They have a single-stranded RNA genome, as two copies of identical strands which during infection of a cell are converted to DNA via reverse transcriptase. This DNA then becomes integrated into the genome of the host cell, generally at some random point. When conditions are right, this newly incorporated DNA is transcribed to produce copies of the original viral RNA genome, which codes for viral protein, and new viral particles are manufactured. One noteworthy feature of retroviruses is that they can only infect cells that are dividing. Figure 2.8a shows a typical retrovirus. There is an inner protein layer, within which are the two identical single-stranded RNA genomes; outside the protein layer is a lipid layer (i.e. the envelope) into which fit proteins that help recognise particular proteins on the outside of cells that are the target of invasion. Human immunodeficiency virus (HIV), the cause of AIDS, is perhaps the best known retrovirus.

In contrast to the retroviruses, **adenoviruses** have a double-stranded DNA genome and can infect non-dividing cells. Many of them are able to naturally infect the cells that line the gastrointestinal and respiratory tract in humans – they are the cause of many different forms of cold and flu. Their structure is relatively simple, with an outer protein coat, consisting, in most cases, of many different proteins, which encloses the double-stranded 35 kbp molecule of DNA (see Figure 2.8b).

There are other types of virus, for example, adeno-associated viruses, but their role in genetic manipulation is modest, so retroviruses and adenoviruses are our chief concern throughout what follows.

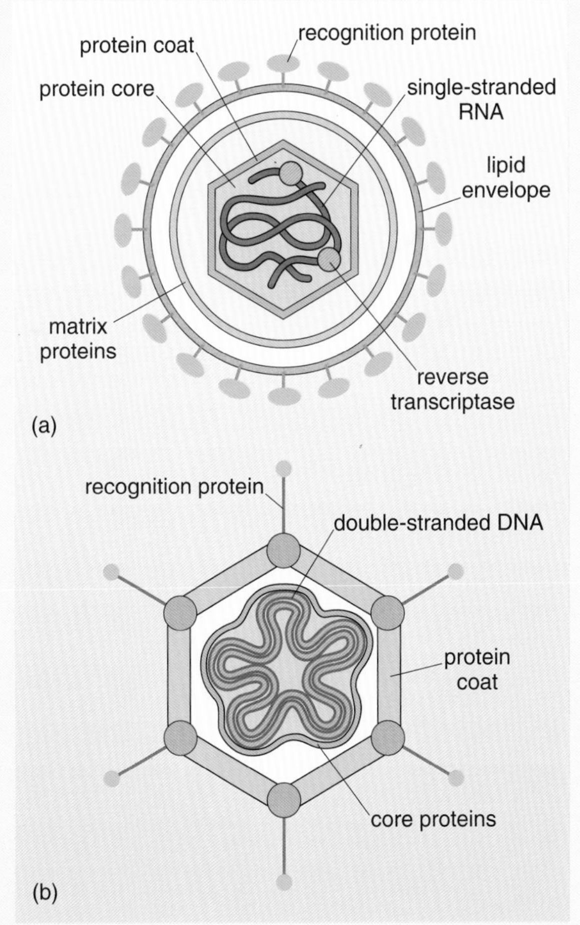

Figure 2.8 (a) A typical retrovirus. The two copies of the single-stranded RNA genome (plus the enzyme reverse transcriptase) are contained within the protein coat, with an outer lipid envelope, which contains recognition proteins. (b) A typical adenovirus, which has double-stranded DNA contained within a coat of many different proteins.

Highly repetitive DNA

Highly repetitive DNA comprises short sequences, often less than 10 bp, but can be repeated from somewhere between hundreds of thousands to millions of copies, often aggregated at particular parts of the chromosome. Another name for such DNA is **satellite DNA**, reflecting the fact that when DNA is subject to a particular form of centrifugation, this DNA type separates to one side of (i.e. as a satellite to) the main component. Different types of such DNA exist (minisatellite and microsatellite DNA) but very little (perhaps none) is transcribed. Rather, they are linked to maintaining the proper functioning of chromosomes, particularly the centromere (which you may recall plays a key part in chromosome separation during cell division) and a special structure at the chromosome ends, called the telomere. There may be additional functions of which we are, as yet, unaware. In the mouse, it has been shown that as many as 10% of the cases of cancers in tissues of the breast, bladder, colon and rectum were associated with mutations in the satellite sequences, although this is generally believed to reflect a generalised increased mutation frequency commonly seen in tumour cells, rather than a specific effect of changes in satellite sequences themselves.

2.4 Achieving complexity

Our picture of how genes work that has just been sketched is far removed from the simple on/off model of genes acting in isolation that dominated thinking until comparatively recent times. Just three brief points should give you a flavour of the subtlety of the processes involving activation and expression of human genes, amply justifying our earlier use of the term 'smart'.

1 Transcriptional controls

The fact that eukaryotic genes generally have promoters has been mentioned before; they also often have one or more elements described as enhancers, response elements and silencers. The details of their function need not concern us, but the nomenclature hints at a variety of 'volume controls' that influence the timing and extent of transcription, largely by their effects on the promoter. Figure 2.9 shows in a very schematic and simplified way something of the control processes involved; you'll appreciate that the details vary enormously from gene to gene. In this instance, an enhancer sequence is far removed from the point of transcription. There may also be downstream regulation of the same gene, with adjacent or distant control DNA sequences. The products that prime and modulate gene transcription in this way, by up to 1000-fold, are termed **transcription factors** and most seem to be proteins that bind to parts of promoters and/or enhancers. Sometimes transcription factors bind to silencer sequences and turn off transcription, rather like we saw in the *lac* operon, though it's not known how important this process is in the human genome. The overall impression is that, in eukaryotes at least, gene expression seems to be regulated very significantly at the level of transcription. For the genes that we know most about, this is achieved through the combined influence of numerous transcription factors from different sources.

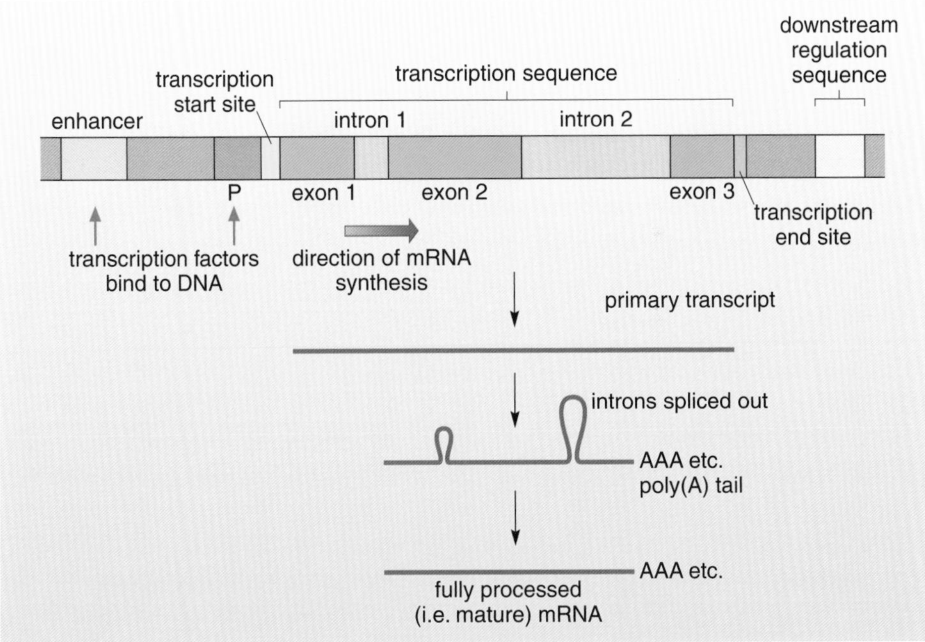

Figure 2.9 A schematic and general representation of some features of eukaryotic gene expression. In this instance the upstream regulator is an enhancer, able to bind one or more transcription factors, as can the promoter, P. Gene expression is also influenced by a downstream site. The gene consists of three exons and two introns. Splicing out of the RNA sequences derived from introns produces mRNA (which may be of many different types) via alternative splicing. (The poly(A) tail will be described in Section 3.1.)

2 Alternative splicing

Alternative splicing is a process whereby the same mRNA primary transcript (i.e. the initial product of transcription) can be processed in different ways. The primary mRNA transcript is cut and sealed at different points, so producing a range of different mature mRNAs, each encoding a distinct amino acid sequence. Thus the splicing process shown in Figure 2.9 may not always be exactly as shown – perhaps exon sequence 2 is included in some of the mature RNA produced but left out of others. So different types of protein might be produced from the same gene –in this hypothetical case, proteins with identical end sequences but different 'middles'. It is estimated that as many as 40% of human genes may produce different mRNA via different types and degrees of cutting and splicing transcribed RNA. One example is the gene *troponin T*, which is especially important in muscle tissue. Which of the 80 or so differently spliced forms of its mRNA that predominate reflects the muscle type and the demands that are placed up on it, by exercise for example. At least one 'genetic' disease seems attributable to problems that occur in the processing of mRNA. The process of alternative splicing is now seen as the key reason why organisms (such as humans) can function so well with comparatively few genes – and also explains why organisms in many ways so different – humans and chimpanzees are often so compared – have DNA that is so nearly identical. A comparatively low gene count becomes a lot more explicable when one considers the unusually large number of *proteins* typical of highly complex animals such as humans.

3 Post-translational modifications

After translation, protein products can undergo one or more of a whole range of post-translational modifications. Sometimes a carbohydrate component is added (glycosylation); in other circumstances, a phosphate (phosphorylation) or methyl (methylation) group is added to particular amino acids. Some proteins are unable to fold spontaneously but require 'molecular chaperones' to help get them into shape. Proteins may be produced as large precursors that have to be cut down to size in a precisely determined way before becoming functional; you'll come across one such example (the hormone insulin) in the next chapter. Some diseases are thought to originate because mutations influence one or more aspect of post-translational modification of proteins.

What these three points hint at is a picture of genes that do not work in isolation, but cooperatively and flexibly. Genes are subject to intricate control mechanisms, the effect of which is to produce a vast repertoire of gene products of enormous richness and sophistication. Such a picture is worth bearing in mind as we begin to explore in the next chapters how individual genes can be picked up and moved about.

Summary of Chapter 2

DNA is a double-stranded macromolecule that carries information; it consists of intertwining polynucleotide chains, where the inner core comprises A (adenine), G (guanine), C (cytosine) and T (thymine). The base-pairing rules permit DNA replication, although errors can arise during the process, which either persist (as mutations) or are repaired.

A traditional (and simplistic) view of gene function is that a particular gene is responsible for the production of a corresponding protein. Transcription is the production of mRNA with a base sequence that corresponds to one of the DNA strands, though with U (uracil) replacing T. Translation occurs on ribosomes and involves the progressive build-up of a polypeptide chain via an assembly line that associates triplet sequences (i.e. codons) in mature mRNA with matching anticodons on corresponding tRNAs, to which are attached particular amino acids.

Eukaryotes have split genes, with non-coding sections (introns) not contributing to the mature mRNA active at the ribosome. Bacterial genomes have mostly protein-coding sequences. RNA splicing occurs in eukaryotes; one or more types of mRNA can be fashioned by 'splicing' of the initial RNA product of transcription. Base substitution (alteration of a single DNA nucleotide) within introns is unlikely to have an effect; within coding sequences, effects on protein structure are more likely, though not inevitable.

Genes operate interactively, subject to the effect of numerous controlling products, often produced by distant genes. A gene's promoter is where a matching RNA polymerase responsible for transcription binds. Neither the size of the genome nor the number of genes accurately reflects complexity.

Single (or very low) copy DNA includes the coding sequences of 'unique' genes, occupying a tiny fraction of the total genome, plus families of similar genes. Moderately repetitive DNA can be repeated several thousand times. It includes genes for rRNA and tRNAs. Most of the moderately repetitive DNA has no known function. It also contains transposable elements, able to copy and insert themselves within the genome, often causing mutations. Highly repetitive DNA comprises short sequences, repeated huge number of times; such DNA is rarely transcribed and its function is uncertain.

Question 2.1

(a) What distinguishes homozygous and heterozygous allele combinations?

(b) Distinguish between introns and exons.

(c) In what respects do DNA and mRNA differ?

(d) How do the processes of transcription and translation differ?

(e) What is the function of the enzyme RNA polymerase?

(f) Suggest why the genetic code has been described as 'redundant'.

(g) Which regions of the human genome are non-coding?

(h) How do chromosomal mutations differ from base substitution mutations?

Question 2.2

(a) Explain in a few sentences how the genomes of prokaryotes (bacteria) and of eukaryotes differ. (b) How can a eukaryotic gene produce more than one type of protein? (c) Explain why the total number of types of protein present in a cell differs from the number of genes that the cell contains.

Question 2.3

The term 'junk' DNA is sometimes used to refer to parts of the human genome. What types of DNA sequence is the term likely to refer to and do you think the term is a useful and accurate one?

Question 2.4

A summary of some of the key points from Sections 2.1–2.3 is provided in Figure 2.10 (overleaf). To check your understanding, progressively work through the different sections, starting with 'the genetic material' and following the connecting lines. Then complete the diagram by listing the characteristics of eukaryote genes in the bottom-right circle.

Question 2.5

Look back at Figure 2.4. Think more about the implication there that a stretch of DNA is like a piece of music on a tape. Does the analogy fall down in some respects? Concentrate on factors such as the comparability of 'genes' and 'songs' and the gaps between these components.

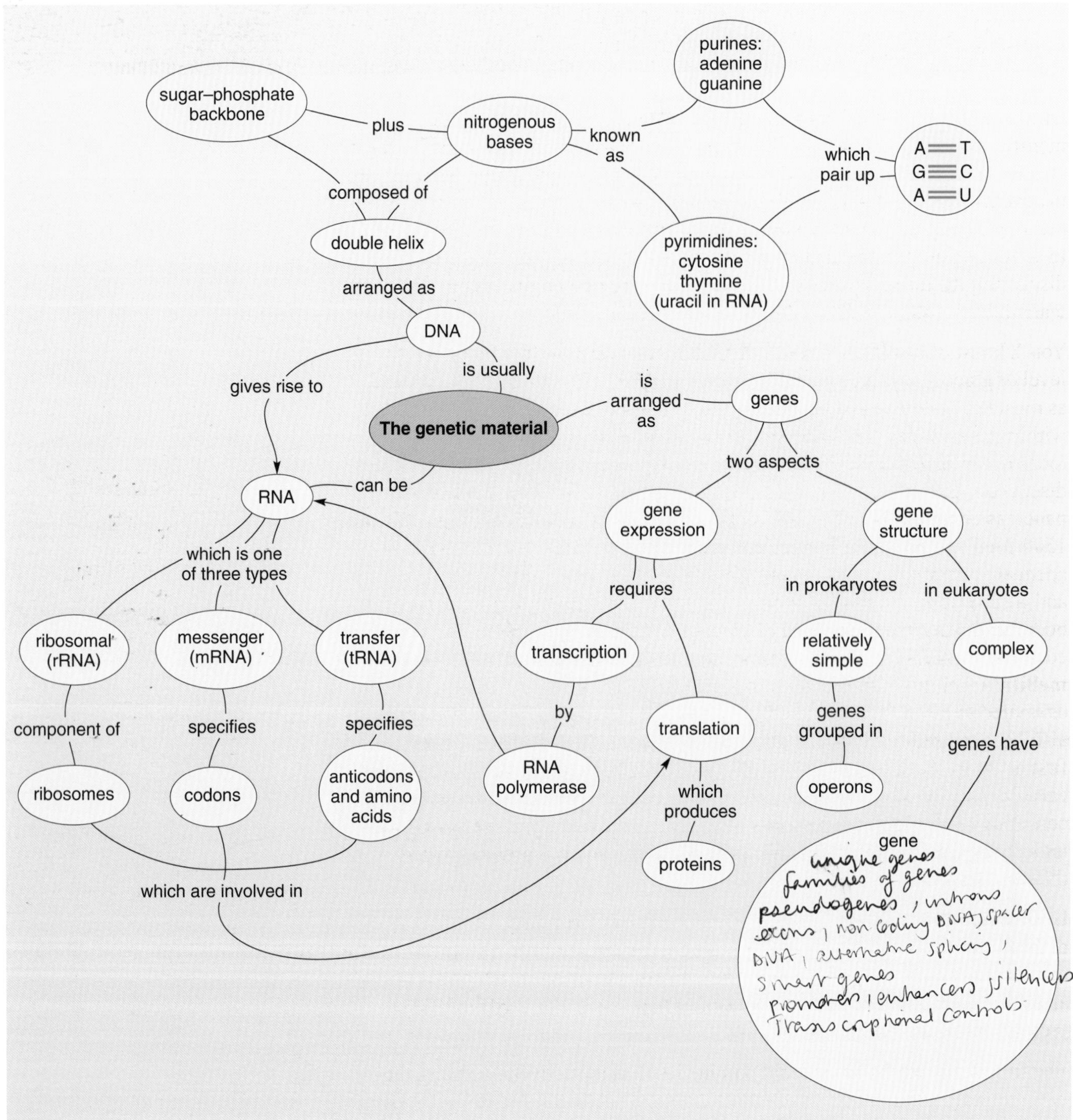

Figure 2.10 A summary diagram of key points from Sections 2.1–2.3. Fill in the circle labelled 'gene'. Suggestions are given in the answer to Question 2.4 on p. 161.

Genetic manipulation of bacteria; producing human insulin

Chapter 3

One of the first practical uses for genetic engineering was the genetic modification of the bacterium *Escherichia coli* to produce human insulin. This chapter tells the story of how this important advance came about. Not only are the events of interest in themselves, but they introduce some of the pioneering techniques that genetic engineers used for transferring genes from one organism to another – information to be built upon as you work through this topic. Before discussing the technicalities of how bacteria were first engineered to manufacture insulin, some background information is helpful.

You'll know of insulin as just one of the hormones responsible for controlling the level of glucose in the blood and the rate at which it is absorbed into tissues such as muscles. Insulin is synthesised naturally in special secretory cells (β cells) within the pancreas. These cells, together with other hormone-secreting cells are located in nodules called 'Islets of Langerhans' (or 'Islets' for short) after their discoverer, the 19th century anatomist Paul Langerhans. A typical human pancreas contains about 5×10^5 islets and each islet contains between 1000 and 1500 β cells. If insufficient insulin is produced, glucose is not taken up to an adequate extent by the tissues, where it is needed; levels of blood glucose rise and glucose is excreted in the urine. If this condition is allowed to persist, the body becomes rapidly depleted of glucose and the patient passes into a diabetic coma. This condition is known as Type 1 or **'insulin-dependent' diabetes mellitus** (mellitus = sweet, from the glucose in the urine) and is currently estimated to affect some 170 000 adults in the UK alone. Type 1 diabetes has also been termed 'early-onset diabetes', reflecting the fact that symptoms often first develop in the early years of life. By contrast, Type 2 diabetes, frequently called 'maturity-onset diabetes', more often occurs later in life and although this condition also reflects the patient's inability to deal with glucose effectively, its underlying cause is not an insufficiency of insulin and is therefore treated differently, by dietary control.

Until the development of a method of making human insulin, people with Type 1 diabetes were treated with insulin purified from the pancreases of cattle (bovine insulin) and pigs (porcine insulin). Whilst this source material is readily obtainable as part of the discarded offal after slaughter, the use of non-human insulin presents two main problems.

The first is that whilst bovine and porcine insulins are active in humans, they differ slightly in structure from human insulin. This difference can be recognised by the immune system in about 10% of patients, leading to an allergic reaction at the site of injection and the removal of the injected insulin from the circulation. Furthermore, although industrial methods are available that are capable of purifying animal insulins to a very high level, there is always the risk that tiny amounts of contaminating proteins can get into the preparations, which will also be recognised by the patient's immune system and set up an allergic reaction. Raised awareness of prion diseases such as vCJD have now increased concerns about the risks of contamination of this type, as you'll appreciate from Topic 1.

The second problem was that of supply. By the mid-1970s it had become clear that whilst the worldwide incidence of Type 1 diabetes was increasing inexorably, the availability of animal pancreases was failing to keep pace, due to a reduction in the amount of meat in Western diets. The principal manufacturer of bovine and porcine insulin, Eli Lilly, predicted that this shortage would become acute by the early 1990s, compromising what for them was a large and lucrative market. It was for this reason that Eli Lilly sponsored a symposium in Indianapolis in May 1976 to discuss the possibility of making insulin by the emerging technology of genetic engineering.

3.1 Obtaining DNA that codes for human insulin

Just what was needed to get bacteria to make this human protein? First, it is necessary to produce a length of DNA that can code for the desired protein. Secondly, it must be inserted into a bacterium in such a way that the bacterium can read the genetic code and produce the protein. The first problem is considerable enough – identifying the tiny fraction of DNA responsible for insulin production is akin to 'looking for a needle in a haystack'. One approach might be to look for the mRNA transcribed by the insulin gene in the cytoplasm of β cells of the human pancreas, but you'll appreciate that such cytoplasm will contain a great array of different types of mRNA, along with the other forms of RNA you know about.

In the case of insulin, there is a further complication. When insulin is synthesised naturally, a single, large, inactive polypeptide called preproinsulin is first produced, which immediately folds in to the structure shown in Figure 3.1a. (Though preproinsulin is the immediate product, we'll follow the usual convention and refer to the gene that produces it as the 'insulin' gene – this is the gene referred to in Table 2.1, where you'll see that it's relatively modest in size.) However, 'mature' insulin consists of two protein chains, derived from the original, continuous, preproinsulin polypeptide chain, shown as Figure 3.1a. There is a shorter A chain, consisting of 21 amino acids, attached to a longer B chain (30 amino acids) by two disulfide (–S–S–) bridges (Figure 3.1c).

- ■ How do the disulfide bridges shown in Figure 3.1 arise?
- ■ You may recall from earlier studies that the amino acid cysteine (present in preproinsulin at the sites shown in Figure 3.1a) has thiol (–SH) groups on its side-chain which can bond to other cysteine groups via the formation of a disulfide bridge.

Figure 3.1a shows there are four cysteines in the A chain and two in the B chain. Figure 3.1a also shows a third disulfide bridge, between two cysteines within the A chain. The importance of all three disulfide bridges is that they help stabilise the three-dimensional structure (conformation) of the mature insulin molecule, which is essential for its action.

In addition to the A and B chains, preproinsulin consists of a signal sequence (or 'tail') at the end of the B chain, and a sequence of 22 amino acids that comprise the C chain which joins the A and the B chains in one continuous sequence, Figure 3.1a. In β cells, the signal sequence directs the molecule to the appropriate part of the cell and is then removed by a **protease**, which is a polypeptide-splitting enzyme, giving rise to proinsulin (Figure 3.1b). Proinsulin is finally converted to insulin by removal of the C chain (Figure 3.1c). This rather complicated production sequence serves the important function of making sure that the A and B chains are in the correct orientation for the right disulfide bridges to form. Since any one cysteine is chemically capable of linking to any other, without this 'lining-up' mechanism the possibility of mistakes could be quite high.

Such trimming of longer precursor proteins to make the shorter ones that are actually needed is a common phenomenon and is just one example of the more wide-ranging phenomenon of post-translational modification referred to in Chapter 2. The problem is that although this particular example occurs naturally in β cells, it does not do so in bacteria – the production of insulin is not normally part of *E. coli*'s repertoire! So researchers were faced with a quandary. Should they use the 'natural' genetic sequence and try to find a way of carrying out the post-translational modification on the preproinsulin that the bacteria would produce, or try to make 'artificial' genes corresponding to each of the A and B chains and then try to link the two chains together in the laboratory? In fact, three research teams entered the race to make the first human insulin. Two of the teams, one based at Harvard headed by Walter Gilbert and another at the University of California, San Francisco (UCSF), headed by Bill Rutter and Howard Goodman, chose to use the 'natural' sequence. Another team headed by Walter Boyer and Stanley Cohen (from Stanford University) and funded by the newly formed biotechnology company Genentech opted to generate artificial DNA sequences for the A and B chains. At this time, genetic engineering was emerging as 'big business', especially in the US, so the fierce competition between these groups reflected not only the usual academic desire to 'get there first' but an awareness of the great commercial gains to made by those first past the post.

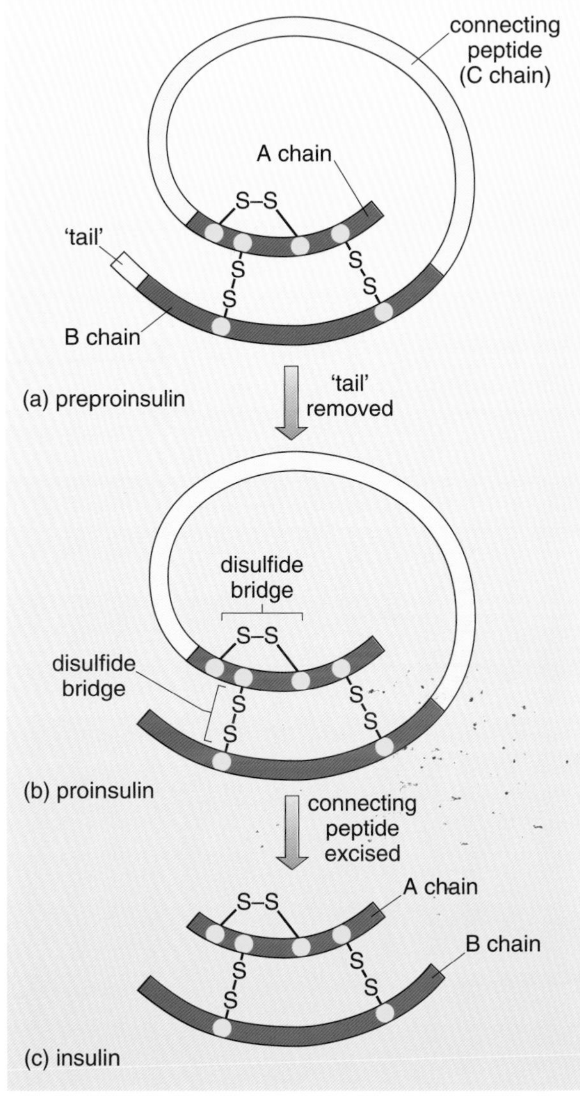

Figure 3.1 Post-translational modification in the production of insulin. (a) The gene product is the insulin precursor, preproinsulin. The locations of the amino acid cysteine are shown as yellow circles. (b) Removal of a short 'tail' section produces proinsulin. (c) Excision of the connecting peptide (i.e. amino acid sequence), also called the C chain, leaves the mature insulin molecule, i.e. the A chain and the B chain joined together via two disulfide bridges.

It is important to remember that when these projects started in 1976, the scientists were operating at the very frontiers of possibility. Many reagents that can now be bought from catalogues had to be made in the laboratory and techniques that are now standard had to be painstakingly developed by trial and error. A procedure that took two years in the mid-1970s can be accomplished within a few weeks in a modern laboratory. The technical stages that the two sets of groups needed to go through are, however, very similar to those used today and so it is instructive to see exactly what they did and how the various problems were overcome.

Let's first take the problems faced by the groups from Harvard and UCSF, who were pursuing the 'natural' gene. Their first main problem was to identify a coding sequence for preproinsulin. It would have been extremely laborious at the time to analyse the entire DNA of a cell in order to identify the miniscule sequence that coded for preproinsulin – remember this was work conducted well before the Human Genome Mapping Project. Furthermore, characterising the make-up of the insulin gene would have been some way short of providing the key information required.

■ Recall from Section 2.1 why this is so?

▒ Although it was not fully realised in 1976, you will be aware that eukaryotic genes are characterised by the presence of non-coding introns which separate the coding sequences of DNA, the exons. Remember that introns are removed, leaving a mature mRNA sequence that can be translated into the desired protein. The preproinsulin gene has two introns which together account for 1.4 kilobases or 67% of the entire gene (see Table 2.1).

Instead of focusing on the actual gene that codes for preproinsulin, both groups concentrated on isolating mature preproinsulin mRNA from cells that were known to be making it.

■ Which cells are these?

▒ They are the β cells of the Islets of Langerhans.

They would then use this mRNA to make a DNA sequence that would be the equivalent of the original gene, minus the introns. How this was achieved is a fascinating example of pioneering genetic engineering, well worth following in some detail.

Because human pancreases are not easily obtained in sufficient quantities, both groups decided in the first instance to see whether they could carry out the procedures using the rat insulin gene. This decision was also guided by a very practical, but non-scientific, consideration. At that time, the transfer of human genetic material into bacteria under US regulations could be carried out only in a Class 4 laboratory. Class 4 laboratories provide the highest level of containment of biological materials. In the 1970s, Class 4 laboratories were almost exclusively run by military biological weapons establishments and not available to civilian researchers. In fact, when the Harvard group eventually attempted to insert a human gene into *E. coli*, they had to obtain special permission from the UK Ministry of Defence to use the facility at Porton Down, Wiltshire and the UCSF group used a Class 3 laboratory in France, where regulations were not so stringent. This restriction did not apply to the Genentech group, because they were using artificial genes. Although these genes were designed to code for a human protein, they did not count in law as 'human' genes and therefore were exempt from regulatory restrictions applying to the cloning of human genes.

The isolation of naturally occurring rat β cells needed very large numbers of pancreases. As you will recall, each islet contains not much more than a 1000 β cells and each islet is itself invisible to the naked eye. The UCSF team therefore undertook the tedious and labour-intensive task of dissecting out whole rat pancreases, up to 200 at a time. The tissue was digested by the enzyme collagenase, which breaks down the connective tissue but leaves cells intact, and the islet cells were separated by centrifugation in a density gradient. In this technique, a tube is filled with a solution that increases in concentration, and therefore density, from the top to the bottom. The mixture of cells is then added to the tube and the whole lot spun in a centrifuge at many thousands of revolutions per minute. Different types of cell vary very slightly in density and by the end of the run the β cells become concentrated in a layer at the point in the density gradient that equals the density of those particular cells. (You may recall from Section 2.3 that much the same technique, though using much higher speeds of revolution, is used to identify the satellite bands, containing highly repetitive DNA.)

Altogether, 200 rat pancreases yielded about 50 mg of cells. This was the starting material for isolating preproinsulin mRNA. The Harvard team, however, decided to use a rat tumour called an insulinoma. Tumours of this type also occur very rarely in humans and are characterised by an uncontrolled proliferation of β cells which are able to produce insulin. By harvesting these cells and growing them either in animals or in tissue culture, it was possible to obtain a much richer source of β cells. Both teams, however, needed to demonstrate that preproinsulin mRNA was present in their preparations.

Earlier it was mentioned that only a small proportion of the total RNA that can be extracted from a cell is accounted for by mRNA.

■ Recall the other types of RNA likely to be present.

▩ Ribosomal RNA (rRNA) and transfer RNA (tRNA), see Section 2.3. Most of the RNA present in a cell is rRNA.

Fortunately, it is relatively easy to separate mRNA from the other two types of RNA. This is because nearly all eukaryotic mRNAs are characterised by a 'tail' of between 50 and 250 adenine nucleotides which are added after transcription by an enzyme, poly(A) polymerase (PAP). The poly(A) tail, shown in Figure 2.9, seems to stabilise mRNA, making it less susceptible to breakdown by enzymes within the cell. When a mixture of different types of RNA is passed through a filter to which is attached sequences of thymine nucleotides, the poly(T) bases pair with the poly(A) tails of the mRNA and the mRNA remains stuck to the filter, from which it can be subsequently extracted.

An added complication mentioned at the beginning of this section is that there would be very many different forms of mRNA within the β cells. A number of 'housekeeping' genes are present in β cells, for example those concerned with producing the enzymes of glycolysis, i.e. the early stages of glucose breakdown in the cytoplasm. All such enzymes would be produced from corresponding mRNAs – for our purposes, 'contaminating' the sample. Individual mRNAs can be separated by a technique called **gel electrophoresis**. Because of their phosphate groups, RNA (and DNA) molecules are negatively charged. This means that if they are put in an electric field with a positive electrode at one end and a negative electrode at the other, they will migrate towards the positive electrode. The trick is to conduct this experiment with the mRNA embedded in a polyacrylamide gel. The polyacrylamide slows down the rate at which the mRNA molecules migrate. Smaller molecules become less entangled in the gel and move fastest, whereas larger molecules move more slowly. Separation of different mRNAs is therefore dependent on their length. The gels are set up so that the original mixture is put

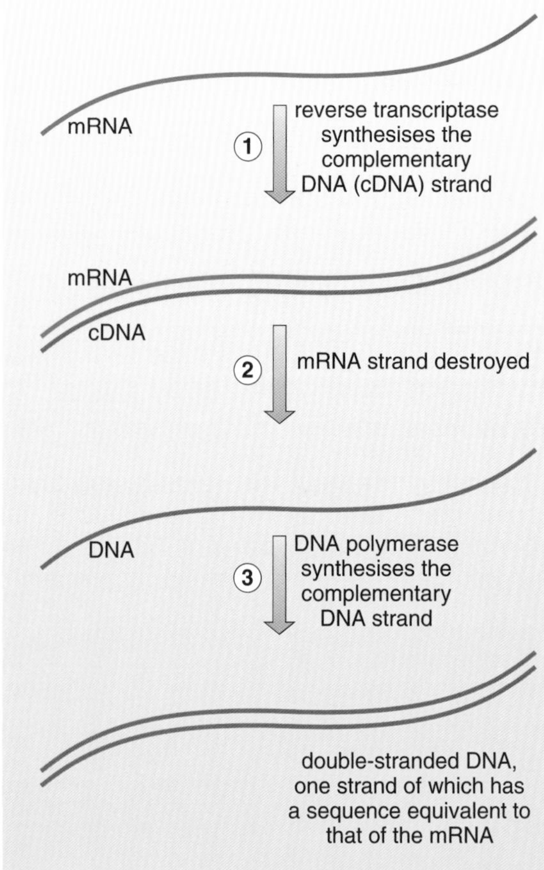

Figure 3.2 Obtaining genes using mRNA. Step 1: isolated mRNA acts as a template for reverse transcriptase. Step 2: the mRNA strand is broken down. Step 3: the single-stranded cDNA acts as a template for DNA polymerase, which synthesises the complementary strand; double-stranded DNA results.

into the end of the gel that is nearest to the negative electrode. After the electricity has been turned on for some time, the shortest molecules of mRNA will have moved the furthest and be nearest to the positive electrode whilst the longer molecules will remain closer to the negative electrode.

The presence of the correct mRNA can be deduced from its predicted size and the fact that preproinsulin mRNA is made only by β cells. The researchers therefore expected to see an mRNA molecule about 450 bases long (including the poly(A) tail) that appeared only in extracts from β cells. This was indeed what was found.

The next stage was to make a DNA copy of the appropriate mRNA, using the enzyme reverse transcriptase. Box 2.1 mentioned that reverse transcriptase is typically produced by retroviruses. Since these viruses are capable of replicating only in a cell, they must first make DNA copies of their RNA genomes that can be read, transcribed and translated by the machinery of the host cell. Reverse transcriptase is the enzyme that makes this possible and it has a vital role in the obtaining genes from mRNA templates, as shown in Figure 3.2.

In order to make a DNA copy, the mRNA was therefore incubated in a solution with reverse transcriptase plus the four DNA nucleotide precursors – of adenine, thymine, cytosine, and guanine. A primer is also necessary to initiate DNA synthesis. It was mentioned earlier that all mRNAs have a poly(A) tail and so a universal primer consisting of a short thymine sequence serves this function with any mRNA. The immediate product of reverse transcriptase (see Figure 3.2, step 1) is a single-stranded DNA that is complementary to the strand of mRNA and is called **cDNA** The mRNA template strand is broken down (step 2) and then the enzyme DNA polymerase synthesizes the complementary strand, resulting in double-stranded DNA helix (step 3).

3.2 Inserting the insulin gene into bacteria

The researchers now had the 'gene' that they had been seeking in the form of a length of cDNA. How could the appropriate cDNA be introduced into *E. coli* in such a way that it would be copied and hopefully be translated into a protein?

One method of introducing foreign genes into bacteria is by using small rings of DNA called **plasmids**. Plasmids occur naturally in bacteria and are quite separate from the large circular DNA molecule that forms the single bacterial chromosome. Figure 3.3a shows both structures within the cell of *E. coli* and Figure 3.3b shows a typical, simple plasmid in greater detail. The ability of many bacteria to resist antibiotics is attributable to the presence of genes located on a plasmid, as in Figure 3.3b, rather than on their chromosome. Note too that

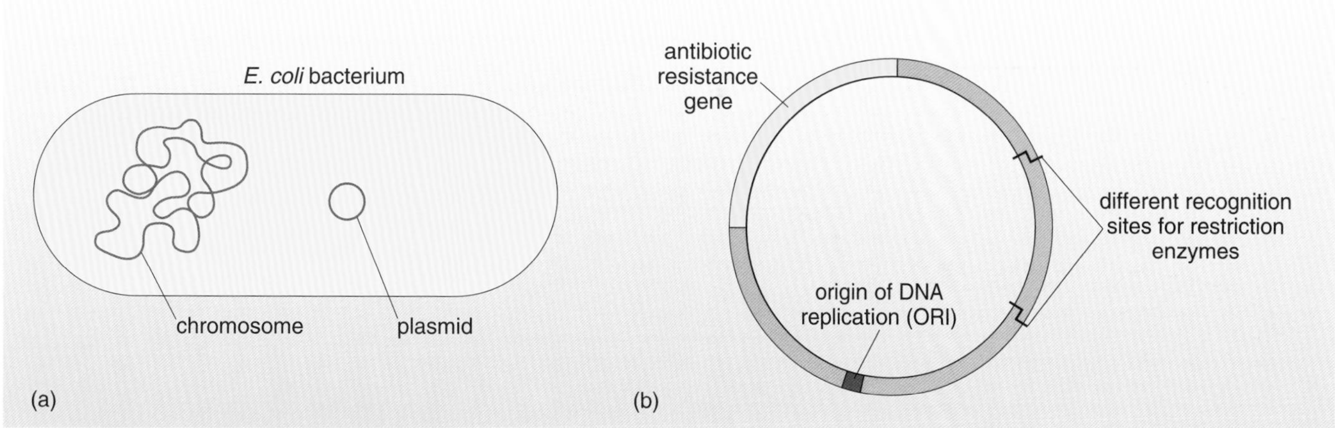

Figure 3.3 (a) A plasmid within a bacterium, adjacent to the main chromosome. (b) A plasmid in more detail, showing a gene that confers resistance to an antibiotic, plus two recognition sites for restriction enzymes.

plasmids typically contain a short DNA sequence responsible for the initiation of their replication, called the **origin of replication (ORI)**. What is also of great convenience for genetic engineers, is that the genes carried on plasmids are recognised by the host bacterium and can be switched on. So, theoretically, if it were possible to insert a new gene into a plasmid, and get the plasmid into a bacterium, the bacterium would start to make whatever the gene coded for, in this case, preproinsulin.

Plasmids replicate naturally in bacteria, beginning at a specific site, as shown in Figure 3.3b, and then pass into the bacterial daughter cells during cell division. Once a plasmid with an added gene (i.e. a **recombinant plasmid**) has been introduced into a single bacterium, all the progeny of that cell would therefore also contain the recombinant plasmids and such cells could be grown in culture indefinitely. It is therefore only necessary, in theory, to succeed in introducing a plasmid into one cell in order to produce, eventually, enough cells to fuel an industrial production line. The insertion of a piece of DNA from one source into another DNA sequence, and the subsequent copying of that modified DNA in such a way is called **cloning**. Any agent able to bring about such a transfer is called a **cloning vector**. Different types of plasmids, either those from bacteria or artificially constructed, are just one type of cloning vector. Cloning is a phenomenon we'll return to later in the topic; for the moment, think of it as a process of 'biological photocopying' of a particular gene.

In order to insert (or splice) a new gene into a plasmid it is necessary first to cut the plasmid at a predefined point and 'persuade' each end of the new gene to join to the cut ends of the plasmid, so that a new DNA loop is formed that includes the new gene. The molecular tools that make this very precise operation possible were first discovered in 1970. They are enzymes called **restriction endonucleases** or, more commonly, **restriction enzymes**. Such enzymes are able to cut double-stranded DNA at particular short base sequences, about 4–6 bp long; the plasmid in Figure 3.3b has two such sites. Each restriction enzyme cuts DNA at one unique sequence, called a recognition site, and no other. Restriction enzymes are produced naturally by bacteria and form part of the bacterial cell's defence against invading viruses. Because of their specificity, they are able to cleave viral DNA. (Not surprisingly, the DNA of the bacterial host is resistant to its own restriction enzymes; the sequences at risk are modified, normally by methylation of those bases.)

There are currently about 70 restriction enzymes commercially available; Table 3.1 lists nine of the more commonly used ones, together with the sequences they cut. One of the tricks in splicing a new gene into a plasmid is to use the same restriction enzyme to cut the ends of the gene that is being inserted and the plasmid, so that the cut ends match exactly. In practice, this is not too difficult to achieve. If the gene does not itself have a suitable sequence close to each end, it is possible to make short synthetic sequences that do contain the appropriate target sequence for the restriction enzyme. These artificial sequences are then attached to each end using the enzyme DNA ligase – the naturally occurring enzyme mentioned in Section 2.2 in the context of DNA repair.

The first three letters of the name of a particular restriction enzyme refer to the bacterial species from which the enzyme was derived, so '*Eco*' refers to *E. coli.* The abbreviation that follows, e.g. 'RI', denotes the strain of bacterium involved. Note that some restriction enzymes can act on more than one target sequence. *Hind* II, for example, can act when either C or T occupy the Py positions, and with either A or G in the Pu positions.

Table 3.1 The characteristics of some restriction enzymes, with cleavage points indicated by vertical arrows.

Enzyme	Source	Target sequence and cleavage points
Hind II	*Haemophilus influenzae*	G T Py ↓ Pu A C C A Pu ↑ Py T G
Hae III	*Haemophilus aegyptius*	G G ↓ C C C C ↑ G G
Bal I	*Brevibacterium albidum*	T G G ↓ C C A A C C ↑ G G T
Alu I	*Arthrobacter luteus*	A G ↓ C T T C ↑ G A
Eco RI	*Escherichia coli*	G ↓ A A T T C C T T A A ↑ G
Hpa II	*Haemophilus parainfluenzae*	C ↓ C G G G G C ↑ C
Pst I	*Providencia stuartii*	C T G C A ↓ G G ↑ A C G T C
Hind III	*Haemophilus influenzae*	A A G C T ↓ T T ↑ T C G A A
Bam HI	*Bacillus amyloliquefaciens*	G ↓ G A T C C C C T A G ↑ G

Provided the cut ends of the plasmid correspond to the correspondingly cut ends of the gene being transferred, they can be joined together. Looking at Table 3.1 you will notice that some restriction enzymes, such as *Hind* II and *Bal* I, make a straight cut whereas others, such as *Eco* RI and *Pst* I, make staggered cuts. The staggered cuts leave a short sequence of single-stranded DNA two to four bases long. When two sequences of DNA that have been cut by the same restriction enzyme are brought together, the complementary unpaired short sequences pair together. This is important as it makes rejoining DNA sequences much easier by holding the two ends together whilst DNA ligase acts on them to make a permanent link. Such unpaired end sequences are referred to as **'sticky ends'**. You can see how valuable they prove by following the sequence of events shown in Figure 3.4, where DNA from two different sources is joined, in the form of plasmid. The result is a recombinant plasmid, which combines DNA from the two different sources.

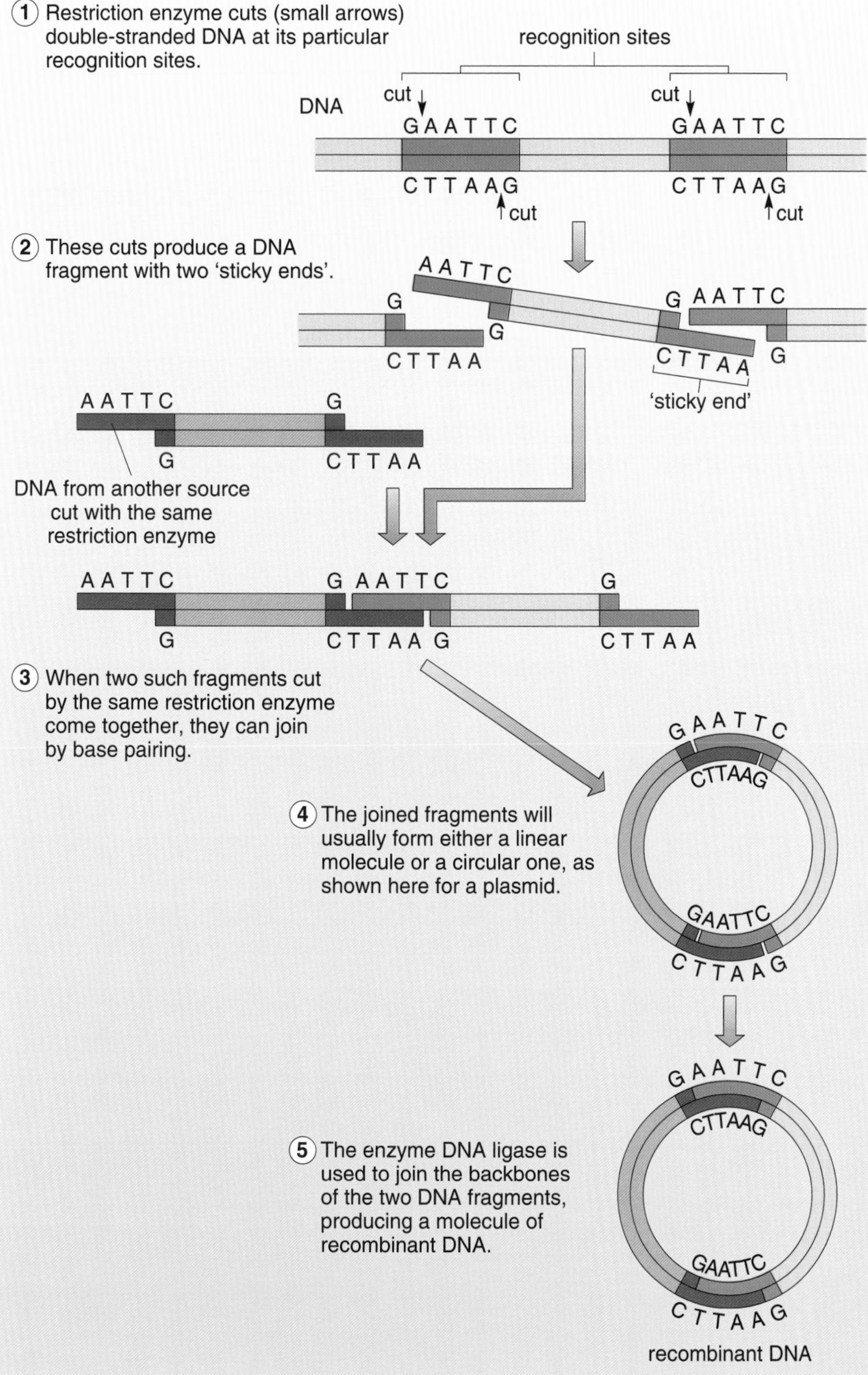

(1) Restriction enzyme cuts (small arrows) double-stranded DNA at its particular recognition sites.
recognition sites
DNA
cut
GAATTC
CTTAAG
cut
(2) These cuts produce a DNA fragment with two 'sticky ends'.
AATTC
G
CTTAA
'sticky end'
DNA from another source cut with the same restriction enzyme
(3) When two such fragments cut by the same restriction enzyme come together, they can join by base pairing.
(4) The joined fragments will usually form either a linear molecule or a circular one, as shown here for a plasmid.
(5) The enzyme DNA ligase is used to join the backbones of the two DNA fragments, producing a molecule of recombinant DNA.
recombinant DNA

Figure 3.4 Use of restriction enzymes, in this case using the same restriction enzyme on both source DNAs. The sticky ends produced mean that DNA sequences from two different sources can be joined, in this instance to form a recombinant plasmid, shown in step 5.

- Which of the restriction enzymes listed in Table 3.1 has been used to cut the two source DNAs shown in Figure 3.4?

- *Eco* RI, which has a recognition site in Figure 3.4 identical to that identified in Table 3.1.

There are a number of artificial plasmids that are compatible with *E. coli*, but the one chosen by all three groups of researchers on the insulin project was one called pBR322 which had been recently developed by researchers Bolivar and Rodriguez at the University of California. The advantage was the large number of different restriction enzyme cleavage sites it contains. Figure 3.5 shows the site of action of a few restriction enzymes – including a number from Table 3.1 – that are effective in this plasmid. This particular plasmid is also distinguished by two genes for antibiotic resistance. One of these confers resistance to the antibiotic ampicillin and the other confers resistance to tetracycline, the significance of which will become clear later.

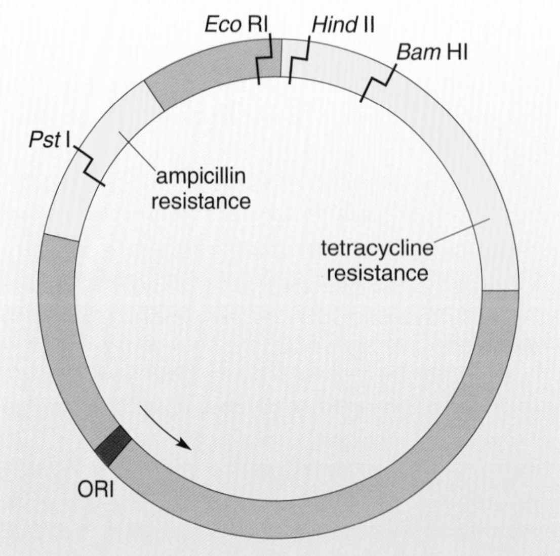

Figure 3.5 Structure of the plasmid pBR322, showing only those cleavage sites that correspond to Table 3.1 restriction enzymes. The arrow shows the direction of plasmid DNA replication.

Section 2.1 reminded you that for a gene to be expressed, it normally must be inserted next to a sequence called a promoter. This is where RNA polymerase attaches, initiating the transcription of mRNA. Given the way in which the insulin gene was obtained by the research teams, there would be no associated promoter. So how can one be introduced? Promoters are specific to different types of organism and so the insulin gene needed to be inserted next to an *appropriate* promoter, i.e. one that will work with *E. coli* RNA polymerase. The bacterial promoter chosen was that linked with the so-called lactose or *lac* operon, which you read about in Section 2.3. If you look back to Figure 2.6 you'll see that the β-galactosidase gene is one of the three concerned with the metabolism of lactose and that all three come under the influence of the same promoter.

So, the researchers made a cut at the *Eco* R1 site in pBR322 and inserted a complex of three different components – the *lac* operon promoter, plus the β-galactosidase gene (i.e. *lacZ*, see Figure 2.6) with the attached preproinsulin gene. The resulting recombinant plasmid is shown schematically in Figure 3.6.

If the system worked, in the presence of lactose, the bacteria would make a hybrid protein consisting of the β-galactosidase protein, with preproinsulin attached to the end of it. The researchers would then need to separate the preproinsulin section from the β-galactosidase. In order to do this, they hit on the ingenious idea of incorporating a DNA triplet for the amino acid methionine at the beginning of the preproinsulin sequence. When the methionine-containing protein is treated with the chemical isothiocyanate, one of the bonds that links this methionine with its neighbour is broken. All the researchers needed to do then was to treat the hybrid protein with isothiocyanate and the preproinsulin would drop off. This method could not have been used had preproinsulin itself contained methionine, but it so happens that this amino acid is not present.

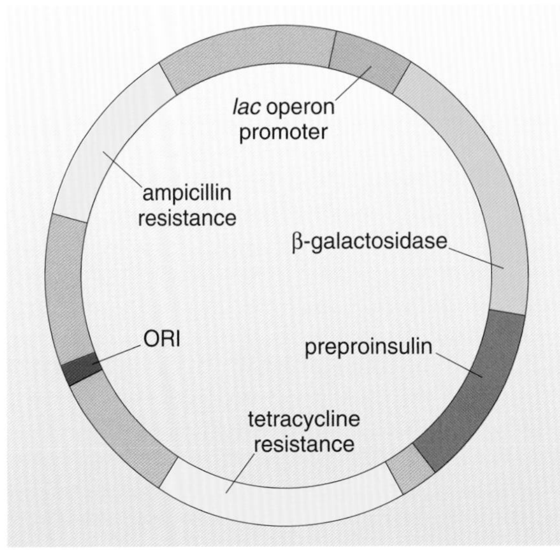

Figure 3.6 The pBR322 plasmid with the *lac* operon promoter–β-galactosidase–preproinsulin gene construct inserted.

- ■ Why would the method not have worked had preproinsulin contained one or more methionines?
- ■ The isothiocyanate would have caused break(s) in the preproinsulin protein chain.

Having prepared a suitable plasmid as a vector, it was necessary to persuade *E. coli* to take it up. Bacteria do not normally take up plasmids very readily, because they have cell walls consisting of complex carbohydrates that are impermeable to relatively large structures like plasmids. It is, however, possible to make these cell walls temporarily porous by subjecting the bacteria to a 'heat shock'. First, they are cooled on ice in the presence of calcium ions; then the plasmids are added. After a further 15–30 minutes on ice, the mixture is heated to 42 °C for a few minutes. Even using this technique, the uptake of plasmids is not always high and it is necessary to examine the bacteria to identify ones that had successfully taken up one or more of the plasmids, i.e. become transformed.

This process of identification of transformed bacteria is, in fact, more straightforward than you might think. First, you will recall that pBR322 contains genes for ampicillin and tetracycline resistance. 'Normal' bacteria are very unlikely to have genes of this type. The value of these resistance genes now becomes evident. Think about bacteria that have taken up the plasmids; such bacteria will be resistant to both antibiotics. If the bacteria are grown on media containing ampicillin and tetracycline, the bacteria that have not taken up the plasmids will die and the ones with the plasmids will survive and grow. So, these genes – very often generally termed **marker genes** – allow genetic engineers to identify which bacteria have taken up plasmids and which have not.

But a further complication is that not all bacteria will have taken up the *recombinant* versions of the plasmid – once a plasmid such as pBR322 is opened up by restriction enzymes, it may simply re-seal itself without incorporating the DNA sequences of interest. So some bacteria will have taken up a recircularised, *unmodified* plasmid. To try to prevent the formation of non-recombinant plasmids, the cut plasmids are treated with the enzyme alkaline phosphatase (AP) to remove their terminal phosphate groups. However, the action of AP isn't 100% efficient, so a proportion of non-recombinant forms do get through.

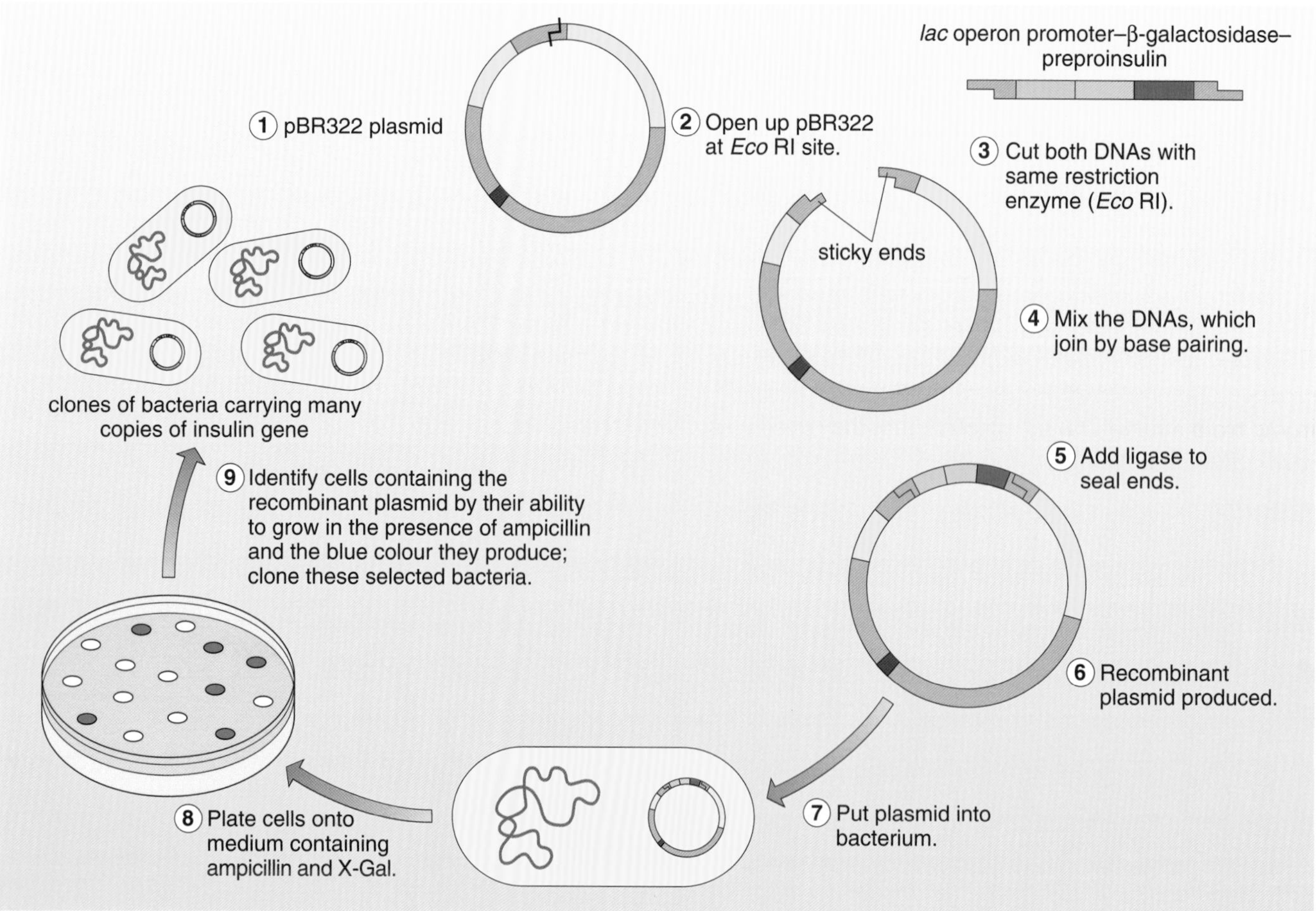

Figure 3.7 A pioneering method of cloning a gene in bacterial cells. Plasmid pBR322 is the starting point (step 1), which is then opened by *Eco* RI (step 2), and the *lac* operon promoter–β-galactosidase–preproinsulin gene construct (also obtained using *Eco* RI) is added (step 3). The DNAs are mixed (step 4), ligase is added (step 5) and the recombinant plasmid is formed (step 6). Steps 7–9 show the production of bacterial colonies, some of which contain the gene of interest. (This is a simplified description in order to illustrate the basic principles of this form of gene cloning. In particular, the construction of the recombinant plasmid involves more stages than shown in steps 2–4.)

But is it possible to tell which bacteria contained plasmids that had successfully incorporated the *lac* operon promoter, and therefore by implication, the β-galactosidase–insulin gene? The presence of β-galactosidase protein can be detected readily by growing the bacteria on an artificial substrate called **X-Gal**. β-galactosidase breaks down X-Gal (normally colourless) to produce free X, which is a blue dye. So if colonies of bacteria grow in the presence of ampicillin and tetracycline and produce a blue dye, there is a very good chance that the bacteria have taken up the recombinant pBR322 plasmid. The full sequence of events is summarised in Figure 3.7.

The final stage is to confirm that the bacteria are synthesising preproinsulin. First, it is necessary to convert preproinsulin to insulin by treating it with a suitable protease, which partially breaks down the protein. This enzyme excises the C chain and cuts off the tail sequence, to leave insulin. Insulin was detected by a technique called **radioimmunoassay**. Radioimmunoassay depends on antibodies that bind very specifically to particular molecule, in this case insulin. The insulin produced by the bacteria is allowed to bind to the antibody and then further insulin, which has been radioactively labelled, is added. The more insulin from the bacteria already bound to the antibody, the fewer sites will be available for the radioactive insulin to bind. The less radioactive insulin bound to the antibody therefore, the more insulin is being produced by the bacteria. Those bacteria found to produce insulin can be encouraged to reproduce to form colonies and their insulin product harvested.

3.3 A better system? – synthesis of artificial genes

Using techniques of the type outlined, both the Harvard and UCSF teams were able to show that insulin could be made in bacteria. Since that time, much the same technique has been extensively used to transfer genes into bacteria and to get the transferred gene to be expressed. Such methods provide a convenient means of making relative large amounts of complex proteins that are often difficult to extract in useful quantities from their 'natural' source or to synthesise by chemical means.

However, it was the Genentech team that won the race in that they eventually produced the system that is now used to manufacture human insulin. It is perhaps ironic from a historical perspective that they used a slightly different approach to the revolutionary method just described.

Remember that instead of trying to extract preproinsulin mRNA from β cells and produce cDNA, this team decided to make *artificial* genes for the A and B chains. They did this by synthesising DNA molecules that contained the sequences of DNA triplets that coded for the amino acids in each chain.

■ Are artificial genes produced like this likely to be identical with the natural gene?

■ No; recall the presence of introns in the natural gene. Also, you'll know from the earlier discussion of the genetic code in Section 2.1 that many amino acids are coded for by more than one triplet. Researchers can choose any triplet that can code for a particular amino acid and so it is very unlikely that they will, by chance, choose for each amino acid the triplet that occurs in nature.

■ Given that the A chain consists of 21 amino acids and the B chain of 30, what would be the minimum length (in base pairs) of each of the artificial genes?

■ A chain: $21 \times 3 = 63$ base pairs; B chain: $30 \times 3 = 90$ base pairs.

Using plasmids, each of these artificial genes was inserted separately – attached to *lacZ* in much the same way as the preproinsulin cDNA gene – into different populations of *E. coli*. The insulin A chains and B chains made by this method were then mixed together under appropriate conditions to make functional insulin. Insulin made by this method was licensed for clinical use in the USA in 1982.

Whilst the artificial gene method might seem more straightforward than isolating mRNA and using it to make cDNA, it is not easy to make very long sequences of DNA artificially without error. The method therefore only works with relatively short polypeptides and most subsequent attempts to clone mammalian proteins in bacteria used the mRNA to cDNA route.

3.4 Helping bacteria cells produce foreign proteins

What we have seen is that it is possible to use bacteria to clone eukaryotic genes and to get round some of the problems posed by the complicating presence of introns in genes such as that for insulin. But there is still a problem about the fate of many such products of eukaryotic genes within bacteria. For example, some are rapidly degraded. Fortunately, sufficient is known about the protease enzymes that bring this about to produce engineered strains of *E. coli* less able to degrade such protein products. Another problem is that many eukaryotic genes contain control sequences linked to particular forms of transcription and translation that are unlikely to have any counterpart in prokaryotes. You may recall the types of post-translational modification identified in Section 2.3 – we saw a very clear example in the case of insulin.

■ In what form is insulin produced by the process shown in Figure 3.7?

■ As inactive preproinsulin, i.e. the product of initial translation.

It helps therefore to incorporate into vectors a number of 'control' sequences that increase the efficiency of transcription and translation. These processes are different between prokaryotes and eukaryotes, so this is often far from straightforward. For example, there are components concerned with signalling the initiation of translation (often as a ribosome binding sequence) and its termination. Effective vectors also include a site where DNA synthesis begins, as in Figure 3.3 and 3.5, to allow their replication. Also, as you have seen, since cDNAs and synthetic genes have no promoter, one must be provided, just as in the modified version of pBR322 shown in Figure 3.6. Generally, a promoter typical of the host cell is positioned just upstream from the site of insertion of the foreign gene. You already know of the importance of marker genes, such as those for antibiotic resistance.

A vector that is engineered in such a way, suitable if possible for the transfer of any one of a number of foreign genes, is termed an **expression vector** and Figure 3.8 shows the features of such a vector for use in bacteria such as *E. coli*, again based on the *lac* operon. The precise details of the tasks particular DNA sequences perform need not be of concern; it's more important that you remember that their overall aim is maximise transcription and translation of the inserted DNA.

The different methods by which expression of the human insulin gene was achieved in the 1970s were, at that time, pioneering research at the very forefront of what has now become today's GM technology. The approach utilised by Boyer and Cohen (Stanford) was registered as one of the first big biotechnology patents which, over the subsequent years, yielded many millions of dollars for Genentech, UCSF (University of California, San Francisco) and Stanford in royalty income. In the laboratory today, the entire procedure could be achieved in just a matter of days. Further to this, with the completion of the genome projects from many hundreds of different organisms, researchers can pick and choose any gene they like from just about any species they like.

The use of expression vectors in GM technology is widespread, in a great variety of applications. Those used for prokaryotes are unlikely to be suitable for gene transfer into eukaryotes and you'll see in Chapter 4 how yet more elaborate vectors and techniques of transfer have to be constructed for gene delivery to plant cells, though they share some of the features shown in Figure 3.8.

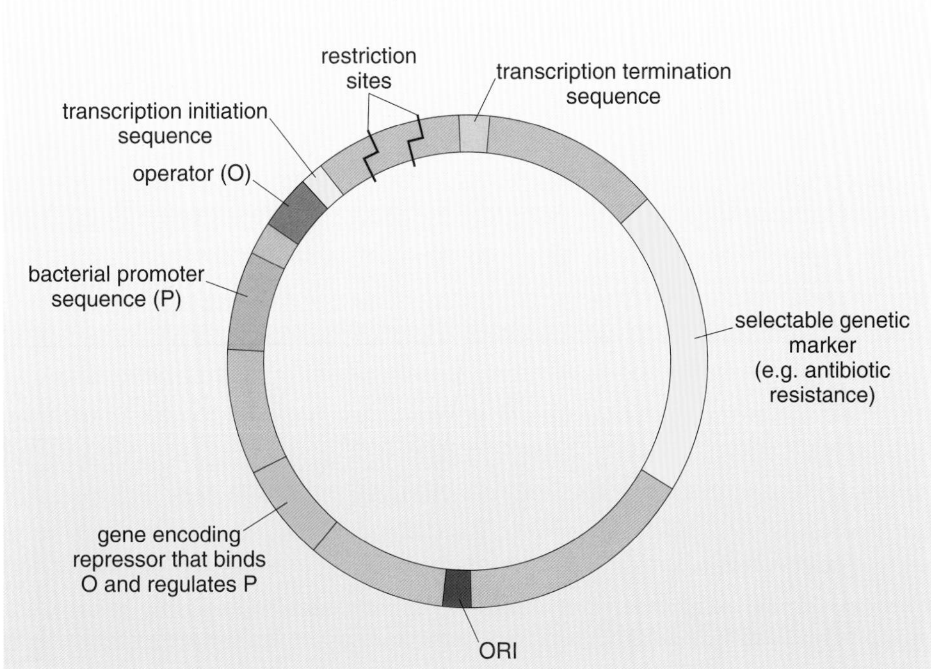

Figure 3.8 An expression vector, based on the *lac* operon, with bacterial transcriptional and translational control sequences. From Figure 2.6, recall the role of the repressor, which binds at O and hence modifies the promoter's ability to trigger transcription. The gene that produces the repressor is incorporated in this particular expression vector.

Summary of Chapter 3

A landmark event in genetic engineering was the transfer of the gene for human insulin into the bacterium *Escherichia coli.* Type 1 diabetic individuals are deficient in insulin; the hormone is produced initially as preproinsulin and subsequently cut during post-translational modification to form two chains of unequal length, linked by stabilising disulfide bridges.

To transfer the insulin gene into bacteria, double-stranded DNA was obtained from isolated mature mRNA using reverse transcriptase and DNA polymerase, to produce cDNA. The resulting DNA has a base sequence that corresponds to the coding sequences of the gene from which the mRNA was initially derived, i.e. intron sequences are absent. Restriction enzymes splice open bacterial plasmids – small, circular pieces of DNA, some artificially created, e.g. pBR322 – which often include genes for antibiotic resistance.

The *lac* operon promoter, which is linked with β-galactosidase production and is normally located on the main bacterial chromosome, was inserted in pBR322, along with the downstream β-galactosidase gene and the preproinsulin DNA sequence. Those *E. coli* progeny that demonstrate resistance to antibiotics had taken up pBR322; those where β-galactosidase synthesis can also be demonstrated (using X-Gal) had taken up the recombinant plasmid, containing the preproinsulin gene. After bacterial production of the preproinsulin, post-translational modifications have to be carried out. Insulin is more routinely produced from two separately cloned bacterial lines, via plasmids containing 'genes' for chains A and B respectively. Sophisticated expression vectors are able to increase the expression of genes transferred in bacteria, by incorporating sequences that control transcription and make translation more efficient.

Question 3.1

Identify the techniques that are used with pancreatic β cells to (a) separate mRNAs from other types of RNA, (b) separate insulin mRNA from other mRNAs present.

Question 3.2

The genes that encode for antibiotic resistance are often naturally present on bacterial plasmids, rather than on the main chromosome; why is this location helpful to genetic engineers?

Question 3.3

During the procedure shown in Figure 3.7, a plasmid such as pBR322 may not take up the *lac* promoter–β-galactoside gene–preproinsulin gene construct. The plasmid may simply re-seal itself or two plasmids may join together to form a single larger circle. How can bacteria that take up such non-recombinant plasmids be identified?

Question 3.4

A variant of the technique shown in Figure 3.7 uses restriction enzymes that have target sites *within* the β-galactosidase gene on pBR322; the recombinant plasmid hence contains the human insulin gene *between* two fragments of the β-galactosidase gene. How might those bacteria containing this recombinant plasmid and those containing the unmodified pBR322 plasmid be distinguished, using X-Gal?

Question 3.5

In cloning genes such as human insulin, why is it (a) advantageous to construct cDNA from mature mRNA, rather that the primary mRNA transcript? (b) difficult to work out the (then unknown) DNA sequence for the A and B chains from the known amino acid sequence of the polypeptides for which they each code?

The genetic manipulation of plants

Chapter 4

4.1 Introduction

In the next two chapters of the topic, we will consider the genetic manipulation of plants, and the production of GM crops. A great deal has been written about the science of GM crops and the controversial issues surrounding their introduction around the world. In the study time available, we will focus on a small number of selected issues.

In this chapter you'll have the opportunity to learn more about the science that has been used to engineer a range of GM crops, and examine both the science and social concerns relating to the development of a nutritionally enhanced rice, known as 'Golden Rice'. The chapter will extend your understanding of the techniques described in Chapter 3.

Chapter 5 will explore in greater detail some of the social issues surrounding the development of GM crops. These issues have been selected for their intrinsic interest and for the light they throw on all four of the course themes. You will explore some of the underlying ethical issues, some of the problems that occur when GM issues are communicated within and outside the scientific community, and how the supposed risks attached to GM foods might be evaluated. You will consider how public concerns about GM crops might be sampled as a prelude to decision making, attempting to balance the different interests of experts, industry and the consumer.

You are likely to have your own feelings and opinions about the development of GM crops and food. We would like you to explore these feelings before you embark on the study of these chapters, by taking five minutes to fill in an online survey as part of Activity 4.1. The questions were developed to assess the views of participants in a UK-based public debate called *GM Nation?*. We will explore this public debate in some detail in Chapter 5, and you will have a second opportunity to fill in the survey. You may find it interesting to see if your opinions change as a result of studying the scientific and social issues.

Your own experience of the GM controversy is likely to have been shaped by events in the country where you live. However, GM technology in plants raises issues of global importance, approached and resolved in very different ways, that often mix local, national and global perspectives. In India for example, attitudes to GM have been shaped in part by concerns about the influence of foreign multinationals, as opposed to home-grown technologies. India's Government supports local research into high-protein potatoes, high-yield mustard and drought- and salt-tolerant rice. But it has banned the import of maize or soya flour from US aid agencies, after several Indian environmental organisations protested against the GM content of such products. In the US, there is a generally high level of acceptance and utilisation of GM foods and there is no requirement to label products derived from **transgenic crops**. Clearly, many factors outside science influence decision making, and these may well differ between countries. We will explore some of these issues in Chapters 4 and 5, but initially, it is useful to have an overview of the position of GM crops globally.

Activity 4.1

Allow 40 minutes

Part (a) – 10 minutes

Visit the S250 course website and fill in the *GM Nation?* online survey. Do not spend a great deal of time considering your answers – the idea is to get a quick snapshot of how you feel now.

Part (b) – 30 minutes

The idea of this part of the activity is to gain an overview of what types of GM crops are being grown around the world. GM crops were first grown commercially in 1995 and the data here are for the year 2004. Begin by examining Figure 4.1, and Table 4.1.

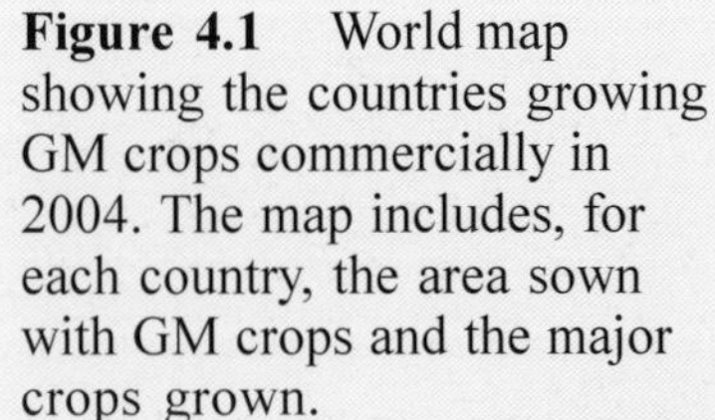

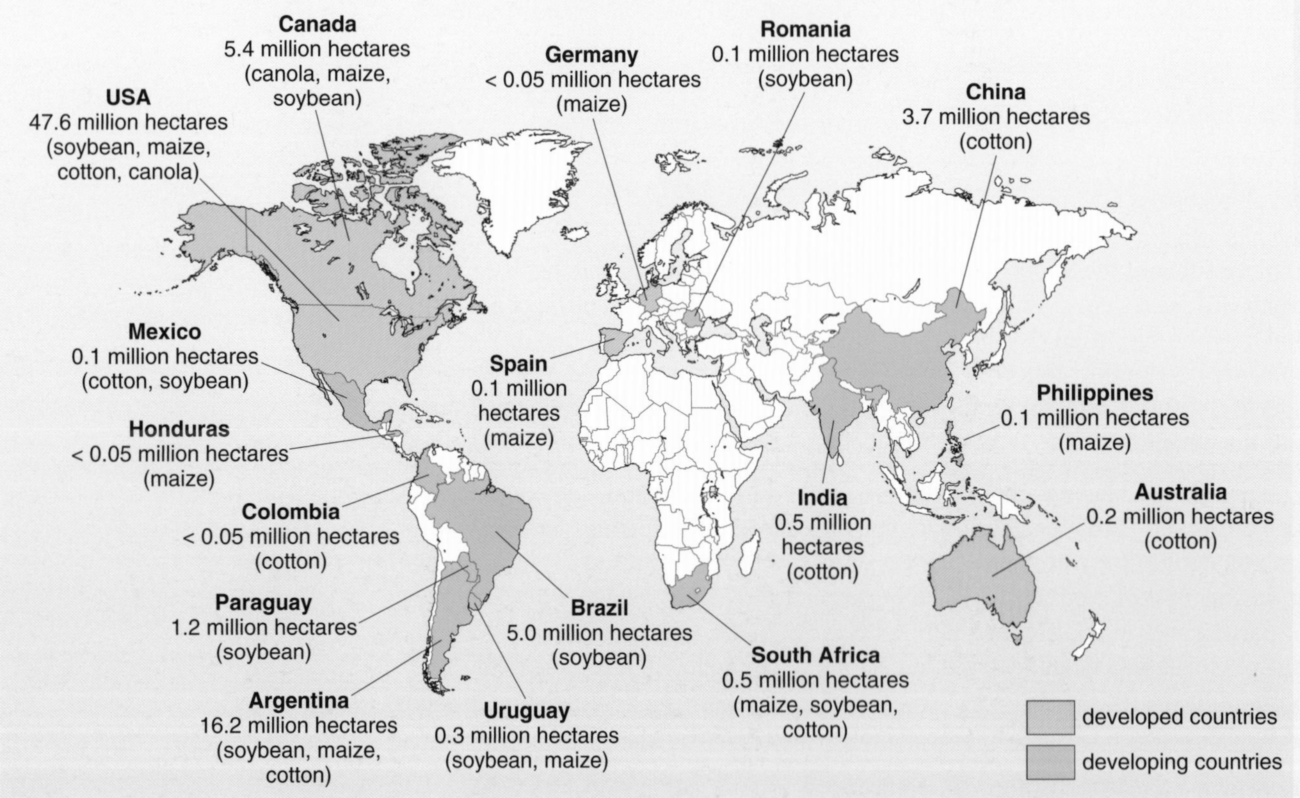

Figure 4.1 World map showing the countries growing GM crops commercially in 2004. The map includes, for each country, the area sown with GM crops and the major crops grown.

Table 4.1 The take-up of GM crops in 2004.

This table gives the area (in millions of hectares) given over to the cultivation of each type of GM crop: herbicide-tolerant, insect-resistant, and with both attributes combined. No other GM crops were grown on a significant scale.

Crop	Herbicide tolerance	Insect resistance	Herbicide tolerance and insect resistance combined	Total
soybean	48.4	–	–	48.4
maize	4.3	11.2	3.8	19.3
cotton	1.5	4.5	3.0	9.0
canola (oilseed rape)	4.3	–	–	4.3
total	58.5	15.7	6.8	81.0

Using the data in Figure 4.1 and Table 4.1, try to get an overview of which GM crops are grown and where:

(i) Which countries form the top five in terms of total area of GM crops, and what percentage of the area sown with GM crops is grown in these countries?

(ii) Given that a reasonable estimate of total area of cultivated land in 2004 would be approximately 1400 million hectares, what percentage of the world's cultivated land is used to grow GM crops?

(iii) In 2003 it was estimated that 47.3 million hectares were sown with GM crops in developed countries, with 20.4 million hectares in the developing countries. Find the areas sown in 2004 and calculate the percentage increase in each case. Comment on any differences you observe.

(iv) Use your answers to (i)–(iii) to write a few sentences (no more than 100 words) summarising the position of GM crops in global agriculture in the year 2004. It is important that you write down your thoughts at this stage, because you will be asked to look back at your ideas when you tackle later activities.

4.2 Genetic modification of plant cells

Your answers to Activity 4.1 will have revealed that the initial development of commercial GM crops has focused on the introduction of two traits: herbicide tolerance and insect resistance. However, many other traits have been introduced into crops that have yet to be grown commercially on any scale. These traits include characteristics such as resistance to viral, bacterial and fungal infections, stress tolerance (for example to high levels of salt in the soil), changes to flower pigmentation, and modification of plant nutritional content. You will explore the current global state of play in an activity at the end of this chapter, and it may be revealing to discover which, if any, of these traits have become commercially significant since this topic was written (2006).

At this point we will begin to explore how these transformations are carried out. Many of the techniques used to modify *E. coli* cells to produce insulin, discussed in Chapter 3, will again be relevant, but transformation of plant cells provides unique challenges, as they are much more resistant to accepting foreign genetic material. Luckily, a naturally occurring soil bacterium, ***Agrobacterium tumefaciens***, has evolved that overcome these challenges.

Flowering plants are classified as monocotyledonous and dicotyledonous. Monocotyledonous plants (monocots) have narrow leaves with parallel veins, and include the grasses. Dicotyledonous plants (dicots) have broad leaves with branching veins, an example would be a broad-leaved tree such as an oak.

4.2.1 Crown gall disease: genetic engineering in nature

A. tumefaciens causes **crown gall disease** in a wide range of dicotyledonous (broad-leaved) plants. The infection normally occurs at the site of a wound in the plant. The disease gains its name from the large tumour-like swellings, or galls, that occur on the stem, branches or roots of the plant. (Tumour induction is specific to these plants and is unrelated to gene-induced tumour formation in animals.) The galls often occur at the crown of the plant, the point where the

Figure 4.2 A crown gall on the trunk of an eastern red cedar, *Juniperus virginiana*. Unusually, in this instance the bacterium has infected a monocot. (The soil has been removed from the roots.)

main roots join the stem (Figure 4.2). During an infection, the bacterium transfers part of its DNA into the plant's cells. The DNA becomes integrated into the plant's genome, causing the production of galls and changes in cell metabolism.

A. tumefaciens can be modified to allow foreign genes to be incorporated into the genome of plant cells. In order to understand the processes involved, it is important to understand how 'natural' infection occurs.

Most of the genes involved in crown gall disease are not borne on the chromosome of *A. tumefaciens* but on a plasmid, termed the **Ti** (tumour-inducing) **plasmid**.

- ■ You have already met bacterial plasmids in Section 3.2. What are their main features?
- ■ A plasmid is a circle of DNA separate from the chromosome, capable of replicating independently in the cell and of being transferred from one bacterial cell to another.

The Ti plasmid is large, between 200 and 800 kb in size. However, a relatively small (12–24 kb) region of the Ti plasmid, called the transfer DNA (T-DNA), is integrated into a host plant chromosome during the infection process. This region is indicated in Figures 4.3 and 4.4; it contains the genes coding for both gall formation and for the synthesis of **opines**. Opines are modified amino acids. They are synthesised by plant cells within the crown gall and provide a source of carbon (and sometimes nitrogen) for *A. tumefaciens*, but cannot be used by the plant itself. Essentially, the bacteria hijack the biochemical machinery of the plant cells, using them to generate a food source that only it can utilise. You may notice in Figure 4.4 that the genes encoding bacterial enzymes used in opine **catabolism** (i.e. its breakdown) are also present in the Ti plasmid, but they are located outside the T-region.

The genes responsible for the transfer of the T-DNA into the host are also located outside the T-DNA region itself. These genes make up the **virulence region** and they encode proteins that facilitate the transfer of the T-DNA, and its integration into the plant cell's genome.

An overview of the events in crown gall formation is given in Figure 4.3.

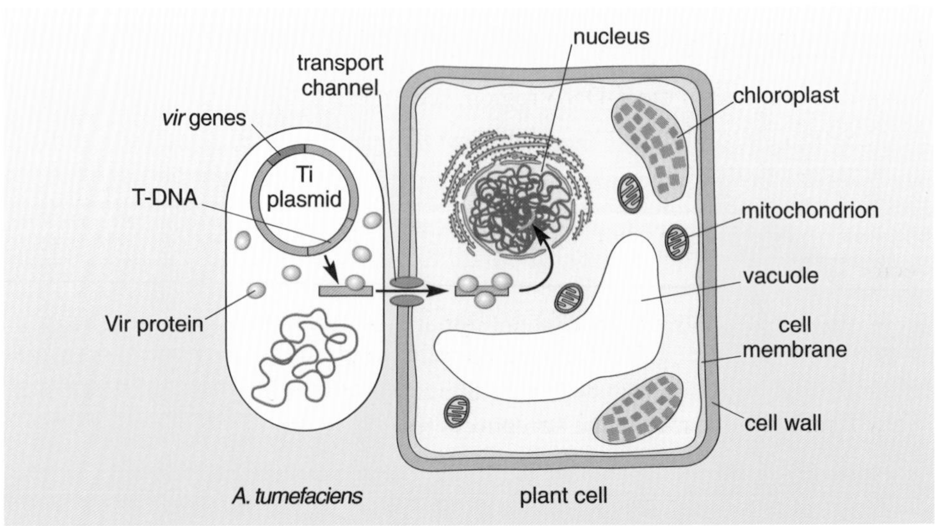

Figure 4.3 How *A. tumefaciens* genetically transforms plants. *A. tumefaciens* contains a tumour-inducing (Ti) plasmid, which contains both virulence (*vir*) genes and a transfer-DNA (T-DNA) region. The bacterium attaches to a plant cell, and the T-DNA and Vir proteins are transferred to the plant through a transport channel. Inside the plant cell, the Vir proteins promote the integration of the T-DNA into the plant genome.

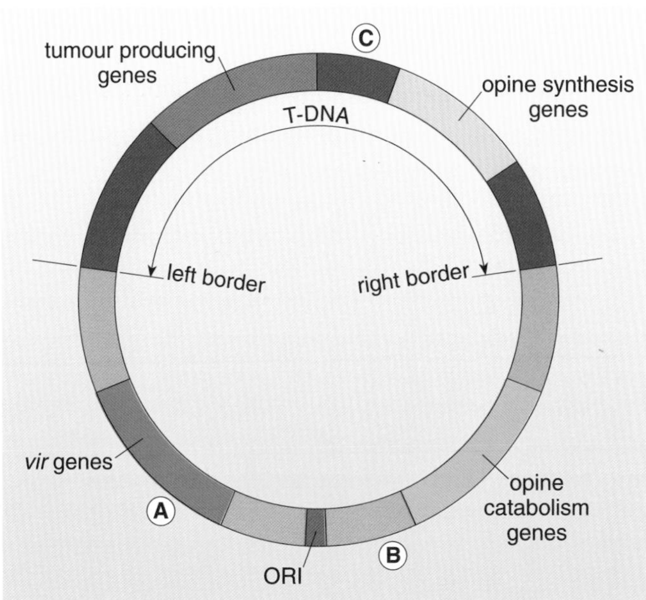

Figure 4.4 An enlarged representation of the Ti plasmid. The T-DNA has left and right borders at its extremities and includes genes that produce tumours and opines. Outside the T-DNA is the virulence region. This is a cluster of genes that encode proteins that facilitate the transfer of the T-DNA into the host. The origin of DNA replication (ORI) is a sequence specific to *A. tumefaciens* at which DNA copying starts, allowing the plasmid to be copied within the bacterium (see Section 3.2). Three positions, A, B and C, are marked for use in the question in Section 4.2.2.

4.2.2 Using *A. tumefaciens* to genetically modify plant cells

Genetic engineers have capitalised on the fact that part of the DNA from the Ti plasmid of *A. tumefaciens* is integrated into the plant genome during the infection process. Ti plasmids can be isolated and a foreign gene spliced in at an appropriate point, making it possible to transfer the novel gene into the plant.

- In Figure 4.4, three positions on the Ti plasmid are marked by letters A, B and C. Which would be the best place to insert the foreign gene?

- Position B is evidently no use since this part of the plasmid is not transferred during infection. Position A looks attractive but although the genes in this region facilitate the gene transfer they are not themselves transferred. This leaves position C; only the T-DNA is integrated into the plant genome, so the foreign gene would need to be inserted somewhere in this region.

The principle underlying the use of the Ti plasmid as a vector for plant transformation is that any gene placed between the left and right border sequences (i.e. within the T-DNA region, see Figure 4.4) will be transferred into the infected plant cell. However, as already mentioned, the Ti plasmid is rather large and, as such, difficult to manipulate using the techniques described in Chapter 3. Special procedures have been devised that allow the use of a much smaller 'artificial' Ti plasmids. We will describe one such procedure, the binary vector system.

An artificial Ti plasmid (Figure 4.5a) is generated that contains the gene we wish to transfer and a plant selectable marker gene (such as one for resistance to the antibiotic kanamycin) between the left and right borders from the T-DNA region. We will return to the role of the kanamycin resistance gene below, but you'll appreciate from Chapter 3 that its purpose is to allow us to detect whether plant cells have taken up the foreign gene.

The commonly accepted definition of an **antibiotic** is that it is a chemical which kills or inhibits the growth of bacteria. You are probably familiar with the use of antibiotics to treat bacterial infections. A more precise definition would be that antibiotics are substances produced naturally by various organisms (usually bacteria, fungi or plants) in order to limit the growth of, or kill other organisms. The organisms affected are usually, but not always, bacteria. Some antibiotics, like kanamycin, are toxic to plant cells; other antibiotics, like streptomycin are not. In fact streptomycin is used to minimise losses from certain bacterial diseases of apples and pears.

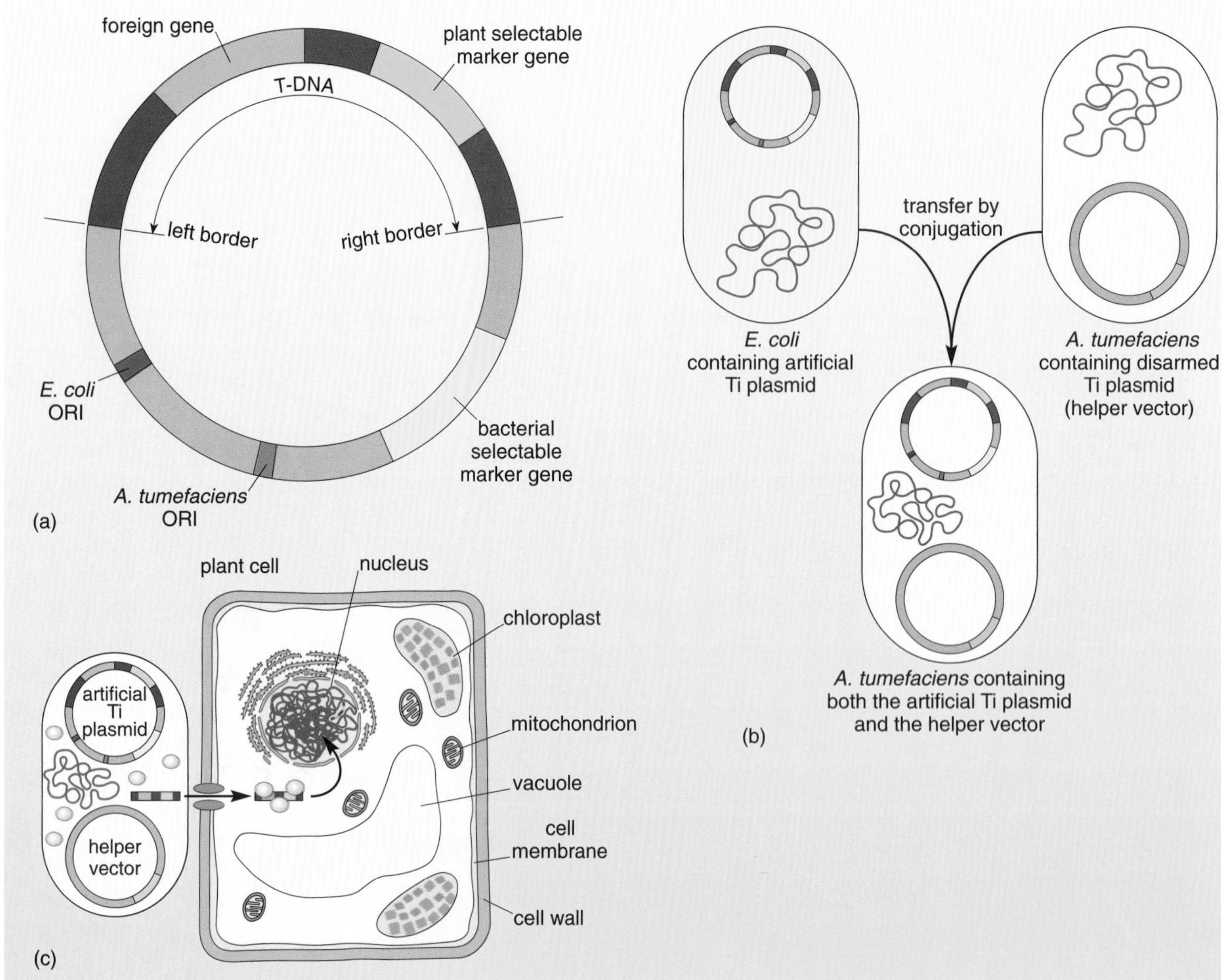

Figure 4.5 The production of transgenic plants using *A. tumefaciens*. (a) The artificial Ti plasmid. The T-DNA region will be transferred to the plant cell, and contains the foreign gene and a plant selectable marker gene. The marker gene will allow the identification of plant cells that have taken up the foreign gene. (b) The artificial Ti plasmid is generated in *E. coli*, and then transferred to *A. tumefaciens* containing a helper vector. This second plasmid contains the *vir* region which encodes the proteins that facilitate DNA transfer from the bacterium into plant cells. (c) The T-DNA section is transferred from this modified *A. tumefaciens* into the plant cell's genome.

It is important that the artificial Ti plasmid contains origins of replication (Chapter 3) so that it can be copied both in *A. tumefaciens* and in *E. coli.* Most of the manipulations required to modify the Ti plasmid are carried out in *E. coli* as indicated in Figure 4.5.

- What features of a normal Ti plasmid (Figure 4.4) are missing from the artificial Ti plasmid (Figure 4.5a)?

- The tumour-producing genes, the virulence region and the genes coding for opine synthesis and catabolism.

■ Which of these features is essential to allow transfer and integration of the genes in the T-DNA region?

■ Only the virulence region is necessary. The tumour-producing genes and the genes related to opine synthesis and catabolism are not required. We do not want the modified plants to produce galls, or for the transgenic plants to synthesise opines – it would utilise valuable resources.

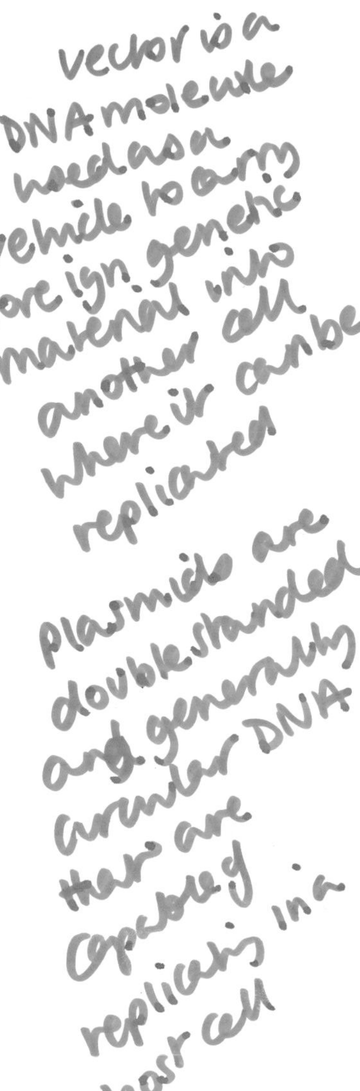

So, having constructed the artificial Ti plasmid, we now need a technique that allows the features of the virulence region to be present in the *A. tumefaciens*. Using the binary vector system, this problem is solved by including the virulence region (*vir*) in a second plasmid. This is called a disarmed Ti plasmid (see Figure 4.5b) because the entire T-region has been removed. This is often referred to as a **helper vector** and we will use this simpler term.

The artificial Ti plasmid is transferred from *E. coli* to *A. tumefaciens* containing a helper vector (Figure 4.5b) via a process known as **conjugation** – a term used to describe direct transfer of genetic material from one bacterium to another.

The modified *A. tumefaciens* containing both the artificial Ti plasmid and the helper vector is then used to infect the target plant cells. On infection, the virulence genes are activated and the DNA between the left- and right-hand borders of the artificial Ti plasmid is transferred to a plant chromosome. The full process is summarised in Figure 4.5.

4.2.3 From infected cells to transgenic plants

Unlike the 'natural' infection process, where only the cells at the site of the crown gall are affected by the inserted T-DNA, scientists wanted to introduce new genes into all the cells of the plant. Fortunately, most plant cells are **totipotent**, which means that any cell from any part of the plant is capable of dividing into cells that can form any or all of the plant's tissues. This means that, using appropriate growth hormones and other tissue culture techniques, a single infected plant cell can be induced to divide and form an entire, new, fertile plant.

In order to produce genetically modified plants, *A. tumefaciens* carrying the artificial Ti plasmid and helper vector are incubated with plant fragments (explants) for 48 hours. The explants could be leaf discs or **cotyledon** (seed leaf) slices or root segments. They have a cut surface and the wounded cells produced by the cut are the sites of DNA transfer from *A. tumefaciens*. The explants are then placed on culture plates containing nutrient medium, kanamycin and a growth regulator to stimulate the division of the cells to produce new plants.

■ What is the purpose of the kanamycin?

■ Kanamycin is used to selectively kill plant cells that have not been transformed.

Remember that genetically modified plant cells contain the kanamycin resistance gene, which we introduced as a plant selectable marker gene (Section 4.2.2 and Figure 4.5a). This means that modified plant cells can produce an enzyme that breaks down the otherwise toxic kanamycin. Untransformed cells cannot produce the enzyme and are killed.

New tissue develops at the site of wounding on the explants. New shoots that develop from this tissue are separated from the explant and induced to root. The plantlets that develop can be tested for the appropriate phenotype. If the results are positive, the plantlets are allowed to develop into mature plants.

The modified plants initially produced are crossed with established high-yielding varieties, using conventional plant breeding methods. The offspring are repeatedly crossed with the established varieties until a true-breeding transgenic line is produced.

Box 4.1 The gene gun – biolistics

Transformation via *A. tumefaciens* has been successfully practiced for many years and is now the main route used to create transgenic dicots. However, until relatively recently, this gene transfer method was thought to be of little use with monocots. This was a problem, because so many of the world's staple crops, like rice and wheat, are monocots. Alternative methods for transformation of plant cells have been developed, and microprojectile bombardment, sometimes referred to as **biolistics** (ballistics using biological components) is probably the most important. In this technique, a particle gun (or gene gun) literally shoots genes into plant cells. The DNA to be delivered is attached to tiny gold or tungsten balls (1–2 μm in diameter). These are put onto a disk which is placed inside the gene gun. A blast of high pressure gas propels the disk forwards at roughly the same speed as a bullet leaving a rifle. A screen stops the disk and the tiny gold or tungsten balls are launched towards the target cells. The balls penetrate the cell membrane and release the DNA-carrying particles. In a minority of cases, the DNA particles will then be successfully integrated into the host cell's DNA.

4.3 Common traits introduced by GM

We will now look briefly at the science underlying the traits introduced into commercial crops, which you explored in Activity 4.1.

4.3.1 Insect resistance

Insect damage causes huge losses of agricultural crops each year. For example, without control measures it is estimated that over 35% of current global cotton production would be lost. Insect control by conventional means is big business, and the sale of insecticides generates many billions of dollars of revenue for multinational companies. Unfortunately, insects develop resistance to insecticides over time, and this can force farmers to use ever increasing amounts to achieve control. This increases the costs to the farmers, and deposits ever larger amounts of toxic chemicals into the environment.

If plants could be genetically engineered to produce their own insecticides, the costs and hazards of insecticide spraying might be reduced or removed altogether. A number of strategies to genetically modify plants in this way have been developed, but the only crops that have been grown commercially at the time of writing (2006) have been the so-called **Bt crops**. These have been modified so as to produce an insecticide derived from ***Bacillus thuringiensis*** (**Bt** for short), another common soil bacterium.

When growing conditions are not optimal, *Bacillus thuringiensis* forms spores that contain protein crystals toxic to insects. Bt comprises a large number of subspecies and each one produces its own particular toxin. So, for example, *Bacillus thuringiensis* subspecies *kurstaki* produces a toxin that kills the larvae of Lepidoptera (i.e. moths and butterflies) and a toxin from the subspecies *israelensis* is effective against Diptera such as mosquitoes and blackflies.

Spore preparations derived from *Bacillus thuringiensis* have been used by organic farmers as an insecticide for several decades. When the target insect ingests the Bt spore, the protein crystal dissociates into several identical subunits. These subunits are a **protoxin**, i.e. a precursor of the active toxin. Under the alkaline conditions of the insect's gut, digestive enzymes (proteases) unique to the insect break down the protoxin to release the active toxin. The toxin molecules insert themselves into the membrane of the gut epithelial cells, setting in motion a series of processes that eventually stop all the cell's metabolic activity. The insect stops feeding, becomes dehydrated and eventually dies. The protoxin requires both alkaline pH and specific proteases before it can be converted to its active form. It is considered unlikely that humans or farm animals would be affected by the protoxin, as initial digestion in mammals occurs under acidic conditions. In addition, there are no binding sites for the toxin on the surface of mammalian intestinal cells.

Epithelial cells are the closely packed cells that cover both the outer surfaces of the body and the walls of internal cavities (e.g. gut, respiratory system) in animals.

These properties of Bt spores do make them a particularly appropriate form of insecticide, but there are a number of limitations. The spores are not toxic on contact – they must be eaten by insects during the feeding stage of their development, i.e. when they are larvae. Spraying has to be carried out when most of the insect population are at this stage in the life cycle. In order to encourage insects to eat the spores, they have to be mixed with appropriate insect attractants. Another limitation is that once boring insects have penetrated into the stems or roots of the plants, any spraying will be ineffective, as the spores remain on the surface of the plant.

■ What would be the advantages of modifying a plant in order to produce the Bt toxin?

■ The toxin would be present in the plant throughout the growing season, protecting the plant at all times. If the toxin is expressed in all cells, the insects will be affected irrespective of whether they are feeding on the surface or have bored into a root or stem.

Several crops have been modified so as to be insect-resistant by incorporation of Bt genes. These include tobacco, tomato, potato, cotton and maize. The insertion of the Bt gene directly into the genome of the crop allows the plants to produce Bt protoxin in their own cells. In most instances, the transfer of the Bt gene into crops has been mediated by *A. tumefaciens,* but microprojectile bombardment (Box 4.1) has also been used.

However, initial attempts to introduce the gene into a variety of crops did not produce plants with an effective defence against insect attack. Initially, the levels of the protoxin produced in the plant cells were too low to be effective. The problem was that the protoxin genes were not well expressed in plant cells. A number of strategies were adopted to increase the levels of expression, including the following.

- A shortened version of the gene was used, producing a smaller, but equally toxic, protein. This seemed to make it easier for the plant cell's biochemical machinery to produce the protoxin, and increased levels of expression a little.
- A particularly powerful promoter sequence was incorporated into the plant genome, alongside the shortened gene. This increased the levels of expression such that an enhanced insecticidal effect was observed.
- A synthetic version of the gene was produced, containing the DNA triplets more commonly used in plants rather than those found in bacteria. This resulted in approximately 100 times more expression of the protoxin in the plant cells, and provided the plants with significant protection against insect attack.

Theoretically, producing Bt crops, which express high levels of the Bt protoxin in their cells, should confer constant insect resistance, and therefore remove the need for application of any insecticide dusts or sprays. In practice, the system is not completely effective, and the number of insecticide applications is reduced rather than eliminated altogether.

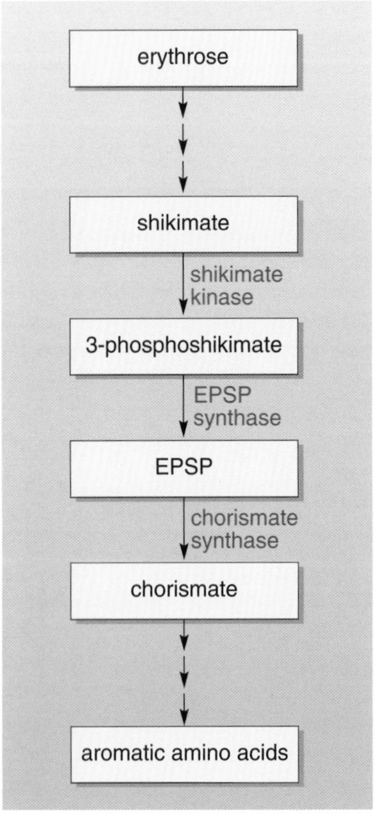

4.3.2 Herbicide tolerance

As you discovered from Activity 4.1, herbicide tolerance is the trait most commonly incorporated into commercial GM plants. A crop can be made tolerant to herbicide by inserting a gene that causes plants to become unresponsive to the toxic chemical. Before considering how the genetic manipulation can be achieved, it is useful to understand a little about how herbicides act.

Many herbicides work by inhibiting a key plant enzyme necessary for growth (if you're not exactly sure what this means, see Box 4.2). The herbicide glyphosate (also known as Roundup™) is the world's largest-selling herbicide. It is a broad-spectrum herbicide which can kill a wide variety of monocot and dicot weeds. It is particularly effective because it is transported downwards in plants and so has the advantage of killing the roots of perennial weeds.

Glyphosate inhibits EPSP synthase, an enzyme that is involved in the shikimic acid pathway (see Figure 4.6). The enzyme catalyses the conversion of 3-phosphoshikimate to the compound EPSP. (If you are interested, this stands for 5-enolpyruvylshikimate-3-phosphate, but this level of detail doesn't really concern us here!). EPSP is converted, via a series of biochemical reactions, into essential aromatic amino acids like phenylalanine, tyrosine and tryptophan. Glyphosate acts by binding with EPSP synthase, and in doing so, prevents the enzyme from catalysing the reaction. If the shikimic acid pathway is blocked in this way, the plant is deprived of these essential amino acids and cannot make the proteins it requires. The plant weakens and eventually dies.

Figure 4.6 Plants produce a number of amino acids via the shikimic acid pathway. Shikimate, a substance derived from the simple 4-carbon sugar erythrose, is converted via a sequence of steps into chorismate, which is the precursor of several essential aromatic amino acids. The herbicide glyphosate prevents the production of chorismate by inhibiting EPSP synthase. If you find following this sequence difficult, the information in Box 4.2 should help.

Box 4.2 Reading biochemical pathways

You may have come across biochemical pathways in your earlier studies, and you should also recall the simplified pathways in Chapter 5 of Topic 4. A key feature of all biochemical processes is that they take place in stages. Substances are made or broken down by an orderly sequence of linked chemical reactions called a **metabolic pathway**. Each chemical reaction in the pathway is catalysed by an enzyme. If the enzyme is not present, the rate of the reaction will usually be negligible. The precise mechanisms of these individual reactions form a fascinating area of study, but for our current purposes you do not need to have anything more than an outline.

To illustrate how these metabolic pathways are represented, we will look at an imaginary sequence of reactions, in which a substance A is converted into substance E by a sequence of four reactions:

$$A \xrightarrow{\text{enzyme 1}} B \xrightarrow{\text{enzyme 2}} C \xrightarrow{\text{enzyme 3}} D \xrightarrow{\text{enzyme 4}} E$$

Note that it is usual to represent the chemical transformation with a simple arrow, and to write the name of the enzyme catalysing the transformation beside the arrow. Such sequences usually focus on the most important chemical substances involved, and the less interesting participants are not included in the scheme. For example, many reactions will involve the gain or loss of phosphate groups or water molecules, but these are often omitted.

If for some reason, we wanted to block this pathway, we might try to prevent the action of one or more of these enzymes, a process known as inhibition. If, for example, we were able to effectively inhibit enzyme 2 in our sequence, we could slow or stop the conversion of substance B into substance C. This might cause the build up of substance B, and also prevent the production of our end product, substance E. The disruption of pathways in this way often severely damages an organism, and can kill it.

If crops can be made resistant to glyphosate, then the herbicide can be applied during the active growing phase without fear of damage to the crop. In the early 1980s, the biotechnology company Monsanto set about introducing glyphosate tolerance using a strategy that could be termed ‘overproduction’. Petunia plants were selected that were expressing high levels of the enzyme EPSP synthase. The mRNA corresponding to the EPSP synthase gene was isolated and cDNA prepared, in a way comparable to that described in Chapter 3. The cDNA was incorporated in an appropriate Ti plasmid, and the ‘gene’ was then used to produce transgenic plants using *A. tumefaciens* mediation. These showed 40- to 80-fold enhanced levels of EPSP synthase. The idea was that when glyphosate was applied, a proportion of the EPSP synthase would be inhibited, but sufficient quantities of enzyme would be produced to allow the shikimic acid pathway to function normally. Although the modified plants did show increased tolerance to glyphosate, the level was insufficient for commercial use and many of the plants showed growth retardation following glyphosate application.

Towards the middle of the 1980s, a different approach was explored. The idea was to discover an organism whose EPSP synthase had a reduced affinity for glyphosate but still had normal enzyme activity, so that the shikimic acid pathway could still operate normally. Although glyphosate is very effective in killing plants, some bacteria are able to tolerate it and these bacteria were potential sources of a gene coding for a glyphosate-tolerant EPSP synthase. One such gene was introduced into maize, using microprojectile bombardment (biolistic) transformation (Box 4.1). The novel EPSP synthase gene allowed the transgenic plants to continue producing aromatic amino acids in the presence of glyphosate, and conferred high levels of tolerance to the herbicide.

4.4 Golden Rice: a case study

In the previous section, you explored the science related to the development of the two traits found in the early commercial GM crops. Their production has been driven by commercial imperatives, and some of the widespread criticism of these crops has reflected a suspicion that they meet the needs of the multinationals' shareholders, rather than those of wider society.

As biotechnological techniques have become more sophisticated, new types of crop have become possible, and in this section we will explore the early stages of the development of one such 'second generation' GM crop, Golden Rice. The development of this crop differs both in the level of technological challenge, and in the type of ethical issues that arise. The rice has been modified to contain a precursor of vitamin A – a vital constituent missing from the diet of millions of impoverished people in developing countries.

4.4.1 Vitamin A deficiency

Vitamin A, more properly known as retinol, is an important chemical intermediate in a number of biochemical processes in mammals. It is involved in vision, and is found in the rod cells of the retina of the eye. These cells are particularly important in seeing at low light levels, and night blindness is a symptom of vitamin A deficiency (VAD). Vitamin A is also involved in the proper functioning of the immune system. Children suffering from VAD are prone to serious infections, and often die from relatively minor illnesses, like diarrhoea or measles. The World Health Organisation in 2003 estimated that between 100 and 140 million children worldwide were vitamin A deficient, of whom between 250 000 and 500 000 become blind each year. Of these, half died within 12 months of losing their sight.

Many plants and bacteria can produce vitamin A from simpler molecules, but mammals cannot. Humans can either ingest vitamin A directly, or produce it by the chemical cleavage of one of a group of molecules called **carotenoids**. Carotenoid molecules contain 40 carbon atoms, and mammals can chemically cleave a number of them to produce either one or two molecules of the 20-carbon retinol. A number of related carotenoid molecules are found in the human diet. The ones that can be converted into vitamin A are referred to as the provitamin A carotenoids. The commonest of these is β-carotene (see Table 4.2).

Table 4.2 Estimates of the retinol provided by common dietary carotenoids using the Retinol Equivalent (RE) and Retinol Activity Equivalent (RAE) scales. (See text for explanation.)

	Colour	**Mass (μg) equivalent to activity of 1 μg of retinol (RE scale)**	**Mass (μg) equivalent to activity of 1 μg of retinol (RAE scale)**
Provitamin A carotenoids			
α-carotene	orange	12	24
β-carotene	orange	6	12
β-cryptoxanthin	orange	12	24
Other common dietary carotenoids			
lutein	red	n/a	n/a
zeaxanthin	yellow	n/a	n/a
lycopene	red	n/a	n/a

The bioconversion of provitamin A carotenoids into retinol is not efficient, and different provitamin A carotenoids provide different amounts of retinol when processed by the human system. Various methods have been used to gain a rough idea of how much retinol a carotenoid will produce. Until very recently, the concept of a Retinol Equivalent (RE) has been widely used. This is a measure of the mass of a given carotenoid that will be converted to 1 μg of retinol in the human body. You can see from Table 4.2 that according to this system, it takes 6 μg of β-carotene to produce 1 μg of retinol. In recent years a number of nutritionists have argued that RE values overestimate the level of retinol produced by a factor of two. They propose a new scale, and use the term Retinol Activity Equivalent (RAE). Some institutions, like the WHO, still use REs, but this may change over the life of this course.

Whether REs or RAEs are used, estimates of dietary requirements can only be very approximate, as the precise value will depend on the source of the food, how it is prepared, and other aspects of the diet. In particular, in order to absorb the retinol, a certain level of fat is required in the diet. The efficiency with which different individuals metabolise the provitamin A carotenoids will also differ.

Nevertheless, the concept of retinol equivalents is useful to help measure the amount of vitamin A in the diet.

■ According to the WHO, a woman aged 25–50 should consume a recommended dietary allowance (RDA) of 800 μg Retinol Equivalents (REs) each day. If it were the sole source of retinol in her diet, what mass of β-carotene would a woman have to consume each day to meet this requirement?

■ Using REs, the table above indicates that 6 μg of β-carotene is roughly equivalent to 1 μg of retinol, so the RDA in terms of β-carotene is 6×800 μg = 4800 μg of β-carotene.

Figure 4.7 Carrots aren't just orange. (1)'Normal' (i.e. orange) carrots, in which the main pigment is β-carotene, with some α-carotene. (2) Yellow carrots; the main pigments are xanthophylls like zeaxanthin. (3) Red carrots; main pigment lycopene. (4) White carrot, with no pigments. (5) Purple carrots; here the pigments are not carotenoid compounds but a class of compounds called anthocyanins. Allegedly these carrots all taste the same!

This quantity of β-carotene could be found in approximately 40 g of raw carrots (Figure 4.7). If the estimate was calculated using RAEs, the figure would be 80 g of raw carrots.

The carotenoids form an important part of a balanced diet. A number of studies have suggested that they may have anti-cancer properties, perhaps resulting from their ability to act as **antioxidants**.

Vitamin A itself occurs in animal products, particularly in meat, liver, eggs and milk. Carotenoid compounds are found in a variety of vegetables and fruit. We have seen that β-carotene is found in carrots. Lycopene is found in relatively high concentrations in tomatoes.

■ What sort of diet will minimise vitamin A deficiency (VAD)?

■ Given the wide variety of foods that contain vitamin A and carotenes, any reasonably varied diet that contains sufficient fat will provide adequate sources of vitamin A.

VAD is a disease of poverty, found where people are unable to afford an appropriate diet. It is prevalent in countries where rice is a staple, particularly in South Asia. The rice plant itself does contain carotenes: they are found in both the leaves and the husks. Rice that has not been milled, brown rice, can therefore be an important source of both dietary fibre and carotenes.

However, white rice is often considered more palatable, and in many countries cultural issues surround the type of rice that is eaten. Unprocessed brown rice is seen as fit only for the lowest in society. Another factor is that milled rice is more easily stored. The husk contains a high proportion of oils which can degrade, causing the rice to become rancid if it is stored for a long time.

A strategy for ridding the world of VAD?

In July 2000, *Time* magazine announced that a potential solution to VAD had been found – 'Golden Rice' (Figure 4.8). This was a variety of rice that had been genetically modified to introduce β-carotene into the endosperm (part of the grain of the rice). The name arises from the fact that the otherwise white grains of rice are given a golden colour by the presence of carotenoid compounds.

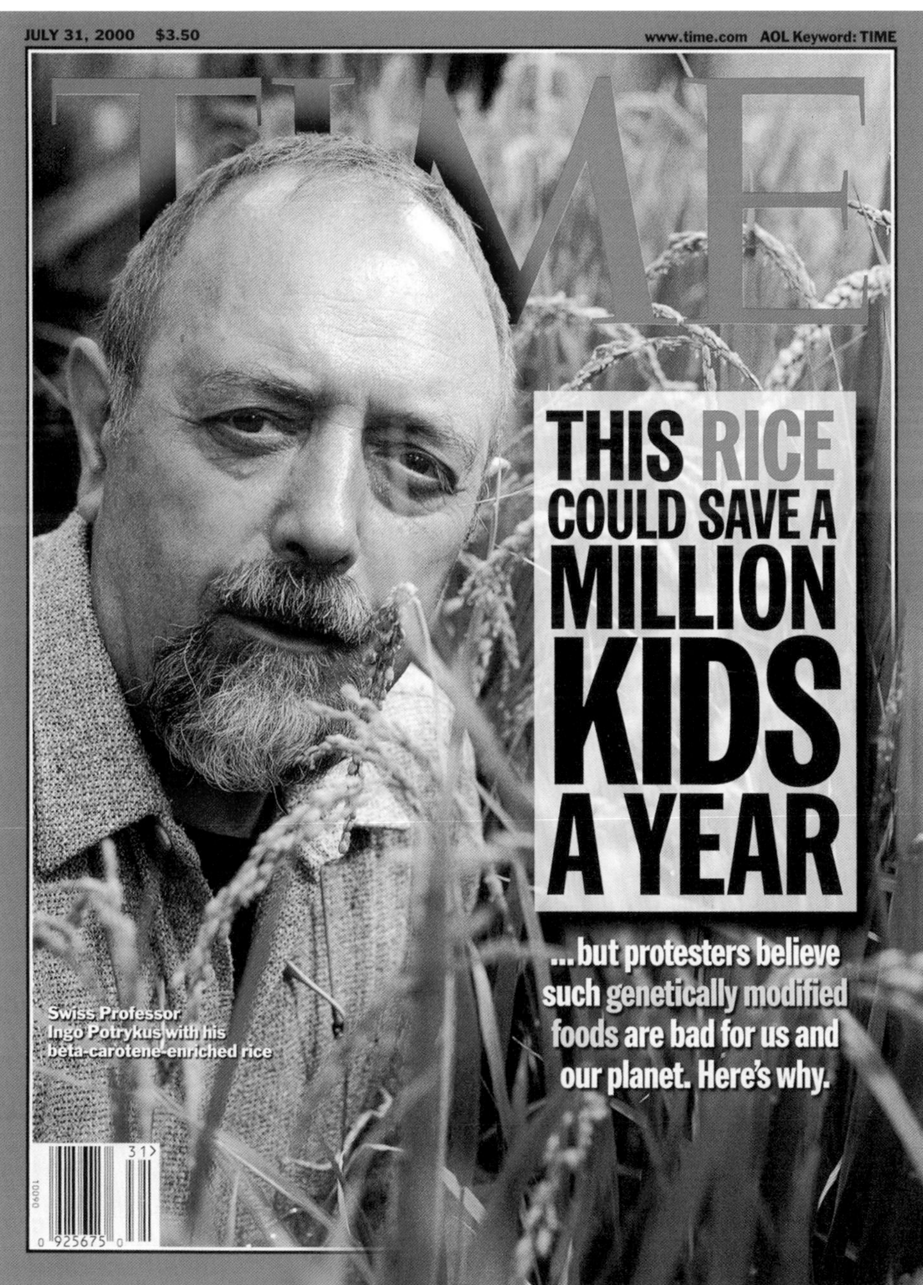

Figure 4.8 *Time* magazine announces the development of Golden Rice. Note that even at this early stage a dispute was raging about the benefits, or otherwise of this technology.

2000

The announcement came at the height of the global controversy over genetically modified crops. The previous year had seen thousands of anti-globalisation and anti-GM protesters gather outside the meeting of the World Trade Organisation in Seattle. Crops had been destroyed both in the UK and abroad. In India, peasant and trades union activists targeted the crops and offices of the company they saw as the major villain in the 'Cremate Monsanto' campaign. The share prices of the biotechnology companies suffered, and at one point the respected Deutsche Bank had advised against investments in companies involved in GM crops, declaring 'GMOs are dead'.

Many of the proponents of GM crops hoped that Golden Rice would prove more politically acceptable than the earlier, more obviously commercial crops. Here, potentially, was a technological solution for what people across the political spectrum could agree is an urgent humanitarian problem. We will explore further some of the debates about this new crop later in the chapter, but first we will examine the science involved.

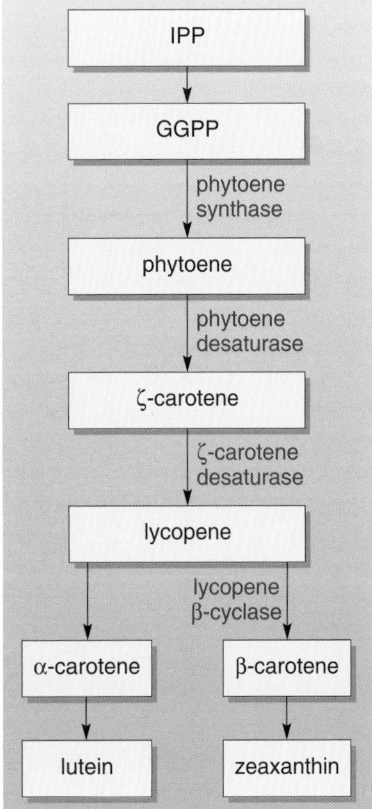

Figure 4.9 Carotenoid biosynthesis in plants. Carotenoids are produced in a series of interlinked steps within plastids, a type of organelle found in plant cells (not to be confused with plasmids which we met earlier). They are derived from a common precursor, isopentenyl diphosphate (IPP). The first step in the carotenoid pathway is the combination of two molecules of geranylgeranyl diphosphate (GGPP) to produce phytoene. (The symbol 'ζ' in ζ-carotene is the Greek letter 'zeta'.)

4.4.2 The science behind Golden Rice

Modifying crops to produce the Bt toxin (Section 4.3.1) was, in some ways, relatively simple. The toxin is a single protein and can therefore be produced as a result of the insertion of a single gene into the plant's genome. Similarly, introducing herbicide tolerance (Section 4.3.2) typically involves modifying the action of a single enzyme, and therefore modification again involves the insertion of a single gene.

β-carotene is not a protein. It is a hydrocarbon, i.e. a compound containing only hydrogen and carbon atoms. (Topic 4 Appendix shows the structure of β-carotene.)

- Is β-carotene coded for by a gene?
- Not directly; genes generally code for proteins. However, β-carotene is produced by a series of biochemical reactions, each of which is catalysed by a specific enzyme. Each of these enzymes (which are proteins) will be coded for by a specific gene.

The series of reactions that produces β-carotene in plants begins with the compound isopentenyl diphosphate (abbreviated as IPP). A common intermediate in many of the biochemical pathways from IPP, geranylgeranyl diphosphate (GGPP), is present in rice endosperm, but conversion to β-carotene was expected to require a four-stage process, involving four separate enzymes (Figure 4.9).

- Given that GGPP is already present in the cells of the rice endosperm, how many genes have to be introduced to allow its conversion into β-carotene?
- The process involves four stages, each catalysed by its own enzyme. In order to produce these four enzymes, four genes would have to be introduced.

The development of β-carotene-enriched rice was first proposed in 1992, by German and Swiss scientists, Peter Beyer and Ingo Potrykus respectively. At the time, the work seemed almost ludicrously ambitious. To attempt to introduce a single protein via insertion of a single gene was difficult enough, but to introduce four at once was surely too difficult. Potrykus had approached Nestlé, one of the world's largest food corporations, to fund the work, but was turned down. Eventually, he persuaded the Rockefeller Foundation, a charitable institution, to provide the funding to start the work.

Potrykus' team planned to introduce each gene separately into individual rice plants, and then perform conventional crossing experiments in an attempt to produce a plant with all four enzymes active in the endosperm. Their method of choice was to use microprojectile bombardment (Box 4.1) on cells from immature rice embryos. The initial results were encouraging, and introduction of phytoene synthase was unproblematic. Phytoene was shown to accumulate in the endosperm, and the plants were healthy and fertile. However, repeated attempts to introduce the second enzyme in the sequence, phytoene desaturase, failed to produce healthy plants.

The project appeared to have reached a dead end, but a new member of the project team came up with some radical new ideas. Xudong Ye had just finished his doctoral research in a related area, and was eager to continue his studies with Potrykus. Unfortunately his time with the group was limited, and he could devote only one year to the work, as he planned to go to America. In order to have any prospect of success within the timescale, and after discussion with his colleagues, he proposed restarting the work, using a new approach. His plan was:

- To introduce the genes using *Agrobacterium*-mediated transformation.
- To insert a bacterial gene encoding an enzyme that would convert phytoene directly to lycopene, in effect performing two steps of the sequence in a single transformation.
- To introduce the genes for all three enzymes that were needed at once.

The proposed simplified pathway is summarised in Figure 4.10.

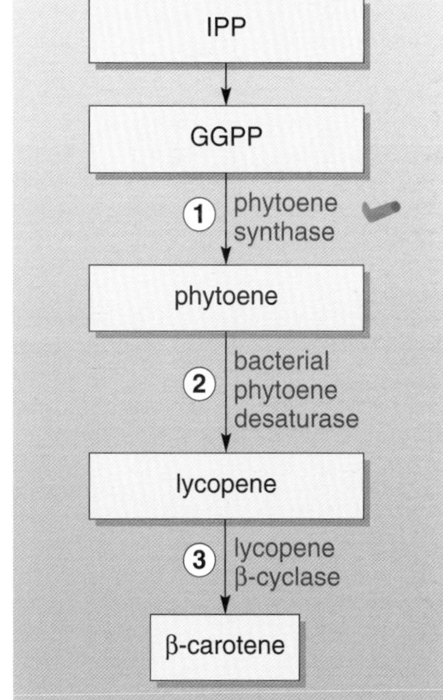

Figure 4.10 Proposed simplified route to β-carotene. What was proposed was that β-carotene would be produced in the rice endosperm by a three-step sequence: (1) GGPP would be converted to phytoene in the normal way, catalysed by phytoene synthase produced by a gene from a daffodil. (2) Phytoene would be converted directly to lycopene, catalysed by bacterial phytoene desaturase. (3) Lycopene would be converted to β-carotene, catalysed by lycopene β-cyclase, again produced by a daffodil gene.

Introducing sequences for three enzymes would be easier than introducing four, but despite using the generally more effective *Agrobacterium*-mediated Ti plasmid method, this would still be attempting to do a great deal of transformation all at once.

■ Why do you think that Potrykus and his co-workers initially used the less effective biolistic transformation method?

■ Rice is a monocot, and you may recall that, until relatively recently, the *A. tumefaciens* method was restricted for use with dicots (Box 4.1).

The necessary genes had to be isolated, cloned and spliced into the T-DNA of a Ti plasmid, using the techniques we have discussed in Sections 3.2 and 4.2. Remember that each gene sequence requires a promoter as well as the gene itself.

■ What is the role of a promoter sequence?

■ The promoter 'turns on' the gene, i.e. it causes the cell's machinery to start transcribing the sequence of DNA (see Section 2.1).

In this case, the promoter needs to be one that is specific to the endosperm, so that the gene will be expressed in the endosperm and not in any other part of the plant. Further sequences are also required, including antibiotic resistance genes or other selection markers, sequences that allow some of the enzymes to be bound to a membrane within the cell, and sequences that produce proteins facilitating transport of the enzymes from the cytoplasm of the cell into specific organelles. The details of these sequences do not really concern us here, but it is important to appreciate that in order to introduce a gene for each enzyme, a whole series of sequences have to be introduced.

The team undertook two experiments, in each case using *A. tumefaciens* and the binary vector system described in Section 4.2.2. The technique involved the infection of immature rice embryos, rather than fragments of mature plants.

- Experiment 1: The team produced *A. tumefaciens* with an artificial Ti plasmid containing the series of sequences necessary to introduce active phytoene synthase and the bacterial phytoene desaturase. They attempted to infect around 800 immature rice embryos, of which 50 were found to have taken up the sequences. These embryos would be expected to produce only the first two of the enzymes required, those needed to convert GGPP to lycopene.
- Experiment 2: The team produced two types of modified *A. tumefaciens.* Type A contained all the sequences necessary for active phytoene synthase and the bacterial phytoene desaturase enzyme, as previously. Type B contained the series of sequences necessary to introduce the final enzyme in the biosynthesis, lycopene β-cyclase. 500 immature rice embryos were infected with both types of *A. tumefaciens* at once. Sixty embryos could be shown to have been infected by type A, but only 12 to have been infected by both types of *A. tumefaciens*.

The team was able to grow the 50 rice embryos from Experiment 1 and the 12 doubly infected embryos from Experiment 2 into mature rice plants. They allowed the plants to self-fertilise, and go on to produce a crop of rice (Figure 4.11).

■ Look again at Figures 4.9 and 4.10. Assuming the enzymes are expressed and active in both cases, what intermediates from the β-carotene pathway would you expect to see produced in the rice grains from each experiment?

■ From Experiment 1 we might expect to see increased levels of lycopene, compared to unmodified grains. In Experiment 2 we would expect to see increased levels of β-carotene.

As lycopene is red and carotene is yellow-orange, if significant amounts of the products were present we might expect Experiment 1 to produce red rice grains, while Experiment 2 would produce the expected 'golden' rice. In fact, both experiments produced grains that showed a more or less intense yellow colour (Figure 4.11). Both lines could be shown to contain β-carotene, along with lutein and zeaxanthin, which are also products of the carotene biosynthetic pathway.

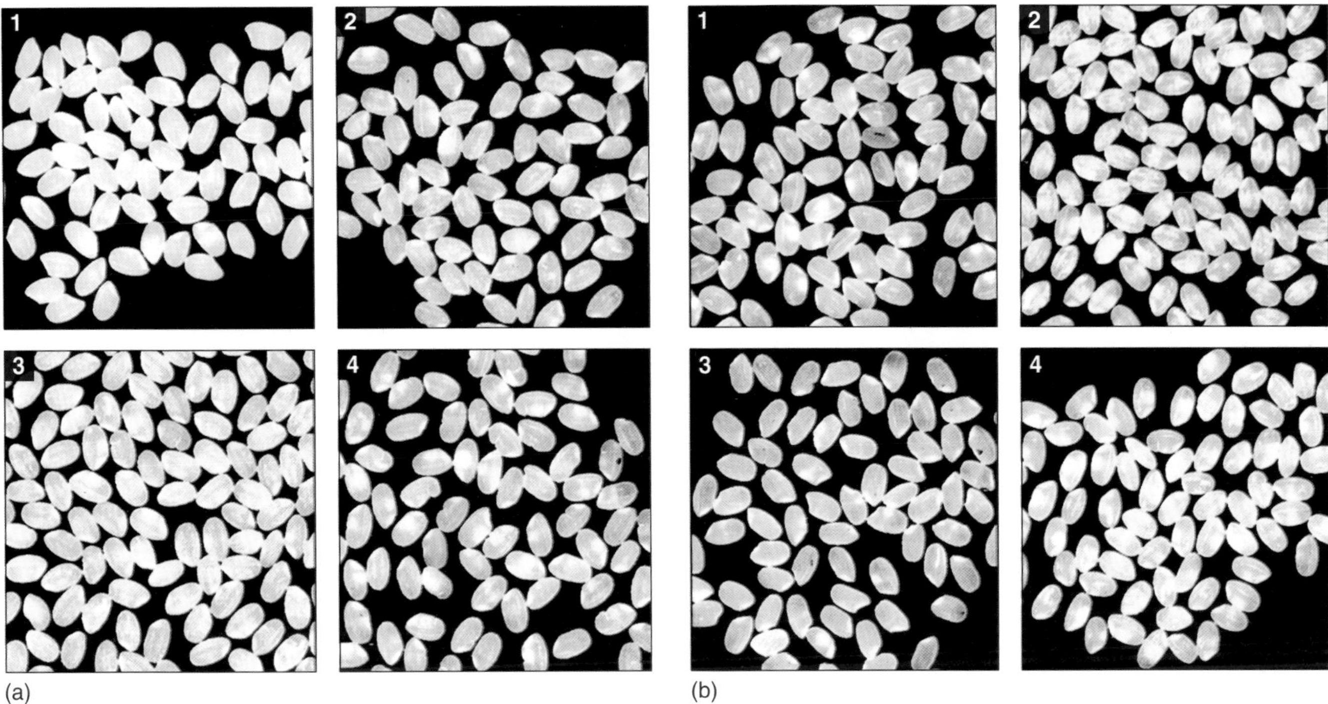

Figure 4.11 Polished rice grains derived from Experiments 1 and 2. (a) Panel 1 shows unmodified rice, the control; panels 2, 3 and 4 show rice derived from three different plants from Experiment 1. (b) Panels 1 to 4 show rice derived from four different plants from Experiment 2. Note that at lower concentrations, β-carotene will give a yellow rather than an orange colouration.

- We predicted that Experiment 1 might produce red rice. What has happened?
- The rice unexpectedly showed a yellow colouration, strongly suggesting that any (red) lycopene produced had been converted to yellow β-carotene. It appears that the rice grains are able to produce their own lycopene β-cyclase. It may be that at high concentrations of lycopene, the production of this enzyme is induced, or it may be that the enzyme is already present.

The fact that only two of the three genes had to be introduced was an unexpected bonus, and remember that initially the expectation was that four genes would be necessary. Subsequent work in a number of research teams has concentrated on introducing the genes for phytoene synthase and phytoene desaturase.

A great deal of work remained to be done before anyone could imagine the rice being grown for human consumption, but this genetically modified rice represented a huge technical breakthrough. Whatever your opinions about genetic manipulation, it is hard not to admire the ingenuity of the work.

4.4.3 Golden Rice in the public domain

In January 2000, the successful experiments were announced in a paper published in the American journal *Science*. This, in itself, is significant. Generally, work on genetic manipulation would be published in one of a number of more specialist journals. Publication in a journal like *Science* indicates that this was important work, likely to be of interest to a wider audience. In its 'Notes for Authors', the journal states that 'Priority is given to papers that reveal novel concepts of broad interest'. This rules out the majority of research work, and publication in *Science* is seen as a huge achievement in its own right.

Publication of a paper in a journal like *Science* tends to serve two purposes. First, it announces new results to a community of specialists within a particular area of science, in this case biotechnologists and crop scientists. Secondly, it promotes the work to a wider audience of scientists outside the specialism, including journalists, sociologists of science and interested members of the public.

To emphasise the importance of this work, the paper was accompanied by an extended editorial by Mary Guerinot (a member of the journal's editorial panel) explaining its significance. 1700 copies of the editorial were circulated to journalists across the world. It made clear the expectations of the work, and placed it firmly in the context of the debate over GM crops:

> The road to better nutrition is not paved with gold and, hence, agribusiness has not centred its efforts on the nutritional value of food. The work that culminated in the production of golden rice was funded by grants from the Rockefeller Foundation, the Swiss Federal Institute of Technology and the European Community Biotech Program. Like the plant varieties that made the Green Revolution so successful, the rice engineered to produce provitamin A will be freely available to the farmers who need it most. One can only hope that this application of plant genetic engineering to ameliorate human misery without regard to short-term profit will restore this technology to political acceptability.

The 'Green Revolution' refers to the large increases in agricultural productivity resulting from the introduction of new varieties, fertilisers and irrigation techniques during the 1960s in the developing world.

Activity 4.2

Allow 10 minutes

Read the above short extract carefully and try to summarise the key points Guerinot is making. Use no more than 50 words.

You may have also noticed that Guerinot implies that the Green Revolution was an unproblematic 'good thing'. This is hotly disputed by those who have campaigned against GM, particularly those based in developing countries (see, for example, Extract 4.1 overleaf).

The promotion of the work by *Science* and others did not go unnoticed. We have seen that news magazines like *Time* took up the story. Potrykus counted 30 TV broadcasts and 300 newspaper articles in the first year. The biotechnology industry saw the development of Golden Rice as a chance to capitalise on some good publicity. Monsanto and other biotechnology companies initiated a multimillion pound advertising campaign.

The campaigners against GM were also quick to respond. One of the most prominent amongst these was Vandana Shiva, an Indian ecological activist. Her article was widely reproduced on the Internet, an edited extract is reproduced here as Extract 4.1, which you should read now.

Extract 4.1 The 'Golden Rice' hoax – When public relations replaces science

by Dr Vandana Shiva

Golden rice has been heralded as the miracle cure for malnutrition and hunger of which 800 million members of the human community suffer.

Herbicide-resistant and toxin-producing genetically engineered plants can be objectionable because of their ecological and social costs. But who could possibly object to rice engineered to produce vitamin A, a deficiency found in nearly 3 million children, largely in the Third World?

Unfortunately, vitamin A rice is a hoax, and will bring further dispute to plant genetic engineering where public relations exercises seem to have replaced science in promotion of untested, unproven and unnecessary technology. The problem is that vitamin A rice will not remove vitamin A deficiency (VAD). It will seriously aggravate it.

It is a technology that fails in its promise. Currently, it is not even known how much vitamin A the genetically engineered rice will produce. The goal is 33.3 μg/100 g of rice.

Even if this goal is reached after a few years, it will be totally ineffective in removing VAD. Since the daily average requirement of vitamin A is 750 μg and one serving contains 30 g of rice, on a dry weight basis, vitamin A rice would only provide 9.9 μg, which is 1.32% of the required allowance.

Even taking the 100 g figure of daily consumption of rice used in the technology transfer paper would only provide 4.4% of the RDA. This is a recipe for creating hunger and malnutrition, not solving it. Besides creating vitamin A deficiency, vitamin A rice will also create deficiency in other micronutrients and nutrients. Raw milled rice has a low content of fat (0.5 g/100 g). Since fat is necessary for vitamin A uptake, this will aggravate vitamin A deficiency. It also has only 6.8 g/100 g of protein, which means less carrier molecules. It has only 0.7 g/100 g of iron, which plays a vital role in the conversion of β-carotene to vitamin A.

A far more efficient route to removing vitamin A deficiency is biodiversity conservation and propagation of naturally vitamin A rich plants in agriculture and diets. In spite of the diversity of plants evolved and bred for their rich vitamin A content, a report of the major science academies of the world has stated:

> Vitamin A deficiency causes half a million children to become partially or totally blind each year. Traditional breeding methods have been unsuccessful in producing crops containing a high vitamin A concentration, [...] Golden Rice, may be a useful tool to help treat the problem of vitamin A deficiency in young children living in the tropics.

It appears as if the world's top scientists suffer a more severe form of blindness than children in poor countries. The statement that 'traditional breeding has been unsuccessful in producing crops high in vitamin A' is not true given the diversity of plants and crops that Third World farmers, especially women, have bred and used which are rich sources of vitamin A.

Women in Bengal use more than 200 varieties of field greens. Over 3 million people have benefited greatly from a food based project for removing VAD by increasing vitamin A availability through home gardens. The higher the diversity crops the better the uptake of provitamin A.

The reason there is vitamin A deficiency in India, in spite of the rich biodiversity and indigenous knowledge base, is because the Green Revolution technologies wiped out biodiversity by converting mixed cropping systems to monocultures of wheat and rice and by spreading the use of herbicides which destroy field greens.

Genetically engineered vitamin A rice will aggravate this destruction since it is part of an industrial agriculture, intensive input package. It will also lead to major water scarcity since it is a water-intensive crop and displaces water-prudent sources of vitamin A.

Activity 4.3

Allow 30 minutes

(a) Dr Shiva states that Potrykus and the other developers of Golden Rice aim to develop rice containing 33.3 μg of vitamin A per 100 g of rice. In Potrykus's *Science* paper, the authors in fact say that their 'goal is providing at least 2 μg/g provitamin A'. Can you see any discrepancy here? If so, can you explain how it has arisen?

(b) Summarise, in your own words, the main points of criticism in the extract. You should not exceed 100 words.

4.4.4 The ongoing story

At the time of writing (2006), the Golden Rice tale is an unfinished story. Some of the developments of the last five years are summarised here.

One area of ongoing scientific dispute is the question of whether the enriched rice can contribute significantly to the alleviation of vitamin A deficiency. We have seen that Shiva estimated that at best 100 g of rice a day would provide 4.4% of the recommended daily allowance. More sophisticated theoretical models, published since that time, have taken into account differing levels of rice consumption amongst different sectors of the population in Asia. They have estimated that Golden Rice might provide between 1 and 15% of the RDA. These are theoretical studies; as yet, the rice has not been produced in sufficient quantities to test how much vitamin A it might provide when cooked and eaten. When expressed as a proportion of the RDA, the quantities of vitamin A supplied appear modest. However, when vulnerable people like children and nursing mothers are suffering from poor diets, even such modest increases might have a significant impact on health.

It remains a point of contention, however, whether the money spent on developing Golden Rice might not be better spent elsewhere. One alternative would be to integrate vitamin A supplementation with vaccination campaigns. Such campaigns have proved effective in reducing the effects of childhood VAD in Vietnam and the Philippines. We have seen that ecological campaigners like Shiva argue for educational campaigns to encourage the growth and consumption of green vegetables as a source of vitamin A.

Since the initial publication of the breakthrough, Potrykus and others have continued to work on the project. Recent results have seen the technology used on the more widely consumed Indica rice varieties rather than the short-grain Japonica variety used in the initial work. Like many other biotechnologists, they have also moved away from using antibiotic resistance markers, reflecting the concern that the resistance might be transferred to wild bacteria.

This is an interesting instance of the way that public concerns can influence the way that science is carried out. There is little direct evidence that such transfer of antibiotic resistance has taken place, but public concern over the issue has been widespread since the early days of genetic modification. The response of scientists has been to develop a range of other selection markers.

Potrykus and his co-workers have established a Golden Rice Humanitarian Board to facilitate the development of related research in developing countries. Whilst the invention of Golden Rice is registered as belonging to Potrykus and colleagues, many of the basic techniques they used are under patent. Various corporations from the agricultural biotechnology sector, who hold patents on some of the techniques used, have granted licences that allow 'freedom-to-operate for humanitarian purposes'. This is agreed to mean that farmers and traders in developing countries can earn no more than $10 000 per annum from Golden Rice. Various projects are currently underway in the Philippines, Vietnam, India, China, Indonesia and South Africa, but as yet the rice has not been grown commercially.

Recently, a group of scientists working for Syngenta have produced what they call 'Golden Rice 2'. Their work suggested that the relatively low levels of β-carotene produced in the original Golden Rice might be caused by low levels of phytoene. By testing a series of genes coding for phytoene synthase from several different species, they have found that an enzyme from maize gives levels of β-carotene that are up to 23 times greater.

This is where the story has reached in early 2006. You will have the opportunity to explore the story further in Activity 4.5.

Activity 4.4

Allow 30 minutes

Throughout this course you have explored issues where scientific and social controversies are intertwined. The themes of communication and ethical issues have featured particularly prominently in the Golden Rice case study. Write briefly (a maximum of 200 words) about the way the communication theme has arisen here. You should focus on the forms of communication involved, and what the communicators were trying to achieve.

Activity 4.5

Allow 45 minutes

You should now go to the Topic 6 page of the S250 course website, selecting the 'Update your knowledge' link, for a current overview of the global status of GM foods and later developments in the Golden Rice story.

Summary of Chapter 4

At the time of writing (2006) a relatively small number of types of GM crop have been grown globally, in a limited number of countries. The take-up of these crops has been relatively high in countries like the USA and Canada, but very much lower in Europe. However, there is a very rapid increase in the growth of GM crops in developing countries.

The technique most commonly used to introduce new genetic material into dicots has involved the use of a modified soil bacterium, *Agrobacterium tumefaciens*. This naturally occurring bacterium contains a large Ti plasmid which consists of the genes required to facilitate the transfer of DNA to plant cells, alongside the T-DNA region, which is the region actually transferred and incorporated into the plant cell's chromosomes. Novel genes can be spliced into the T-DNA region, and the machinery of the *Agrobacterium* used to transfer them into plant cells. Difficulties in modifying the *Agrobacterium* itself mean that scientists usually create and clone a modified Ti plasmid in *E. coli*, and then transfer this into *A. tumefaciens*. Modified plant cells can be induced, under the right stimuli, to produce entire genetically modified plants.

Commercially grown GM crops currently all display either herbicide tolerance or insect resistance, or both traits combined. Bt crops are insect-resistant crops that have been genetically modified to produce the Bt protoxin, a protein toxic to certain insects. The protein is derived from another soil bacterium, *Bacillus thuringiensis*, and the modification involves the transfer of a single gene coding for the protoxin. Herbicide-tolerant plants have been modified to show greater tolerance for glyphosate. This herbicide acts by inhibiting a key plant enzyme, EPSP synthase, involved in the production of certain amino acids. The modification again involves the transfer of a single gene – in this case, one derived from bacteria – for a novel version of EPSP synthase which is active in the presence of glyphosate.

A GM crop currently under development is Golden Rice, which has been modified to produce β-carotene. It is suggested that this rice can play a role in alleviating vitamin A deficiency in developing countries. Golden Rice was produced by *Agrobacterium*-mediated transfer of several genes into immature rice embryos, which later developed into fertile plants. The process was more complex than the production of either Bt or glyphosate-tolerant crops, in that it involved the transfer of more genes. The potential of Golden Rice to alleviate vitamin A deficiency has been the subject of controversy. Those who oppose GM crops argue that it is not an appropriate or practical solution, and dispute whether the rice can provide enough vitamin A.

Question 4.1

Genetic modification using *Agrobacterium tumefaciens* often involves the use of a binary vector system – using two different plasmids. (a) What are the roles of the two plasmids? (b) Which parts of the plasmids are incorporated into the plant's genome?

Question 4.2

(a) In what way is the protein produced by *Bacillus thuringiensis* toxic to insects? (b) Why isn't this protein toxic to humans and farm animals?

Question 4.3

(a) How does the herbicide glyphosate kill plants? (b) Describe two methods that have been used to attempt to genetically engineer plants to tolerate the effects of glyphosate.

Question 4.4

In what ways do the science and social issues surrounding Golden Rice differ from those surrounding glyphosate-tolerant and Bt crops?

Chapter 5

Social issues and GM crops

Chapter 4 focused predominantly on the science behind a number of transgenic crops, but also explored some of the social issues surrounding the development of Golden Rice. This chapter will focus less on the science as such, but will explore some of the emerging social concerns.

Many of the issues that surround GM crops are ethical. They relate to what course of action is 'right', and initially Section 5.1 of this chapter will explore a number of arguments from the 1999 report of The Nuffield Council on Bioethics, called *Genetically Modified Crops; The Ethical and Social Issues*. (You can access the report in full, via the S250 course website, should you wish.) The point here is not to persuade you to any single point-of-view about GM crops, but to encourage you to think through some of the key ethical issues.

5.1 Concerns about GM crops

There are at least three broad and overlapping areas of concern about GM crops. First, there is a concern that GM products might be detrimental to human health. These include concerns that:

- The use of antibiotic marker genes might increase bacterial resistance to antibiotics. It was noted in Section 4.4.4 that these concerns have led to the development of alternative selectable marker genes.
- New proteins manufactured in GM crops might provoke unwanted allergic responses.
- Novel combinations of genes might have longer-term health effects of an uncertain nature and severity.

Second, there are concerns over environmental effects, which might include that:

- Insect-resistant crops (Section 4.3) may adversely affect benign insect species (so-called non-target species).
- The adoption of herbicide-tolerant crops (Section 4.4) might encourage farmers to use greater quantities of broad-spectrum herbicides, with resulting detrimental effects on wildlife.
- Genes might spread from the crop plant to wild relatives, to produce herbicide-tolerant weeds, far more difficult to control; or insect-resistant weeds, which might affect a much wider number of non-target species.

Thirdly, there are a number of broadly political concerns. For example, as the Nuffield report points out, there is the anxiety that GM crops are 'only one step further in the 'industrialisation' of agriculture'. By this logic, 'it could be that much of the dislike of GM crops stems from guilt by association; they are produced by agrochemical and seed companies and they are an element in 'non-organic' farming'. Concern about the influence of these multinational companies is reflected in widespread opposition to the use of 'terminator technologies', known within the biotechnology industry as GURTs (genetic use restriction technologies). GURTs include a variety of techniques that prevent farmers collecting seeds from GM crops for sowing in future seasons; for example, the seeds from crops modified in this way may be sterile. Opponents of GM crops have argued strongly that in forcing farmers to buy new seeds each year, such technologies are unethical.

We will explore some of these political concerns in Section 5.4, but at this point it may be worth discussing a general issue underlying both health and environmental concerns – the idea that GM crops and food are 'unnatural'.

5.1.1 What is natural?

Many critics of GM feel that the techniques reflect an unwelcome form of 'tampering with nature'. This is a particular concern of some consumers with respect to food. Such a view is sometimes scornfully interpreted as an expression of what is called the 'naturalistic fallacy' – a belief that equates morality with naturalness, seeing what is natural as 'right'. But concerns about GM foods may reflect a more reasoned and defensible position. It might be argued that consumers are not demanding a 'risk-free' existence, but that they are disinclined to add extra risks of uncertain magnitude.

■ Suppose that β-carotene-enhanced 'Golden Rice' could be obtained either 'naturally'– i.e. via conventional plant breeding, or via the 'engineered' route (Section 4.4). Which rice would be acceptable to you?

■ Your answer might be one or other, both, or neither. This is not a question we can answer for you. However, do take a moment to write down the reasons underpinning your choice; it will be useful to come back to them later on. Do you think your choice is based on logic or 'feelings'? Using a similar example, the Nuffield report concludes 'we can see no reason in ethics to draw a distinction'. This is a point of view worth exploring in more detail.

Do GM crops pose unique problems?

It is perhaps overly simplistic to take the line that only 'natural foods' should be commended and that GM plants are unnatural. Arguably, very few of our modern foodstuffs can be termed 'natural', in that they are not derived from naturally evolved crops. Tremendous changes in genetic make-up have been achieved by conventional (i.e. non-GM) breeding methods. Traditional plant breeding involves selection of individuals seen as superior, and then crossing, i.e. transferring the pollen of one superior plant to the female parts of another superior plant of the same species. Whilst those suspicious of GM crops do not argue against this form of production of new crops, it is hard to argue that it is in any way 'natural'. More complex technological procedures falling under the category of conventional plant breeding include:

- **Intergeneric** and **interspecific crossing** between distinct plant genera and species, are commonly brought about artificially, to produce what could be called 'man-made' crops. One example is *Triticale* (Figure 5.1a), which is a hybrid between wheat (*Triticum* spp.) and rye (*Secale* spp.), used in animal feeds and (without any level of public concern) in the manufacture of multigrain bread for human consumption.
- **Haploid breeding** (also known as doubled-haploid breeding) involves the treatment of normal (diploid) plants so as to produce haploid offspring, which have only one chromosome from each pair in the nuclei of their cells. The haploid plants are treated with a chemical that induces each single chromosome to double, producing an exactly identical copy. This means that the plant is homozygous for all traits. The method produces true-breeding crops more quickly than traditional plant breeding, and commercial varieties of barley have been produced in this way.

(a)

(b)

Figure 5.1 (a) *Triticale*, an example of a crop produced by intergeneric crossing. (b) *Linola*, a strain of flax produced by mutation breeding. Used to produce edible linseed oil.

- **Mutation breeding** involves exposing crop plants to appropriate doses of ionising radiation, or another mutagenic agent (see Chapter 2). This raises the rate of mutation, and may 'knock out' one or more genes. Almost all of the resulting mutations are deleterious, and lead to unhealthy and/or infertile plants. Occasionally, a previously unknown feature arises that may be beneficial, and this can be exploited and a new strain developed. It has been estimated that more than 1400 'improved' crop varieties (technically termed cultivars), in a wide range of species (e.g. see Figure 5.1b), have been developed through mutation breeding in the past 50 years, with no evidence of public concern.

These few examples testify to the fact that a form of 'genetic technology' has been part of common agricultural practice for many years. However, these techniques came into widespread use at a time when there appeared to be less public interest in agricultural technology. You might speculate that the introduction of such techniques might inspire a great deal more public concern today.

■ What is distinctive about GM as opposed to these more orthodox methods of plant breeding?

■ It can bring about the selective and specific transfer of one or more genes from radically different organisms.

With more conventional plant breeding, crossing generally requires the combination of two entire genomes, which means that in addition to what may be the single gene of interest, others are brought along in the process. Take a conventional wheat-breeding programme, where the intention is to introduce a foreign gene from a distantly related cultivar into an existing commercial cultivar. By conventional crossing, not only would the new useful gene be introduced, but also a whole range of other genes, much less likely to be advantageous to the newly developed cultivar. It may be that these inadvertently introduced genes produce a readily identifiable feature – perhaps many such plants are tall, in which case the plant breeder can easily identify and eliminate them. More typically, such additional genes are far less easy to eradicate.

Critics of GM claim that the process involves genetic transformation of a type and degree that is unique. They emphasise factors such as the extensive breaking and joining of the DNA of the host genome and what some call 'illegitimate recombination' and 'scrambling' of both foreign and host DNA at the points where transgenes become inserted. By this logic, GM technologies are imprecise and inefficient. It is claimed that the removal of genes from their normal context and randomly inserting them in a totally new genetic environment could lead to 'position effects', resulting in variable levels of transgene expression as well as disruption of host gene function. Critics of GM claim that many of the enthusiastic proponents for GM are following the traditions of genetic determinism (see Chapter 2) and adopting simplistic 'reductionist' modes of thought about the science of genetics. By that 'reductionist' logic, organisms are no more than collections of genes, with each gene acting in isolation. Campaigning organisations such as GeneWatch and Greenpeace have contrasted GM techniques with traditional breeding:

> Natural sexual reproduction methods used in plant breeding preserve the complex gene organisation and regulatory networks that have evolved over vast periods of time.

■ Look back at Section 2.3 and refresh your memory about the organisation of the eukaryotic genome. Are concerns about 'position effects', 'functional integrity' and 'natural sexual reproduction methods' relevant in this context?

■ Indeed they are. Section 2.3 stressed the complexity and subtlety of plant and animal genomes, drawing attention to interactions between genes and the ease with which control mechanisms can be upset. The worry about 'position effects' is genuine, although transgenic crops described in Chapter 4 have, as yet, shown no obvious deleterious effects. It is likely that most deleterious effects of genetic modification, like those of conventional breeding, result in unhealthy or infertile plants, which are not developed further. Commending 'natural sexual reproduction methods' might be seen as being more problematic. Natural processes are often error-strewn and may give rise to unexpected outcomes.

5.1.2 A closer look at ethical issues

Science can define what is practicable, what can be done, but it cannot determine which developments it is right to pursue; this is largely an ethical judgement. One sensible approach in making an ethical assessment is to try to weigh up the benefits of a technology against its potential to do harm. Deciding whether GM technology is acceptable, in ethical terms, then involves a judgement about the plausibility and moral weight of competing sets of claims. Individuals may make widely different judgements based on the same information, exposing different underlying values and different views on how scientific information ought to be applied. Nevertheless, any judgement should begin with an assessment of the possible benefits and risks.

■ From your viewpoint, list two or three potential benefits of GM crop technology and two or three potential disadvantages.

■ In terms of benefits, GM techniques could:

- raise agricultural productivity
- lead to the production of safer, more nutritious foods
- increase food provision to poorer developing nations.

The potential disadvantages are that GM crop technology may:

- harm human health
- damage the environment, including other organisms
- favour the interests of large multinational companies, at the expense of smaller providers.

The Nuffield report suggests that in making a judgement about the claims of a new technology, it is useful to consider the following questions:

- Will the technology promote the general welfare by making for improved food safety or reducing the use of chemical pesticides in agriculture?
- Does the technology pose unknown risks for consumers and the environment that we would be wise not to run if we are concerned about the general welfare?
- What implications does the technology have for the right of consumers – for example, the right to be informed about the food one is eating?
- What implications does it have for the rights of scientists to be free to conduct their research in ways that protect their intellectual integrity?
- Who will be the principal beneficiaries from the introduction of the new technologies and what obligations do they have to compensate losers?

Specific questions of this type lead to the identification of broad principles that help in the process of evaluation:

1. The principle of general welfare: Governments and policy-making institutions should act in the best interests of citizens.
2. The principle that people's rights should be maintained – for example, the right of consumers to have freedom of choice.
3. The principle of justice: both the burdens and the benefits of particular policies and practices should be shared fairly between those affected.

Applying the principles

Trying to use 'guiding principles' of this type does not make assessment straightforward. For example, such principles can't be rigidly applied in an abstract way, reflecting absolutes such as what is 'right' or 'wrong'; their operation depends on context.

We can explore this further by attempting to apply the third of these principles. Justice might be considered to involve directing the benefits of a new technology to those who need it most. At the same time, the role of policy makers is, arguably, to 'strike a fair balance' between the competing rights and welfare of individuals, groups, industry and the state. But achieving justice in this way is again not straightforward. An example would be compulsory labelling of the products of GM crops. Suppose that labelling was very expensive to a relatively poor farmer marketing GM crops, and that the likelihood of harm was generally agreed to be minimal. Many people might take the line that any gains from labelling would be outweighed by the damage to the farmer's livelihood. Achieving justice in this case might involve taking the side of the farmer.

■ But suppose labelling were inexpensive, the manufacturer rich, and that there was strong public demand for it and yet the likelihood of harm was no greater. Would the argument for labelling be more compelling?

- Many would surely argue that a just outcome in this case would be one requiring labelling.

The assessment of what constitutes a just outcome would be quite different if a stronger ethical line was taken; for example, if it was considered that consumers should have the absolute right to know what they are eating, whether or not the products pose any risk. In that case, justice might demand that all products of GM crops are labelled, whatever the effects on the producers.

As the Nuffield report comments:

> The principles at stake are not complex, but their implementation is. Achieving agreement is complicated by the fact that producers have an interest in exaggerating the difficulty of complying with new regulations and pressure groups have an opposite interest in exaggerating the public demand for them.

It is also true that firm ethical principles are of limited value if they are impractical. For example, the segregation of non-GM and GM food is beset with practical problems, and very modest levels of GM 'contamination' are allowed even in food labelled as organic. European Law allows up to 0.9% contamination, while the Soil Association, the body that ratifies organic food in the UK, allows up to 0.1%.

Keeping principles and contextual issues of this type in mind, let's return to the issue of whether GM technology should be encouraged for developing countries. The Nuffield report argued that it should, although they would like to see the responsibility for doing so falling initially to international agricultural research centres, not commercial organisations.

Activity 5.1

Allow 45 minutes

Look back at your answers to Activities 4.1 and 4.5. Considering the ethical issues and the notions of justice that you have explored, answer the following questions. In each case, your answer should be less than 100 words.

(a) In your view, who has benefited from GM-based agriculture so far? Who should benefit?

(b) Would it be ethically justified to develop GM crops for developing countries, if these were to raise yield and profitability at the expense of traditional farming methods?

(c) Some commentators predict that within 10 years, almost all the best varieties of the major crops will be GM. Would it be ethically sound to exclude developing countries from adopting GM crops in such circumstances?

5.1.3 Can GM crops feed the world?

The issue of global food security is at the heart of many of the ethical issues related to GM technology. United Nations population scientists estimate that the world's population will increase by 2 billion over the next 30 years, posing huge challenges for global food production. More than 842 million people are currently chronically hungry. Proponents of GM crops argue that further development of this technology is vital to meet this challenge.

However, a more equal distribution of existing supplies could solve food shortages. In 2002, the world produced enough food to supply an average 2800 kilocalories per head of the global population, exceeding the average daily requirement of 2100 kilocalories. Clearly, the problem is not that we are not producing enough food. Should this point be used to argue against supporting technological progress in food farming in developing nations?

Some people argue that the political difficulties inherent in food redistribution are so severe that other avenues have to be explored. These would include the continued intensification of agriculture, given its likely success in ensuring cheap food supplies in developing countries. GM crops are seen as one element in such intensification. The Nuffield report supports the notion that GM crops have the potential to assist in alleviating world hunger.

■ If the line were taken that GM crops should not become part of agricultural practice in developing countries, can you think of any alternative strategies?

■ Strategies that might be pursued include expansion of agricultural land, improvements in irrigation, increased fertiliser and pesticide input, and sustained use of conventional plant breeding procedures.

The Nuffield report identified problems with each of these options.

- The expansion of agricultural land area has slowed over recent years, reflecting the decreased returns from the land that is available. It is estimated that if world crop yields had not increased threefold between 1960 and 1992, via the Green Revolution, 2600–3100 million hectares of additional land would need to have been cultivated. To avoid such extra land use over the next 20 years, 'we must be able to triple the yields from the world's existing farmland'.
- Increased irrigation has to continue as a priority, but is now said to face 'sharply diminishing returns, increasing marginal costs and hazards'.
- Increased use of fertilisers and pesticides carries obvious disadvantages, not just because of environmental and health effects, but because of their expense and the problems of lax regulatory control.
- It is argued that the gains from conventional plant breeding over the past 40 years are unlikely to be replicated.

This is an area of great contention, and there is no reason to expect that you will agree with the Nuffield Council's conclusion. In the last analysis, their view is based on a belief that political factors make a fairer distribution of food unlikely.

The second generation of GM crops

Much of the present-day debate about GM plants centres around the existing range of GM crops, most of which have been engineered for herbicide tolerance or insect resistance (Chapter 4). One of the implications of this narrow commercial focus is that the benefit that such crops would bring, other than to those multinational companies that produce them, is by no means clear. Weighing up their value on some form of ethical scales might be unlikely to find in their favour.

A range of second-generation crops are currently being developed that might tip the balance in a different direction. You have explored the issues around one such crop, Golden Rice (Section 4.5). Other second-generation GM crops include those that have been modified so as to produce a whole range of pharmaceutical products, including vaccines and drugs of promised relevance to diseases such as HIV, rabies, diabetes and TB. The use of such crops has been termed 'pharming', an issue explored in the press report given in Figure 5.2.

Medical crops coming soon

Human trials of GM drugs could be five years away

Ian Sample
Science correspondent

Human trials of vaccines produced by genetically modified plants could begin within five years, scientists claimed yesterday.

The researchers outlined proposals to grow fields of crops that have been genetically modified to produce vaccines and other pharmaceuticals to treat HIV, rabies, diabetes and TB.

They said field trials of medicine-producing crops were likely to begin in 2006, with safety trials in humans beginning three years later at St George's hospital in London.

Although the team will consider carrying out trials on plots of a hectare (2.5 acres) in Britain, the unfavourable climate and risk of sabotage mean that field studies, and ultimately full-scale growing of the plants, is most likely to happen in South Africa or southern Europe.

Scientists have long known that GM technology can be used to trick a plant's molecular machinery into making a range of medically useful compounds. Instead of using expensive pharmaceutical factories, advocates envisage fields of GM crops being harvested to reap new medicines cheaply, a process known as "pharming".

According to Julian Ma of St George's Hospital Medical School in London, the leader of the £8m project, the primary aim is to provide medicines for the developing world. "The major burden of disease is in the developing world, but these are the countries that do not have access to vaccines", Prof Ma said.

The number of people dying each year from the six major diseases for which vaccines exist is around 3.3 million.

The scientists have already identified genes that can be put into plants to make them produce antibodies or other compounds that can help treat rabies, TB and diabetes.

While no vaccine yet exists for HIV, genes that produce antibodies capable of destroying the virus have been discovered.

A cream containing the antibodies could help reduce the risk of HIV being transmitted during sexual intercourse, but the production technology cannot easily be scaled up.

"Using traditional techniques, you just cannot produce enough," said Prof Ma.

Prof Ma believes GM plants – probably tobacco or maize – offer a cheap way to make vast quantities of vaccines and other drugs. "It looks like the cost of plant-derived products will be 10- to 100-fold less than conventionally derived products," he said.

If the technique is proved, it may be adopted by developing countries, helping to breaking their reliance upon pharmaceutical multinationals.

"Growing and harvesting plants is low tech," Prof Ma said. "We see this as being transferred to countries where they can start up their own industry at a low start-up cost and produce the amounts they need."

Philip Dale, an expert in GM safety issues at the John Innes Centre in Norwich, is advising on possible risks of contamination, where genes from the GM plants get into others.

"The ability to be able to isolate these from other crops is a crucial factor," he said. "There's a possibility of mixing with other crops and that's the basic challenge we have to wrestle with."

Land used to grow the crops will need to be remote from other crops and dedicated machinery will be needed to process them, so that the medicine cannot enter the food chain.

Sue Mayer of the lobby group GeneWatch said the researchers should pledge to make their technology free to all, to prevent it being claimed by pharmaceutical companies.

Friends of the Earth's GM campaigner, Clare Oxborrow, said: "A clear set of criteria must be established to ensure that human health and the environment are protected. Any benefits must genuinely reach those that need them, rather than simply lining the pockets of the biotech and pharmaceutical industry."

Figure 5.2 'Medical crops coming soon', *Guardian* article, 13 July 2004.

The attraction of 'pharming' is that crops offer a considerably cheaper pharmaceutical production route compared to conventional means – between 10 and 100 times so. Of course, environmental and health concerns remain, for example, that genes from such GM crops might escape into similar neighbouring crops, running a risk of unwanted medicines entering the food chain.

Some second-generation crops are promised to be of special benefit to developing countries and the environment. For example, GM crops are under development that may be able to grow in particularly salty soil. This might then make productive some of the estimated 35% of the world's agricultural land that is currently too salty to be of value. In the longer term, it may be possible to transfer bacterial genes responsible for nitrogen fixation from the nitrogen-fixing bacteria into cereal crops. Nitrogen fixation allows certain bacteria, which naturally occur in the roots of leguminous plants such as peas, to convert atmospheric nitrogen into nitrates, which are an essential plant nutrient. If this process could be induced in the roots of cereal crops, it would reduce farmers reliance on nitrate-based fertilisers.

Some supporters of GM technology see a future where beneficial applications of this type will be so numerous and far-reaching, and the contexts of debates therefore so different, that attitudes to GM technology in the near future will be very far removed from present-day anxieties.

5.2 A key point in the controversy over GM crops: the Pusztai affair

Issues of 'fairness' and our obligations to the developing world do not in themselves explain why the issue of GM plants attracts such controversy. This section focuses on an episode in the fraught history of the development of GM foods that had a significant effect on public attitudes in the UK. In particular, we look at the experiments of Arpad Pusztai in the late 1990s at the Rowett Institute near Aberdeen, Scotland. These experiments are of particular interest to us because they reveal a lot about how science is communicated between scientists and to the world at large, and the pitfalls, ill-feelings and confusions that can occasionally emerge in the process.

5.2.1 Pusztai's experiments

Arpad Pusztai was an expert on a type of plant proteins called **lectins**. One such lectin, *Galanthus nivalis* agglutinin, GNA, is found in snowdrops, where it deters sap-sucking insects. GNA is of interest to genetic engineers because, as a natural insecticide, it might be used to introduce insect resistance into a variety of crops, in the same way that we have explored with regard to the Bt protoxin (Section 4.3). Pusztai was funded to investigate whether the consumption of GM potatoes engineered to produce such lectins would have any effect on the growth and immune system of rats.

Pusztai conducted feeding trials both over a short period of 10 days and also over a longer regimen of 110 days. One experiment involved feeding rats with a diet of raw, baked or boiled potatoes over a 10-day period. A proportion of these potatoes were genetically modified to produce GNA, while some of them had GNA added to the unmodified potatoes. It is not clear from Pusztai's account, whether the modified or adulterated potatoes were supplied raw, baked or boiled. Such small details matter enormously; for instance, prolonged boiling substantially reduces the concentration of GNA. The interpretation of Pusztai's results is further complicated by the fact that a diet of potatoes is nutritionally very poor for rats – so much so that Home Office regulations insist that such diets have to be supplemented by added protein if the feeding regimen is conducted for substantial periods of time. Indeed, Pusztai noticed that the rats fed on unmodified boiled potatoes had a comparatively low rate of growth – and those on unmodified raw potatoes an even lower growth rate.

In one experiment, Pusztai looked for differences between rats fed genetically modified raw potatoes expressing GNA and those fed raw unmodified potatoes. He compared the body mass of these animals after their death with their so called 'empty' body mass, where the food present in the lumen of their guts had been removed by flushing. Pusztai took the view that if there was an atypical difference between these two masses, indicating a larger proportion of the diet had remained undigested in the gut, it would suggest that digestion had been affected by the GM potatoes. He did find an unusual difference of this type in one experiment, though it was not evident in another similar experiment. On the basis of this evidence, Pusztai speculated that 'digestion and absorption of nutrients of transgenic potato diets was retarded in comparison with ordinary potato diets'. But you'll appreciate that for such a statement to be any more than speculation, the diets of the two sets of rats would have to be identical in all respects other than the inclusion of potatoes expressing the GNA gene – if this is not so, the differences in the amount of material in the gut could be due to some other cause. It's known that the transgenic potatoes contained 20% less protein than the non-GM potatoes. Normally the experimental design would allow for such a difference by supplementing the GM diet with extra protein; such adjustment do not seem to have been routinely made in all Pusztai's experiments – certainly not in the short-term feeding experiments.

Pusztai found no statistical difference in the growth rate of rats fed transgenic GNA potatoes over the prolonged 110-day period, compared to the growth rate of a control group fed unmodified potatoes without added GNA. Also rats fed unmodified potatoes spiked with added GNA grew at the same rate as rats fed the same diet without GNA.

From his studies of the immune system of such rats, Pusztai concluded that animals that were fed transgenic potatoes became immunosuppressed. However, the majority view of those appraising Pusztai's data was that such effects are variable and inconsistent and that the effect is not statistically significant. Pusztai went further and claimed that when GNA was simply added to unmodified potatoes, there was no effect on the immune system. This implies that it wasn't the product (GNA) that was causing the problem, but something about the process of genetic modification itself. The 'construct' used to make GM GNA potatoes includes a promoter (Chapter 2) derived from a plant virus – cauliflower mosaic virus, CaMV. The virus is non-toxic to humans and widely distributed in nature; it is present in broccoli, for example. The **CaMV promoter** is used in a variety of GM products, so if Pusztai's data were valid, the safety of many GM crops would be under suspicion.

- How could you test whether the presence of a particular promoter (rather than an adjacent gene or its product) was having an effect on animals eating GM food?

- One approach would be to modify potatoes using the same CaMV promoter, alongside another gene, perhaps one that was not functional. Tests would have to be undertaken that such an insertion would make no difference to other nutritional variables in the potatoes, especially protein content. These would be technically demanding and time-consuming procedures.

5.2.2 Communicating Pusztai's findings

In mid-1998, the Rowett Institute released a succession of press releases describing Pusztai's findings. The safety, or otherwise, of GM foods was a hot issue at the time and his preliminary findings gained widespread publicity. Pusztai gave an extended interview to the World in Action TV programme 'Eat up your genes', broadcast in August 1998. He described some of his experiments and outlined his interpretations in ways that helped shape the general tone of the programme, which was highly sceptical about the safety of GM foods in general.

The descriptions of Pusztai's work in the early Rowett press releases were far from clear or consistent, and some of the early claims made were later withdrawn. It was unclear who was responsible for these releases; soon Rowett were sufficiently embarrassed to pronounce that it 'regretted the release of misleading information about issues of such importance to the public and the scientific community'.

Pusztai was suspended from the Institute, in an atmosphere of increasing bitterness and recrimination. It was alleged that the Institute's management came under direct pressure from senior Government ministers to silence Pusztai.

What's especially important to note is that at this time, none of the key data from Pusztai's experiments had been submitted for publication. The work had not been 'peer reviewed' as a means of testifying to the quality of the experiments and the appropriateness of the conclusions. The Rowett then established a four-person audit committee to look at Pusztai's work and they drew the conclusion (posted on the Institute's website) that 'the existing data do not support any suggestion that the consumption by rats of transgenic potatoes expressing GNA has any effect on growth, organ development or immune function'. Pusztai disputed the findings of the audit committee, but they were disinclined to modify their findings in the light of his objections.

Such developments helped fuel the significant amount of press coverage that took place at the time (late 1998), much of it raising doubts about the safety of GM food and expressing a good deal of sympathy for Pusztai, whom many thought had been shabbily treated. Much of the information that fuelled the dispute was available on the Web, including Pusztai's own more detailed account of his experimental design and conclusions, in his 'Alternative Report'.

Pusztai's findings attracted some support from fellow scientists, in particular 20 individuals from 14 countries produced a widely distributed memorandum. But the majority of the other opinions expressed were hostile, focusing on concerns about the rats' inadequate diets, whether appropriate control experiments had been run, the number of rats used in each group and the appropriateness of the statistical tests that had been applied to assess the significance of the data – concerns that Pusztai and his co-author attempted to answer, though not in a way that satisfied critics.

In June 1999, the UK's premier scientific body, The Royal Society, published a review of Pusztai's work. The review process involved the assembly of existing information, the elicitation of further information from Pusztai, his co-workers and his critics and the invitation to six referees (intended to be both independent and anonymous, following standard peer-review practice) to critically evaluate the information available. The Royal Society report claimed that the experiments were poorly designed, with little information on how the GM and control diets differ. For example, the Royal Society team felt that lack of information about differences in the chemical composition between strains of GM and non-GM potatoes meant that firm conclusions were difficult. The use of a diet of raw potatoes for feeding rats was questioned, given that potatoes are renowned for containing high levels of natural toxins. They also pointed out that, as far as they could ascertain, Pusztai's measurements were not conducted 'blind'; which should be standard practice.

■ How might such experiments have been conducted 'blind' and what would have been the advantage in doing so?

■ The scientists performing the measurements – in this instance, measuring body mass or looking for effects on the immune system – should be unaware of (i.e. 'blind to') the particular treatment that any one rat has been subjected to. This is to guard against unconscious bias in the recording and interpretation of results; the risk is that data are recorded in ways that favour expectations (see Topic 4, Section 4.3).

The Royal Society group concluded that:

> The uncertainty and ambiguity of the data urge great caution in the interpretation of the results presented. A much improved experimental design, with stringent controls, would have been needed if the claims made for the study were to be convincing. Even if the results of the particular study had supported the claims that have been made for them, it would have been unwise to use them for making statements about the safety or otherwise of all GM foods.

Pusztai disputed the Royal Society team's findings and expressed strong resentment that he had not been sufficiently involved in drawing up of the Royal Society report. He also emphasised that he and co-workers had

> never inferred from the results of the work with GM potatoes that GM foods were harmful to human beings. Indeed, we have never said that GM potatoes were harmful to anything but rats. However, we have to point out that the genetic modification method we used is almost identical to the methods used in most presently marketed GM foods in the UK without any biological testing.

Pusztai's arguments continue as follows:

> A great deal has been said about the design of the experiments, which is quite remarkable because no design is described in the reports [...] no diets, methods, analytical techniques, rat ages, methods of feeding and other animal experimentation methods are described but as it has been pointed out on innumerable occasions these were reports (and not scientific papers) compiled for people who were fully aware of all these and not written for peer-reviewing. The implication by the RS report that we had bias in our measurements is highly offensive and therefore fully rejected by us.

The one area where Pusztai and the Royal Society review team seem united is in their recognition of the need for further work and clarification, though they do so from different stances. Pusztai continued to defend the quality of his disputed data claiming that 'the data reliably and convincingly demonstrate that the inclusion of GM potatoes in the rat diet had a number of harmful effects on growth, organ development and immune response'. He claimed that though these were preliminary experiments, they were 'well designed, expertly carried out and subjected to correct statistical analysis'. In Pusztai's view 'the results could serve as the basis for further developments'. But the Royal Society review team thought that:

> The only way to clarify the current situation would be to refine the experimental design of the research done to date and to use this as the basis for further studies in which clearly defined hypotheses were tested, focused on the specific differences already claimed. It would be necessary to carry out a large number of extremely complex tests on many different strains of GM and non-GM potatoes. It would be important to ensure that these studies had sufficient statistical power (in the sense that numbers in each experimental group were sufficient to deal with the variability in individual response) to come to a clear conclusion. It would also be important to take adequate account of the age and the susceptibility of the animals and the wholesomeness and adequacy of the entire diet. Careful thought would have to be given to the specific targets for any hypothesised damage.

Formal publication

The first formal, peer-reviewed, publication of part of Pusztai's work came in the *Lancet* in October 1999. Pusztai and his co-author Stanley Ewen had developed the work to include measurements on the effect of GNA potatoes on the structure of the rat intestine. They were looking for any effect of the GM diet on the mucosal cell layer lining the gut. Any increase in thickness would indicate that the diet had prompted increased growth of these layers, seen as a deleterious effect. In their design and analysis, these experiments had much in common with those highlighted in the 'Alternative Report' of October 1998 and the authors' conclusion, that GNA-GM potatoes had effects on gut structure, were in line with previous claims.

GMFoods

It's that man again

Arpad Pusztai is finally publishing a paper about his experiments on modified potatoes. But the meaning of his work remains unclear.

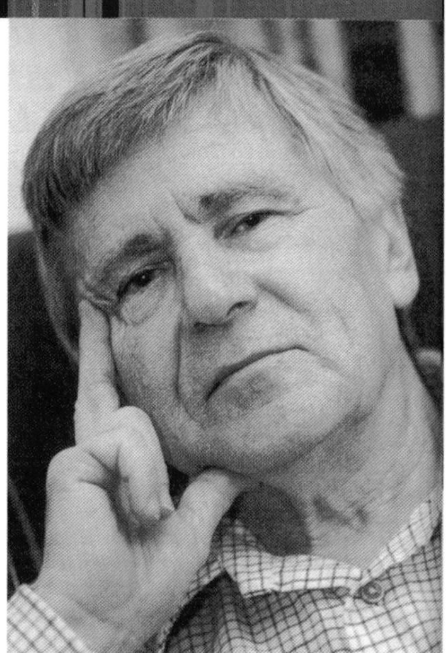

At the centre of the storm: the controversy surrounding Arpad Pusztai's research will not be resolved by his paper in *The Lancet*

At long last, the research that soured many people's taste for genetically modified food is to be published in a scientific journal. More than a year after Arpad Pusztai claimed in a television interview that eating GM potatoes damaged the health of young rats, a paper describing some of his results will appear this week in *The Lancet*.

However, publication is unlikely to settle the issue. *New Scientist* has learnt that *The Lancet* sent the paper to six expert reviewers. Several advised against publication on the grounds that the results are impossible to interpret. David Sharp, *The Lancet's* deputy editor, says that the journal nevertheless published the paper because it was "high time these data were out in the open".

The paper was written by Pusztai, formerly of the Rowett Research Institute in Aberdeen, and Stanley Ewen, a gut pathologist at the University of Aberdeen. It describes an experiment in which young rats were fed potatoes genetically engineered to produce GNA, a type of protein called a lectin. GNA is made by snowdrops to deter sap-sucking insects. Other rats were fed normal potatoes laced with the lectin, and a control group was fed normal potatoes to which nothing had been added. Some rats ate the potatoes raw, some boiled.

After 10 days, Pusztai killed the rats and sent the guts to Ewen, who examined intestinal crypts, the clefts between the finger-like villi that line the gut. Crypts in one part of the intestine, the jejunum, were longer in rats fed raw GM potatoes.

Ewen also counted white blood cells called lymphocytes, which accumulate between cells in the gut lining if it is damaged. He found that rats fed raw GM potatoes averaged 9.3 lymphocytes per crypt, compared with 5.3 in rats fed normal raw potatoes. Rats fed boiled GM potatoes averaged 10.3 lymphocytes, compared with 7.6 for those fed normal boiled potatoes. Although Ewen did not do the same counts on the rats fed potatoes laced with GNA, the paper states that eating lectins does not cause lymphocytes to accumulate in intestinal crypts. Finally, he found that the lining of the caecum, part of the large intestine, was thinnest in rats fed boiled GM potatoes.

Pusztai and Ewen suggest that these changes could be due to the "construct" in the GM potatoes – the package of DNA inserted with the gene for GNA. The construct includes the cauliflower mosaic virus promoter, a genetic switch from a plant virus included to "turn on" the GNA gene.

Constructs containing this promoter are routinely used to genetically engineer plants. "The possibility that a plant vector in common use in some GM plants can alter the mucosa of the gastrointestinal tract and exert powerful biological effects may also apply to GM plants containing similar constructs," concludes a proof of Ewen and Pusztai's paper obtained by *New Scientist*.

However, most experts stress that the experiments conducted by Pusztai and Ewen cannot reveal whether the construct is harmful. To do this, you would have to repeat the tests using GM potatoes containing the construct but lacking the gene for GNA. And many scientists believe that other explanations are more plausible.

The new paper refers to just one of four feeding experiments conducted by Pusztai, and contains few details on the biochemistry of the potatoes involved – information that is crucial to interpreting the results. Ewen says that the experiment was one that Pusztai codenamed D227.

The rats in this experiment are known to have become malnourished. This might in itself explain some of Ewen's observations, says Chris Potten, a gut toxicologist at the Christie Hospital in Manchester. He adds that the way the tissue was prepared – by slitting open the gut and laying it on card – could have altered crypt lengths.

Alternatively, the gut changes might have been caused by toxins made by potatoes called glycoalkaloids. Pusztai didn't measure glycoalkaloids, so nobody knows whether his potatoes were producing more than normal. But information on experiment D227 placed on the Internet by Pusztai suggests that the GM potatoes were biochemically unusual (see Table).

While Pusztai blames the construct for this, other experts say that such changes can occur whenever plants are grown in tissue culture, a technique used both in genetic engineering and in conventional plant breeding. Potatoes are prone to this problem. Propagating by seed can correct it, but this is hard to do with potatoes. "This study is more informative about working with potatoes than it is about GM technology," says David Baulcombe of the John Innes Centre in Norwich.

All of this raises questions about the safety of new varieties of crops in general (see "How safe is safe?", opposite). But it means that we're no closer to knowing whether GM foods pose any special hazard.

Pusztai's new paper doesn't contain any results on stunted organ growth or damage to the rats' immune systems. That's surprising, given the importance attached to these results by Pusztai in February, after they were revealed at a press conference in London (*New Scientist*, 20 February, p. 4). Pusztai did not respond to *New Scientist's* request for an interview about the paper.

Puszai's potatoes

	Starch	Sugars	Potato lectins
Normal	640	82.0	0.067
Modified	596	107.7	0.079

grams per kilogram of dried potato

Altered state: the modified potatoes fed to young rats in experiment D227 were unusual in several ways

Figure 5.3 'It's that man again', *New Scientist* article, 16 October 1999.

Journal to publish GM foods hazards research

James Melkie

The research that did most to raise public alarm over potential health hazards from genetically modified foods is finally to be published, vindicating work that the scientific establishment and government tried to discredit and reigniting the row over the safety of GM technology.

The Lancet, the influential international medical research journal, will next Friday contain a paper showing changes in the guts of rats fed GM potatoes, raising questions as to why these may have occurred. Publication comes 14 months after the scientist Arpad Pusztai first suggested that the food may stunt the rats' growth and sparked concerted attempts by the government and scientific opponents to discredit him.

Dr Pusztai, who last year was forced out of his job at the Rowett Research Institute, Aberdeen, after he voiced his concerns on a television programme, and Stanley Ewen, a senior pathologist at Aberdeen University, offered their evidence to the Lancet late last year. It was reviewed three times by other scientists before being accepted for publication by the journal, which said that all its papers "went through the mill" first.

Dr Pusztai, who had always said the work would be published by an independent scientific journal, yesterday admitted to being "only human" in his satisfaction at the news after being "kicked left, right and centre" by the government and senior scientists. "One of the major mistakes the scientific establishment made was to pick on the wrong man. There will be a lot of people with egg on their faces."

He declined to give details of the Lancet paper, but said: "If they consider it important to publish, it must be an important piece of information." His work had sought to establish whether the effects of GM materials and non-GM materials were "substantially equivalent" in every respect. "Up to now, people have said they are the same. This is not true with GM potatoes. They are compositionally different."

The Royal Society has attacked Dr Pusztai's work as flawed "in many aspects of design, execution and analysis", while Jack Cunningham, the cabinet enforcer in charge of GM policy, said his research had been comprehensively discredited and should not be an excuse for the biotechnology industry to grind to a halt.

Professor William Hill, a member of the Royal Society working group that published its assessment in May, yesterday reiterated his belief that there was no convincing evidence of adverse effects from GM potatoes.

The cabinet office said: "We see no reason to retract what was said earlier this year."

But anti-GM campaigners were delighted by news of publication. Those who had tried to rubbish Dr Pusztai and his work owed him a public apology", said Friends of the Earth's food campaigner, Pete Riley. "Scientific concerns about the safety of GM foods are clearly real." Greenpeace said: "The fact the work is of sufficient quality to be published raises questions about the safety of GM food."

Dr Pusztai's work involved feeding rats with potatoes modified with an insecticide gene from snowdrops. He said they suffered damage to their organs and immune systems. Dr Ewen then examined the animals and found enlarged stomach linings in those fed GM potatoes, extra evidence revealed by the Guardian in February, months after the Rowett Institute had forced Dr Pusztai out of his job.

Dr Ewen said at that time that the researchers had expected no differences between those fed GM food and non-GM food. "But there are differences which cause me concern. We need to know what happens in the mammalian gut with GM food."

Dr Pusztai, 69, said the Royal Society's judgement had been based on "half-cocked selected pieces of information from the Rowett". He had been offered new scientific posts in Europe and planned to publish more information on his work and conduct new research. "For the last 14 months while people have been talking they have been doing nothing. I know of no other work on similar lines. I will be doing it, make no mistake."

His quarrel had been with scientific administrators, not other scientists. "My reputation is higher than ever."

By contrast, he said, the politicians and administrators who had expected the story to go away had made a "ghastly miscalculation".

The Rowett Institute declined to comment.

Figure 5.4 'Journal to publish GM foods hazards research', *Guardian* article, 5 October 1999.

Activity 5.2

Allow 30 minutes

Carefully read though the *New Scientist* and *Guardian* articles (Figures 5.3 and 5.4). Given the information in this section, do you think that this coverage of Pusztai's work is fair, accurate and balanced? Can you find any errors in either article? Give a short written justification of your answer, in no more than 200 words.

Activity 5.3

Allow 15 minutes

It is important that you form your own views about the Pusztai affair, so before reading what follows, spend a few minutes writing down your thoughts about what the saga tells us about communication within the scientific community and between scientists and non-experts. The issue is explored in some detail below, but we don't expect you to produce anything like the detail in Section 5.2.3. Make short notes, no more than 200 words, and refer to them as you read what follows. You may like to annotate the text with your own thoughts. (You will not necessarily agree with every point that we make.)

5.2.3 Drawing conclusions

Sections 5.2.1 and 5.2.2 have summarised some of the major aspects of the Pusztai affair, but it should be said that almost every detail has been the subject of prolonged and heated dispute. Our purpose is not to attempt to denigrate individuals or institutions. Rather, the hope is that the tale carries some general messages of value about how science is undertaken and communicated, which can sometimes become clearer when things go wrong.

Communicating preliminary scientific information via press releases, internal reports and TV programmes is fraught with problems. It's very difficult to establish the credibility of findings without access to formal published scientific papers and without the expertise necessary to understand them. However, scientists increasingly use less conventional methods of disseminating their findings, notably TV and the Internet. In areas of public concern such as GM research, they are often encouraged to do so by the media. The pressure to announce findings early, through the mass media, also reflects the highly competitive nature of many areas of scientific research. Formal publication and peer review tends to be a slow process, and the quality assurance procedures are not perfect. However, a good reason for favouring formal publication is that, in assessing the value of scientific findings, referees set great store upon the fine details of experimental design and interpretation. Errors in either aspect of a paper can force authors to reconsider and improve their experiments, or prevent publication. Once a paper has passed this quality control test, it becomes available to a wider scientific community and the public. One problem in areas of science of commercial interest, like GM, is that much of the work is not freely available for public or scientific scrutiny. A great deal of the work on GM has been performed by commercial companies, or university researchers hoping to exploit its commercial potential. Much of this work is not openly published, for fear of losing competitive advantage.

The Royal Society and Pusztai disputed the role of internal reports. The Royal Society took the view that since the reports were publicly available (via the Rowett website) and at the time the only documents giving experimental details, it was right that they be subject to expert scrutiny. Pusztai felt that this was unfair, as they were aimed at an internal Rowett audience, who shared a knowledge of the procedures used.

It is self-evident that different individuals and institutions took very different meanings away from the episode. It is tempting to look for clarity by emphasising that we should just 'stick to the facts', but what comprise the facts can be very complex and contentious. Facts can be selected and presented in ways that reflect pre-existing beliefs and particular personal contexts. Many such contexts may have little to do with science as such, but they help shape or 'frame' the debate to a significant degree. At the risk of over-generalising, those who had existing concerns about the safety of GM foods saw Pusztai as a brave, pioneering scientist and a victimised whistle-blower. From that point of view, the scientific and political establishment conspired to discredit and excommunicate Pusztai. By contrast, his critics within the scientific community had particular views about professional practice and about where the threshold should be set for the 'burden of proof'; they took the view that Pusztai had fallen short of these exacting standards.

The episode also raises questions about the responsibilities of scientists, their working relationships with their institutions and the scientific community. In particular, the differing responsibilities of the institution (Rowett) and the scientist (Pusztai) are unclear – how and through what channels should the concerns of an individual scientist be conveyed? There are many situations where the broad scientific consensus takes a different view from that of a lone dissenting voice. Such a majority opinion may well be based on sound thinking and proper caution, but sometimes dissenters have been proved correct, and in retrospect the majority can appear to have reacted in ways that reflected an innate conservatism or self-interest.

There can be little doubt that the manner of Pusztai's treatment fuelled the view that an 'aging and frail' scientist was being turned into a martyr. Attempts by Government ministers to undermine his results, combined with what many saw as a high-handed stance from the Royal Society, conveyed the impression of unfairness and intimidation. The sight of scientists quarrelling in public may have helped to erode public confidence in their opinions and generally heighten anxiety about the safety of GM foods. Many within the scientific community bemoaned this increase in public suspicion, but a case could be made that their own behaviour helped engender just such an atmosphere. Even if it were true that Pusztai's work had experimental flaws and was built on questionable assumptions, a more subtle and constructive line of dealing with such a voice was needed.

■ Peer review is often put forward as the 'gold standard' that testifies to the validity of published scientific information. Does the Pusztai episode reveal any shortcomings in the procedure?

■ Episodes such as this, though exceptional, do reveal the system's weaknesses. Reviewers may disagree, or have dubious motives. Editors may take the view (as here) that publication is less about 'quality control' and more an obligation to bring contentious issues out 'into the open'. Scientists may be frustrated by the slow pace of the peer review process, and feel their work needs to be in the public domain more quickly. However, as we've seen, the use of non-standard means of dissemination, prior to publication, can place particular strains on peer review.

5.3 Assessing the safety of GM food

Pusztai and his team were attempting to develop suitable tests to assess the safety of GM potatoes. Typically, testing the safety of GM food involves comparing its composition and/or its effects with that of the conventionally produced food it most closely resembles. We have seen that such comparisons were at the heart of Pusztai's work.

The comparison of GM and conventional crops and food has led to the so-called principle of **substantial equivalence**, which has been used extensively by regulatory authorities. If a GM plant, or food derived from it, is regarded as substantially equivalent to its conventional equivalent, it is assumed that no new health risks are presented, thus paving the way for commercial development.

Some see the operation of this principle as the abandonment of the need for careful safety tests, on the grounds that the GM product is automatically assumed to be essentially identical to 'tried and tested' products. Pusztai was particularly dismissive of the principle. A major motivation of his work on GM potatoes was a desire to develop more rigorous testing regimes. We will spend some time examining how interpretations of this principle have changed over time, and some of the controversy that has surrounded the term. In doing so, we would hope that you gain insight into the way that the scientific assessment of risk influences regulatory decision making, nationally and internationally.

5.3.1 Scientific risk analysis

In the context of national and international legislation on the safety of food and animal feed, much of the thinking about assessing risk has come from the experience of developing legislation to cover potentially toxic chemicals. In this regard, the terms 'risk' and 'hazard' are particularly important. ENTRANSFOOD (European network safety assessment of genetically modified food crops) has defined the terms as follows:

> Risk is defined as the likelihood that, under particular conditions of exposure, an intrinsic hazard will represent a threat to human health. Risk is thus a function of hazard and exposure. Hazard is defined as the intrinsic potential of a material to cause adverse health effects; implicit in the definition is the concept of severity and adversity of the effect.

We might think of these terms with regard to a substance like the common painkiller, paracetamol. Paracetamol has the potential to cause irreversible liver damage, and hence represents a grave hazard. However, this only occurs when the drug is taken in relatively large quantities, so we have to balance this hazard against the risk, i.e. the likelihood that an individual might accidentally or deliberately take an overdose.

You may recall that a similar term: Tolerable Daily Intake (TDI) was used in Section 2.1 of Topic 3, with reference to contaminants in drinking water. TDI is used to refer to contaminants in the diet, while Acceptable Daily Intake (ADI) refers to food additives and similar substances.

Risk analysis therefore has to take into account both the relative hazard of a substance and the likely level of exposure. Determining the relative hazard of a novel substance has generally involved animal testing, i.e. giving laboratory animals a range of doses of the substance and determining the highest dose at which no adverse effects are observed – the No Observable Adverse Effect Level (NOAEL). Acceptable Daily Intakes (ADIs) are then set, often at one-hundredth of the NOAEL. Once the degree of hazard has been determined, this can be combined with information about likely exposure levels to form the overall risk assessment.

5.3.2 Assessing GM foods: substantial equivalence is introduced

In the early 1990s, biotechnology companies were preparing to market the first food products derived from GM crops. This provided a challenge to legislators. There were no precedents to guide them as to how to approve or ban novel food products. The methods used to approve pharmaceuticals, summarised above (Section 5.3.1), did not seem to transfer easily to whole food products.

■ Why might this have been the case?

■ Determining the NOAEL and hence the ADI of a whole food could prove exceptionally difficult; force-feeding laboratory animals large quantities of a single foodstuff would be impractical and ethically unacceptable.

In order to meet this challenge, the Organisation for Economic Cooperation and Development (OECD, see Table 5.1) gathered a group of 60 regulatory scientists nominated by its member governments. In 1993, after two years of deliberation, they published a 74-page report, which concluded that:

> For foods and food components from organisms developed by the application of modern biotechnology, the most practical approach to the determination of safety is to consider whether they are substantially equivalent to analogous conventional food product(s), if such exist.
>
> If a new food or food component is found to be substantially equivalent to an existing food or food component, it can be treated in the same manner with respect to safety. No additional safety concerns would be expected.
>
> Where substantial equivalence is more difficult to establish because the food or food component is either less well-known or totally new, then the identified differences, or the new characteristics, should be the focus of further safety considerations.

This was the point at which the so-called 'principle of substantial equivalence' became firmly established.

■ The report identifies two distinct classes of food or food components derived from genetically modified organisms. What are they?

■ The report made a clear distinction between GM foods that could be considered substantially equivalent and therefore safe, and those where the identified differences or new characteristics should be the focus of further safety assessment.

An increasingly complex system of international regulatory institutions plays an important part in international decision making. You will come across a number of these organisations. Table 5.1 should provide a useful point of reference.

Table 5.1 International decision makers.

—	Codex Alimentarius Commission	Created in 1963 by the FAO and WHO to develop food standards, guidelines and related texts, such as codes of practice.
FAO	Food and Agriculture Organisation	Part of the United Nations, leading international efforts to defeat hunger. FAO aims to act as a neutral forum where all nations meet as equals to negotiate agreements and debate policy.
OECD	Organisation for Economic Cooperation and Development	Representing 30 developed nations, part of its remit is to produce internationally agreed instruments, decisions and recommendations to provide guidelines in areas where multilateral agreement is necessary.
UN	United Nations	The UN's remit includes the development of international law – conventions, treaties and standards – that are intended to play a central role in promoting economic and social development, as well as international peace and security.
WHO	World Health Organisation	The UN's specialised agency for health. Its objective is the attainment by all peoples of the highest possible level of health.
WTO	World Trade Organisation	An international organisation dealing with the rules of trade between nations.

5.3.3 Incorporating substantial equivalence into national and international law

The concept of substantial equivalence very quickly became important in international trade law. The WTO aims to harmonise national food standards to meet international norms. Under its rules, a country could be penalised if it imposed food standards more stringent than those agreed internationally. In this context, international food standards are set by the Codex Alimentarius Commission (Table 5.1). In 1996, a report was issued within the Codex framework, which endorsed the principle of substantial equivalence:

> Establishment of substantial equivalence is not a safety assessment in itself, but a dynamic analytical exercise in the assessment of the safety of a new food relative to an existing food […] The comparison may be a simple task or be very lengthy, depending upon the amount of available knowledge and the nature of the food or food component under consideration. The reference characteristics for substantial equivalence comparisons need to be flexible and will change over time in accordance with the changing needs of processors and consumers and with experience.

Whilst the principle of substantial equivalence has played an important role in the regulation of GM food in both America and Europe, it has been used in different ways on the two sides of the Atlantic.

In the US, the regulation of biotechnology rested on the assumption that the products were not significantly different to their conventional counterparts and that therefore new legislation was not required. This meant that companies were self-regulating, and that there was no requirement to seek approval before marketing a GM food for public consumption. In practice, however, companies wishing to market GM foods voluntarily sought a safety review from the Food and Drug Administration (FDA). The companies provided the FDA with information on the physical composition of the GM food, citing this as evidence of substantial equivalence to existing products. In return, the FDA provided the companies with documentation noting the claim. There is some indication that companies saw this documentation as protection against legal liability. The prospect of huge payouts in lawsuits, meant that, whether it was a legislative requirement or not, in the US companies felt obliged to consult the FDA.

In the European Union, companies wishing to market GM products have always had to seek prior approval before release onto the market, or in the case of GM crops, before they were grown commercially. This arose from an underlying assumption that GM products are inherently different from their conventional counterparts. That is not to say that the EU did not approve GM products or crops. In 1997, the EU passed a regulation (the 1997 Novel Food Regulation) which allowed a simplified procedure for cases where the GM product was substantially equivalent to its conventional counterpart – in that case, companies had to provide scientific evidence to back up the claim of equivalence rather than carry out a full risk assessment.

Initially, it seemed that the fact that the principle of substantial equivalence played a significant part in the regulatory framework on both sides of the Atlantic, might lead to a straightforward 'harmonisation' of trading laws, as desired by the WTO. However, a combination of the very different starting assumptions and the negative public response in Europe led to two very different outcomes.

In the late 1990s, at the same time as international legislative bodies were developing policies based on the principal of substantial equivalence, it was becoming a key point of criticism from non-Governmental organisations (NGOs) and activists. The concept was attacked for downplaying the novelty of the transgenic products. Importantly, it was derided as vague and open to interpretation. We shall return to these points of criticism below.

In 1996–97 shipments containing American GM maize and soybeans were providing a focus of opposition to the opponents of GM food in Europe. By the year 2000, activists had successfully lobbied the major European supermarket chains into dropping GM products.

The widespread public opposition to GM in Europe provided the context for what became a much stricter interpretation of substantial equivalence. In early 1997, the UK Advisory Committee on Novel Foods and Processes (ACNFP) approved the use of a number of Bt maize products for use in processed food. The ACNFP had accepted that the products were only different from normal maize products in that they contained the Bt protein. The Bt protein was deemed safe, conventional maize was already accepted to be safe and therefore the new products were approved.

- In focusing solely on the protein product produced by the transgene, the Bt protein, what assumptions were being made?
- There was an implicit assumption that transferred genes/DNA sequences (the gene encoding the Bt protein; the selectable marker genes, like antibiotic resistance genes; and promoters, like the CaMV sequence) pose no threat. To be fair, the approval was for processed food, so it was unlikely that intact genes remained in the products.

By late 1997, and the passing of the EU Novel Food Regulation, the ACNFP was using a much tighter definition of substantial equivalence. A few months later, a member of the ACNFP described how the committee tightened its definition of substantial equivalence:

> If we must use that criterion alone, then we will tighten its definition. In MAFF's [Ministry of Agriculture, Fisheries and Food] view, a food cannot be regarded as substantially equivalent if it contains any intact GM DNA, so the product must be highly refined to ensure that all the DNA has been denatured.

In the context of widespread public suspicion of GM throughout Europe, this change in interpretation rapidly became official EU policy. What had been designed as an accelerated way of approving new products that could be demonstrated to be substantially equivalent, had become a barrier to approval – the new foods had to demonstrably contain no modified DNA, or any of the protein products of that modified DNA.

5.3.4 A critique of substantial equivalence

In the late 1990s, the principle of substantial equivalence came under sustained attack, and at this point it is worth examining both the points of criticism and the responses. In October 1999, Erik Millstone, Eric Brunner and Sue Mayer published a critical commentary on substantial equivalence in the journal *Nature*.

Before you read some extracts from this article it is worth commenting both on the nature of the article and who the authors are. The article is a 'commentary' published within a respected journal that also publishes formal peer-reviewed papers. The journal's editors argue that it is important to publish 'original and stimulating opinions', without implying any endorsement of the views expressed. Millstone is an academic with a science background who specialises in science policy. Brunner is also an academic, specialising in epidemiology and public health. Mayer is a scientist working for the pressure group GeneWatch. These people are not working biotechnologists, but they have all been active participants in the debates surrounding GM crops.

Box 5.1 contains five key extracts from the article, numbered for convenience. (You will find the full article on the S250 course website, if you are interested.) As you read the extracts, you should undertake the following activity.

Activity 5.4

Allow 30 minutes

As you read the five extracts in Box 5.1, write brief comments on the authors' arguments (in the margins, if you wish). For each extract, you should try to assess the validity of the points being made. Do you agree or disagree? If so, explain your reasons.

Box 5.1 Extracts from 'Beyond Substantial Equivalence'

E. Millstone, E. Brunner and S. Mayer, *Nature*, October 1999.

1 The concept of substantial equivalence has never been properly defined; the degree of difference between a natural food and its GM alternative before its 'substance' ceases to be acceptably 'equivalent' is not defined anywhere, nor has an exact definition been agreed by legislators. It is exactly this vagueness that makes the concept useful to industry but unacceptable to the consumer.

2 The concept of substantial equivalence emerged in response to the challenge confronting regulatory authorities in the early 1990s [...] One obvious solution at that time would have been for legislators to have treated GM foods in the same way as novel chemical compounds, such as pharmaceuticals, pesticides and food additives, and to have required companies to conduct a range of toxicological tests, the evidence from which could be used to set 'acceptable daily intakes' (ADIs).

3 The challenge of how to deal with the issue of risk from consuming GM foods was first confronted in 1990 at an international meeting, of the FAO and the WHO. The FAO/WHO panel report [...] does not use the term 'substantial equivalence' or mention ADIs. It implies that GM foods are in some important respects novel, but it then argues that they are not really novel at all – just marginal extensions of traditional techniques. These inconsistencies are inevitable, given that the industry wanted to argue both that GM foods were sufficiently novel to require new legislation – and a major overhaul of the rules governing intellectual property rights – to allow them to be patented, yet not so novel that they could introduce new risks to public or environmental health.

4 Unfortunately, scientists are not yet able reliably to predict the biochemical or toxicological effects of a GM food from a knowledge of its chemical composition. For example, recent work on the genetics of commercial grape varieties shows that, despite detailed knowledge, going back for centuries, of the chemistry and flavour of grapes and wines, the relationship between the genetics of grapes and their flavour is not understood. Similarly, the relationship between genetics, chemical composition and toxicological risk remains unknown. Relying on the

concept of substantial equivalence is therefore merely wishful thinking: it is tantamount to pretending to have adequate grounds on which to judge whether or not products are safe.

5 Substantial equivalence is a pseudoscientific concept because it is a commercial and political judgment masquerading as if it were scientific. It is, moreover, inherently antiscientific because it was created primarily to provide an excuse for not requiring biochemical or toxicological tests. It therefore serves to discourage and inhibit potentially informative scientific research. [...] If policymakers are to provide consumers with adequate protection, and genuinely to reassure them, then the concept of substantial equivalence will need to be abandoned, rather than merely supplemented. It should be replaced with a practical approach that would actively investigate the safety and toxicity of GM foods rather than merely taking them for granted, and which could give due consideration to public-health principles as well as to industrial interests.

You should now compare your thoughts about these extracts with the comments on Activity 5.4 given on pp. 170–1.

5.3.5 Responses to the critique

A number of responses to the commentary were published in the letters pages of *Nature*, almost all of which objected to the article. For our purposes, a particularly interesting response came from Peter Kearns and Paul Mayers, two scientists associated with the OECD:

> Substantial equivalence is not a substitute for a safety assessment. It is a guiding principle which is a useful tool for regulatory scientists engaged in safety assessments. It stresses that an assessment should show that a GM variety is as safe as its traditional counterparts. In this approach, differences may be identified for further scrutiny, which can involve nutritional, toxicological and immunological testing. The approach allows regulators to focus on the differences in a new variety and therefore on safety concerns of critical importance. Biochemical and toxicological tests are certainly not precluded.
>
> Since the concept of substantial equivalence was first described, several new foods have been assessed and knowledge has accumulated on how to use the concept. In parallel, the OECD, its Governments and others have continued to review its adequacy in food safety assessment and to develop supporting tools. The OECD's task force on the safety of novel foods and feeds, in particular, continues to focus on the application of the concept. This includes work on assessment methodologies when substantial equivalence cannot be applied, as well as efforts to identify the critical nutrients and toxicants found in major crop plants, as a focus for the demonstration of substantial equivalence.

■ Having read this quote, re-read the original OECD definition of substantial equivalence (p. 90). Do you think Kearns and Mayers are making a fair point?

■ The original OECD definition was quite vague, so you could argue that Kearns and Mayers' more rigorous description of an evolving assessment that 'can involve nutritional, toxicological and immunological testing' is consistent with the original. However, it could be argued that their description does not describe actual practice up to that date (1999).

In some ways, Kearns and Mayers' letter gave an indication of the subsequent evolution of safety assessment. In Europe, there was a reluctance to draft further legislation that referred to substantial equivalence. However, whether the principle was mentioned or not, the central idea, that to assess safety of a novel crop some comparison with its traditional counterpart is necessary, has remained at the centre of risk assessment methodologies.

5.3.6 Safety assessment today

At the time of writing (2006), the descriptions of safety assessment for GM crops and derived products are far more rigorous than the vague prescriptions offered in the early 1990s (see Figure 5.5). This might be seen as an inevitable development as scientific knowledge increases and technology improves. However, that would only be part of the story. A fully rounded appraisal of the evolution of safety assessment in this field would have to acknowledge the huge part that both the direct criticism of the principle and anti-GM public protest played in forcing regulatory scientists and authorities to refine and improve their systems.

Figure 5.5 summarises a proposed European approach to the hazard assessment involved in producing a new GM variety and/or food product, as described in the report of the EU sponsored project, ENTRANSFOOD (introduced in Section 5.3.1). This was a working group of industry and academic scientists, regulatory

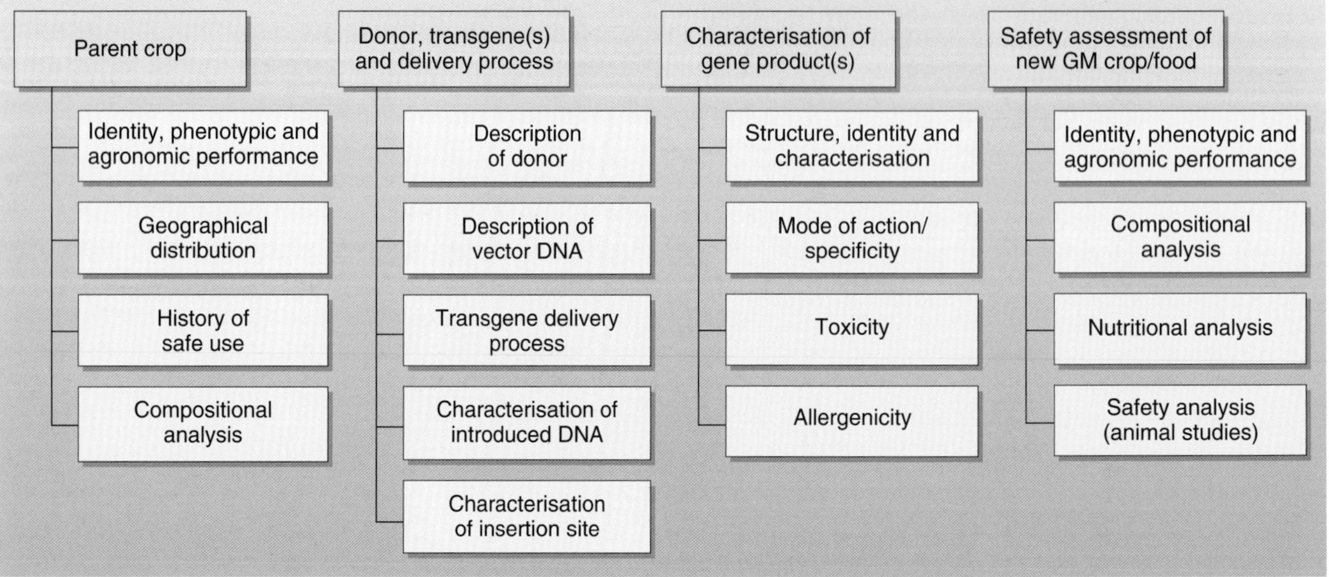

Figure 5.5 A modern assessment method for GM crops.

experts and consumer representatives. The precise details of every step in the procedure need not concern us, but the four stages are:

- Determining the precise characteristics of the parent crop.
- Determining in detail the nature of the DNA inserted and the delivery process.
- Studying the various characteristics of the product(s) of the transferred genes.
- Studying the various characteristics of the new crop as a whole.

Each of these stages requires the detailed study of specific defined aspects. Many of these are themselves the subject of detailed international standards that carry weight in international and national regulations. For example, the OECD publishes documents that provide the international consensus view as to the key nutrients, toxins, allergens and biologically active substances that should to be measured for many of the common species.

Note that the project responsible for the assessment scheme described above was not made up of scientists alone. In Europe, the 1990s saw an increasing involvement of consumer groups and other NGOs in the decision making process. Traditionally, the development of food safety regulations had involved the generation of scientific risk assessments by scientific experts, which were then interpreted by regulatory scientists, civil servants and, in the last instance, elected politicians. From the late 1990s on, partly as a result of the pressure from opponents of GM, Governments and international organisations increasingly have found it necessary to invite consumer groups and other NGOs to take part in the relevant working groups.

The involvement of non-scientists in these working groups reflected a wider change that occurred in the 1990s – the move to attempt much wider consultation with the public over issues of technological and scientific development. In the next section, we will examine this trend in more detail, in particular focusing on the *GM Nation?* debate, an attempt to consult the British public over the development of GM crops.

5.4 Public views and the *GM Nation?* debate

The first genetically modified organisms (GMOs) were created in the early 1970s, but for much of the 1980s biotechnology was a phenomenon confined to the laboratory. In 1988, 'vegetarian cheese', the first food product created using GMOs, was introduced in the UK. This cheese was produced using **chymosin**, an enzyme derived from genetically modified bacteria, rather than the traditional animal product (rennet). Chymosin derived from GMOs is now used to produce 90% of the hard cheeses made in the UK, but these cheeses are labelled 'GM-free' as the enzyme is completely destroyed as the cheese matures. In 1996 the first proper GM food product, tomato puree derived from GM tomatoes (Flavr Savr™) became commercially available in the UK and initially the product sold well. On this evidence, with relatively limited public concern and muted media coverage, the introduction of GM products into our daily lives seemed to be a commercial inevitability.

- In the latter part of the 1990s, a number of events seemed to trigger a change in public perception of GM crops. Can you recall any significant events likely to have contributed to such a change?

- In Topic 1 you explored the UK BSE episode, which raised anxieties about modern agricultural practices and the credibility of scientific pronouncements. Pusztai's experiments (Section 5.2) provided a focus for sustained media coverage in the late 1990s. You may also have recalled the creation of Dolly the genetically modified sheep in 1996, an episode we explore in Section 6.1.

In October 1998, the UK Government brokered a deal with the major biotechnology multinationals that GM crops would not be grown commercially in the UK until more information was available about their possible environmental impact. Approvals for commercial plantings would have to await the results of a series of Farm-Scale Evaluations (FSEs), designed to assess the environmental impact of GM crops. At about the same time, the EU agreed an unofficial moratorium on the approval of new GM products for food or animal feed.

The increasing apprehension about GM crops in the UK and other parts of Europe contrasts strongly with seemingly more muted public concern in other areas of the world. For the UK, it might have been anticipated that the combined influences of the moratorium and the suspension of commercial growing would have reduced public disquiet. But media attention on the FSEs – which took place between 2000 and 2003 – was especially intense. A number of activists expressed their continued disquiet by destroying parts of these trials, though not to the point where their usefulness was seriously jeopardised (Figure 5.6).

In May 2002, the UK Government announced the launch of a 'national dialogue' on the subject. The idea first came from an advisory committee, the Agricultural

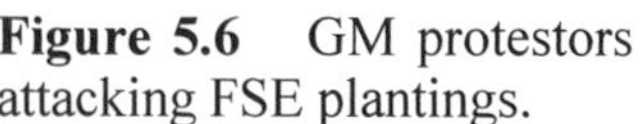

Figure 5.6 GM protestors attacking FSE plantings.

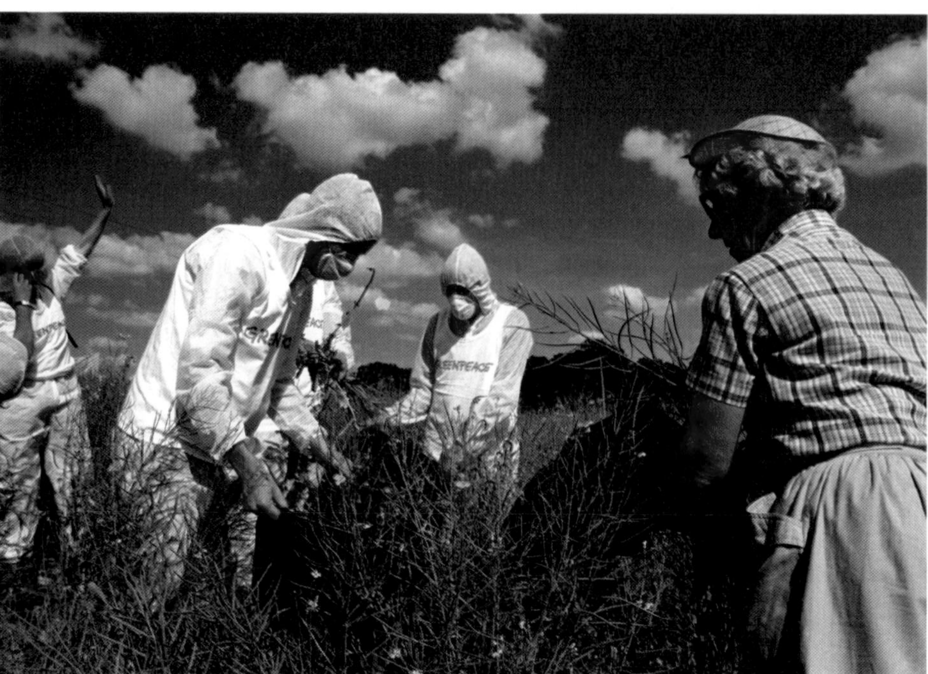

and Environment Biotechnology Commission (AEBC), which was keen to see a broader range of evidence feeding into decision making on GM policy than would be provided by the FSEs alone.

This section will outline how this national dialogue was structured and examine its outcomes. There were three main strands to the national GM dialogue, relating to science, economics and a nationwide public debate. The first two elements will be explored very briefly; but the last strand is of particular interest, for what it tells us about the processes of consultation and communication.

5.4.1 The scientific and economic strands

The GM Science Review

The review was undertaken by the GM Science Review Panel, chaired by the Government's Chief Scientific Adviser, Sir David King. Its role was to assess the evidence available in the peer-reviewed scientific literature. The panel produced two reports, the first in July 2003 and the second in January 2004. The main conclusions of these reports are listed below.

- The risk to human health is very low.
- There is little likelihood of such plants invading the countryside and becoming a significant problem.
- For herbicide-tolerant GM crops, there is insufficient information available to predict with certainty the long-term environmental effects on wildlife.
- Genetic modification is not a homogeneous technology, and therefore its applications needs to be considered on a case-by-case basis.

Both reports highlighted areas of scientific uncertainty – for example, relating to the ease with which GM plants were able to invade new habitats. In neither report is there any claim that GM foods are absolutely safe. However, the panel pointed out that there 'has been no verifiable untoward toxic or nutritionally deleterious effects resulting from the cultivation and consumption of products from GM crops'.

■ How much credibility do you personally attach to such a reassurance about safety?

■ You explored in Section 5.2 and 5.3 the difficulty of assessing safety, and a degree of ambivalence is perhaps inevitable. Commentators sympathetic to GM technology often emphasise the fact that millions of people, particularly in the US, have been eating GM food products for many years, with no apparent deleterious health effects.

■ How convincing do you find this argument about the lack of long-term influence on exposed populations from ingesting GM products?

■ The notion of 'the absence of evidence' of harm should not be seen as equivalent to evidence of the absence of harm.

A credible argument might be that any deleterious effects from GM products are masked by ongoing improvements in healthcare and environmental standards.

Some GM critics have alleged that there is a link between consumption of GM products and an increase in the incidence of food-borne illnesses in the US. Proving such a theory would require thorough **epidemiological studies** – systematic monitoring of individuals consuming GM foods. These are the type of studies that first highlighted the risks of smoking, for example.

The GM Economics Review

Scientists, as might be expected, played a limited role in this review, which was produced by a team dominated by economists. The review sought to evaluate the costs and benefits of commercial development of the GM crops available at that time in the UK. They also looked at possible developments over a 10–15-year period. The members of the team were obliged to recognise the limited 'evidence-base' available on the costs and benefits of GM crops, covering only a short period of time.

They also accepted that the data available were subject to different interpretations. The panel had to deal with the difficulties of predicting unexpected developments – for example, how could unforeseen, and perhaps unforeseeable, adverse impacts on human health be taken into account? It recognised that, in the short term, the negative attitude of consumers would be likely to substantially limit the demand for products containing GM foods, which severely compromises the economic value of the current generation of GM crops.

By contrast, the longer-term prospects for the future developments of GM crops were perceived as more encouraging, with new products bringing presumed health and consumer benefits (see Section 5.1). The panel concluded (a) that it was exceptionally important that the regulatory system 'keep up' with future GM technology and (b) that it is able to 'anticipate and manage people's concerns effectively'.

5.4.2 *GM Nation?* The public debate

The key objective of the national dialogue on GM was to allow the exchange of views and information – members of the public would presumably learn more about the issues; experts and policy makers would learn more of the reasoning behind the public's concerns.

- Can you think of any problems involved in running such a dialogue?
- One problem is the difficulty of sampling public opinion in a representative way, trying to ensure that those involved constitute a representative cross-section of the public. Another problem, given the strongly polarised views on the issue, might be how to encourage a meaningful two-way debate, with both sides listening.

Whether the debate that did occur was successful in solving these problems is a matter of some contention. With that in mind, it's worth examining precisely how the debate was structured.

An independent 11-member Steering Board had executive control; their independence was meant to guarantee a debate at 'arms length' from Government. The make-up of the Board aimed to reflect 'the full spectrum of opinion on GM issues'. In November 2002, the Board launched an initial eight foundation workshops, five in England and one in each of Scotland, Wales and Northern Ireland. The foundation workshops involved selected members of the public, none of whom had significant previous involvement in GM issues, i.e. there were no 'stakeholders'.

For comparison, a ninth workshop was held in Norwich, involving only those already active in the debate – half were supporters, half opponents. The nine workshops were to capture the range of concerns of the public and help frame the issues for debate, i.e. to help set the agenda. They were also used to frame the 13 questions that were used to assess the outcome of the later, full-scale debates. You have already come across these questions in Activity 4.1.

'Stimulus' material was developed, including a video that consisted in the main of footage of conversations between groups of farmers, consumers and scientists. Written stimulus material was made available via a workbook, CD-ROM and interactive website.

The material attempted to show a range of representative opinions rather than provide information. The extract printed in Table 5.2 gives you a sample of the style of the material. (If you wish to view the full material, it is available via the S250 course website.)

Table 5.2 Extract from 'Why GM?', stimulus material developed for the *GM Nation?* debate.

2.1 WHY GENETICALLY MODIFY FOOD?	Sharp differences in perspective on the need for GM, and what benefits and costs it brings, lie at the heart of the GM debate.
Views for	Current GM crops provide environmental, economic and indirect health benefits. In the future they will provide direct health benefits as well. It is important to evaluate and develop GM crops that will help support the world's population in a truly sustainable manner and to help farmers in this country and elsewhere to contribute to this goal. GM crops can benefit the environment by reducing the needs for pesticides and fossil fuels. Future GM crops that can be grown under environmental stresses (heat, cold, drought) will help countries (including developing countries) to improve their food security in a way that is affordable and less damaging to the environment.
Views against	GM will not 'feed the world'. The current food crisis is a problem of distribution not quantity. The evidence so far does not show GM crops lead to reduced use of chemicals. Anything that GM can do, other methods can also do, without bringing risks to the environment. The debate has to be widened beyond a focus on GM alone, to look at the whole question of how we produce our food.

- On the basis of this brief extract, what is your reaction to this style of presentation?
- Many users were critical of the document: the 'for' and 'against' format runs the risk of polarising debate, in that two sides were clearly identified and that alignment to one or the other was implied to be necessary. The material was felt to lack 'depth and substance' and to many, the lack of scientific information was surprising. (It was significant that none of the organisations that were commissioned to work on the booklet were willing to be associated with the final product.)

The *GM Nation?* debate proper took place in three 'tiers'. Tier 1 consisted of six major regional debates, three in England and the remainder in Scotland, Wales and Northern Ireland. Each meeting was fully booked, in halls that had capacities of between 100 and 200. The format of each meeting was the same, with a preliminary showing of the video and subsequent assembly of the audience into 'round-table' groups of about a dozen. A single independent facilitator guided each group through questions specified in the resource booklet; the meeting finished with a general feedback session, with each table electing their own facilitator.

A cascade of Tier 2 and Tier 3 meetings were initiated, of variable format. Around 40 Tier 2 meetings were held by regional and county-level local authorities. Tier 3 consisted of what might best be described as 'grassroots meetings', differing hugely in terms of scale and location – including, as fans of *The Archers* radio series will recollect, one set in the fictional village of Ambridge. Estimates of the number of Tier 3 events range from 400 to 700. Given that such meetings had to take place within a specified six-week period, the supply of speakers was limited; in particular, those who could present the pro-GM stance were under-represented. There is general agreement from those who attended such meetings that both in terms of numbers attending and the general tone of the debate, anti-GM views were dominant.

Printed feedback forms, including the 13 questions you answered in Activity 4.1, were provided to all participants and an on-line version was made available. In all, 37 000 feedback forms were returned and 24 609 people visited the website, 61% of whom submitted forms on line. 1200 letters or emails were received by the Steering Board.

Ten closed 'focus group' discussions were run at the same time as the public debate. These excluded individuals with any prior involvement with the subject. Each group met twice, and in the two week interim, participants were asked to explore the GM issue individually, using resources that they located from newspapers and websites. These were termed 'narrow-but-deep' (NBD) groups and were designed to act as 'control' groups, to balance the likelihood that the self-selecting participants at the public meetings were not representative of the 'silent majority'.

As already mentioned, the debate was initially announced at the end of May 2002, but a number of administrative delays meant that the main public phase of the debate was confined to a brief six-week period in the following year (during June and July 2003) – a good deal shorter than originally intended.

5.4.3 The outcomes of the public debate

Box 5.2 contains an edited version of the Executive Summary of the document *GM Nation? Findings of the Public Debate*. This is a lengthy summary, but it is worth exploring in some detail. The unedited version can be found on the S250 course website.

Box 5.2 *GM Nation?* Findings of the Public Debate

1 People are generally uneasy about GM

Across the different elements of the debate, participants expressed unease about GM. They were uneasy not only about issues directly related to GM technology but [also] about a range of broader social and political issues. The mood ranged from caution and doubt, through suspicion and scepticism, to hostility and rejection. Despite the range of expression, among people who chose to take an active part in the debate, these attitudes far outweighed any degree of support or enthusiasm for GM.

Our analysis of the NBD element suggests that among this sample of the general population people are less emphatic and less definite in their first response to GM issues. [Participants] readily confirmed that they did not feel that they knew much about GM. Although they have strong anxieties about some risks from GM, particularly towards the environment and human health, they are more willing to accept that GM may offer some benefits. However, their predominant mood is one of uncertainty towards GM.

2 The more people engage in GM issues, the harder their attitudes and more intense their concerns

The NBD sample also suggested that when people in the general population become more engaged in GM issues, and choose to discover more about them, they harden their attitudes to GM. Although they are more willing to accept some potential benefits from GM (especially medical benefits and other advantages for developing countries) they become more doubtful about the others and they express more concern/greater unease about all of the risks most frequently associated with GM.

3 There is little support for early commercialisation

There is little support for the early commercialisation of GM crops. Among active participants in the debate, just over half never want to see GM crops grown in the UK under any circumstances.

The NBD sample suggests that the general population does not share [this] unconditional opposition. However, it does suggest that the general population would prefer caution: GM crop technology should not go ahead without further trials and tests, firm regulation, demonstrated benefits to society (not just for producers) and, above all, clear and trusted answers to unresolved questions about health and the environment.

4 There is widespread mistrust of Government and multinational companies

Alongside arguments over the potential risks and benefits of GM itself, both the open debate and the NBD element also highlighted a series of political issues, manifested in a strong and wide degree of suspicion about the motives, intentions and behaviour of those taking decisions about GM – especially Government and multinational companies. Such suspicion is commonly expressed as a lack of trust. [There is a] suspicion that the Government has already taken a decision about GM: the debate was only a camouflage and its results would be ignored. The GM debate also reflects a weakening of faith in the ability or even the will of any Government to defend the interest of the general public. This was supported by the way in which people cited past disasters, especially BSE. They carried a double lesson: first, that Government may not have adequate knowledge and advice to help them take the right decisions; and second, that Government can be too close to producer interests.

The debate also highlighted unease over the perceived power of the multinational companies that promote GM technology, and of such companies in general. People believe that these companies are motivated overwhelmingly by profit rather than meeting society's needs, and that they have the power to make their interests prevail over the wider public interest, both at home and throughout global society.

When given the opportunity to engage in GM issues, people do not rely exclusively on official sources or everyday media. They choose sources that they trust and that mean something in their personal life.

5 There is a broad desire to know more and for further research to be done

In all parts of the debate, both from active participants and the NBD sample, people expressed a very strong wish to be better informed about GM from sources they could trust. They wish to be able to resolve for themselves the contradictions and disputes, claims and counter-claims, in the existing body of information, science and research on GM issues. They want a corpus of agreed 'facts', accepted by all organisations and interests. They also want confidence in the independence and integrity of information about GM – the assurance that it does not reflect the influence of any group with a special interest for or against GM (including Government and business). There was a general feeling that no one knows enough at the moment and that much more research is necessary.

6 Developing countries have special interests

There was a 'debate-within-the-debate' on the potential role of GM for developing countries. In all parts of the debate, there was at least an initial assumption that GM technology might help developing countries produce more food and offer them medical, social and economic benefits. There was then a clear divergence between the views of active participants in the debate and those expressed in the NBD sample. The former rejected, by a majority, the idea that GM technology would benefit developing countries: the latter supported it, and their support slightly increased after people got more engaged in GM issues.

However, in the context of the developing world, opposition to GM was based less on negative feelings towards GM than on the view that there were better and more important ways to promote development, including fairer trade, better distribution of food, income and power, and better Government.

On the issue of benefits to the developing world, people were particularly sceptical about the will of multinational companies to deliver them.

7 The debate was welcomed and valued

Although there was a widespread suspicion that the debate's results would be ignored by Government, people in all parts of the debate were glad that it had happened. People expressed their appreciation for the opportunity not only to express their own views, but to hear those of other people, including experts, to ask questions and acquire new information, and to take part in stimulating discussions. In spite of their suspicions of Government, people expressed a real hope that their efforts in the debate would influence future policy.

It is useful to explore some of the issues raised in the Executive Summary in a little more depth, calling on further information in the main body of the report and from sources critical of *GM Nation?*.

The summary makes clear that many of the participants were sceptical as to whether their views would have any influence.

■ According to the summary, why where participants sceptical?

■ There was a widespread view that the Government had already made up its mind about GM crops. By that logic, the debate was little more than 'window-dressing'. There was a good deal of suspicion about the Government, usually talked of in terms of a 'lack of trust'; the motives of the multinational companies in the forefront of GM development were also regarded with suspicion.

All the elements of the debate were conducted on a very short timescale, which made it more difficult to organise meetings. A number of organisations felt that this meant that the right quality of information could not be provided to the public. Furthermore, the timing of the debate was such that information from the FSEs, and the Science and Economic reviews was not available (Section 5.4.1).

In all three tiers of debate, many more people were 'cautious, suspicious or outrightly hostile' about GM crops than were supportive towards them. A key issue is whether such anti-GM views accurately reflect the views of 'ordinary people'. Those who attended Tier 2 and 3 meetings were 'self-selecting', rather than representative, and already held views about GM. Here's what one critic of the events had to say about the 'non-scientific' nature of the survey:

> But the large size of the sample does not overcome one glaring problem with it. It is, as even its authors concede, a self-selected sample, and therefore is almost certainly not random. As a self-selected sample, it is probably comprised mostly of those with strong opinions on the subject. After all, if you don't give a damn, why would you go to the trouble of writing a letter to a survey unit telling them that you don't give a damn? The fact that tens of thousands of the sort of people who get worked up about GM wrote in to say that they get worked up about it tells us nothing much about the rest of the population, especially when one considers that none of the *GM Nation?* budget was spent on advertising, and so most of the people who knew about it (before the results hit the headlines) were the activists.
>
> (Campbell, 2004)

Opponents of GM technology criticised the lack of publicity too, arguing that many who would have expressed hostile views were not aware of the debate. However, whatever the shortcomings of this debate, other means of gauging public opinion have revealed a comparable degree of public anxiety about GM crops and food.

A common argument against GM crops involves the expression of the precautionary principle (as seen in earlier topics). The *GM Nation?* report summarises the principle as that 'no major technological change should be introduced into the environment and into society until its impacts, including long-term ones, are known and measurable'.

- Can you identify any strengths and weaknesses of the precautionary principle?

- A strength of the precautionary principle would be that it provides maximum reassurance of safety. A major weakness would be that it is unlikely that any fully reliable data set could ever fully quantify the level of risk to human health or to wildlife, in every possible circumstance. Absolute proof of safety is impractical. Many would argue more pragmatically that the absence of apparent harm offers the next best thing. Most technologies have associated elements of uncertainty; banning their adoption would very substantially limit the pace of technological innovation.

The tendency to favour precaution shown by the public was one of several concerns that became evident during the debate. Other concerns included freedom of choice, the power of the multinationals, and 'doing right' by developing countries. What the report says about this plethora of issues is illuminating:

> The public do not view GM as a purely scientific, or environmental, or economic, or political or ethical issue. All of these aspects are important to them. It follows that the public accept no single arbiter of decisions to be made about GM. They do not regard science and the scientific method, or economics and economic analysis, or academics or politicians, or any other discipline as a single source of evidence and guidance. The public seek and trust expertise and authorities that accord with their own arguments and values.

Any debate over a new technology such as GM, has therefore to take in the widest possible range of factors. In the broadest possible terms, the key question becomes 'what type of society would we like to achieve and how might new technology help to achieve it?'

The sociologist Alan Irwin picks up this point, in a way that provides an interesting summary of some of these issues:

> But this isn't just about the risks. The question is: why would anyone accept additional risk – no matter how improbable – if the benefits were not clear? This view that risks make no sense without matching benefits emerged during the GM debate. Whatever the risk, if the need for a new technology has not been demonstrated, why go ahead?
>
> I attended one of the regional GM meetings. Of course, others might have been taken over by hysterical hordes, but what I saw was a mature discussion among mature people. What took place in Harrogate was a calm and intelligent reflection, a serious treatment of serious issues. Surely we should be encouraging that kind of engagement rather than presenting it as a backward slide?
>
> In my experience, there is very little anti-science feeling among the general public – but there can be a sort of 'anti-public' feeling among some of those who claim to speak for science. Members of the public will often express caution about the advantages of new science and technology. But it is no use muttering about Luddism when people are simply asking how society will gain from new medical technologies or biobanks. To some degree, I can understand scientists' impatience to get ahead with what they see as significant progress. Nevertheless, other voices have a right to be heard, without being dismissed as hysterical.
>
> So what's the answer? First, let's recognise that science is too important to be left to scientists alone. We should accept that scientists don't have the monopoly on rationality. Those who are critical of public opinion would do well to join the next consensus conference, citizen's jury or regional debate (although they may have to wait since all of these are in short supply). Once their prejudices about the public are put to one side, they might just find that they have something to learn as well as contribute.
>
> Next, we should appreciate that risks can't be separated from the contexts in which they occur. In the case of GM, that means considering the perceived influence of US companies and the feeling that there are better solutions to world poverty than another technological fix. Honest reflection on the ethical and philosophical issues should not be labelled as procrastination.
>
> Finally, we could move to a culture where public opinion is seen as an essential constituent of progress – rather than as an impediment. Doesn't the representation of the public as risk-averse suggest a decidedly arrogant posture in the face of expressed concerns? Rather than representing citizens as risk-averse, we should be engaging more thoroughly with what people actually want from technical change. Of course, this is no easy option – but there is no sustainable alternative. (Irwin, 2004)

We have spent some time discussing the *GM Nation?* debate. Does the experience help inform how future debates of this type – on nanotechnology, for example – might be conducted to better effect? A common criticism is that the *GM Nation?* debate took place 'too late to influence the direction of GM research or to alter the institutional commitments of key players'. In recent years, a number of commentators have called for processes of public consultation that take place in advance of ('upstream' of) a developing technology. For example, the Royal Society/Royal Academy of Engineers report on nanotechnology calls for a 'constructive and proactive debate [...] at a stage when it can inform key decisions about their development and before deeply entrenched or polarised positions appear'.

Controversially, perhaps a genuine debate, sufficiently far upstream, ought to include at least the possibility of deciding not to go ahead with one or more aspects of new technology.

Activity 5.5

Allow 30 minutes

Now go to the S250 course website to explore the results of your own *GM Nation?* survey.

Summary of Chapter 5

There are two areas of general concern regarding the introduction of GM crops and food: the possible impacts on human health and on the environment. For some critics of GM technology, this reflects a feeling that GM technology is unnatural, as compared to conventional crop breeding. However, many techniques used in conventional crop development, for example, intergeneric and interspecific crossing, haploid breeding and mutation breeding, are highly technological and seem very far from being natural. Critics of GM argue that the newer technology is qualitatively different, and gives rise to new and different concerns.

An ethical judgement about the value or otherwise of GM crops and food will involve an assessment of the potential risks and benefits of the technology, and an attempt to reach just decisions. Achieving justice is complex, but might involve both an attempt to direct the potential benefits of the new technology to those who need it most, and an attempt to strike a fair balance between competing interests. The notion of justice is at the heart of the debate over whether GM crops might form part of a strategy to feed the world. However, it is important not to see the ethical debates in static terms, as 'second-generation' GM crops may change future attitudes.

A key episode in both the story of GM crops and the relationship of science and wider society in the last decade involved the work of Arpad Pusztai at the Rowett Institute. The work in question focused on developing methods for testing the safety of GM food, specifically potatoes modified to express GNA lectin, an insecticide. A series of press releases from the Institute, and televised statements from Pusztai, implied that the work unequivocally demonstrated potential health risks, before any peer-reviewed papers had been published. In the ensuing controversy, Pusztai was condemned both by senior scientists and Government ministers, and was forced to retire. The episode reveals the difficulty of communicating science in areas of heightened public concern.

Assessing the health risk from GM products provided a new challenge for scientists and legislators in the late 1980s and early 1990s. The concept of substantial equivalence was developed to meet this challenge, and involves an assessment as to whether a GM product is 'substantially equivalent' to its conventional counterpart. In cases where the GM product is demonstrated to be substantially equivalent, the product is assumed to be safe. However, the concept of 'substantial equivalence' and the methods used to demonstrate it, have been the subject of sustained criticism. Arguably, the interpretation and the use of the term has evolved, at least partly as a result of this criticism.

In response to the widespread concerns about GM crops and food, in 2002 the UK Government launched a 'national dialogue' over the issue. There were three strands to the debate – a review of the science, an economic review, and a national public debate.

The science review concluded that the risk to health and the environment was low, but that the new technology should be considered on a case-by-case basis. The economic review concluded that in the short term, negative public attitudes were likely to limit the demands for GM food.

The *GM Nation?* public debate appeared to demonstrate that there were, indeed, widespread public concerns over the technology, coupled with mistrust of Government and big business. The participants also expressed a desire to know more and for further, independent research. However, the debate was criticised for sampling an unrepresentative pool of public opinion, and for the way in which the debate was structured. Another criticism of the debate was that it occurred too late to shape the development of the science, technology or regulations. Whilst the precise structure of the *GM Nation?* debate is unlikely to be replicated, public debates of a similar kind are likely to occur in the near future, for example over nanotechnology.

Question 5.1

(a) Give a simple interpretation of the concept of 'justice' that might be appropriate to guide decision makers influencing the introduction of a new technology. (b) Why might this concept of justice be difficult to use in practice?

Question 5.2

(a) Given the experience of the Pusztai affair, what are the difficulties that arise from communicating scientific results via press releases and direct contact with the media? (b) Is it realistic to expect scientists not to communicate in this way?

Question 5.3

(a) What is the principle of substantial equivalence? (b) Why was it the subject of sustained criticism from those opposed to GM crops?

Question 5.4

Participants in the *GM Nation?* debate were broadly opposed to the introduction of GM crops. Does this indicate that the participants distrusted science?

Chapter 6

The genetic manipulation of animals

Up to now, we've been concerned largely with gene manipulation in microbes and in plants, but here our attention turns to comparable processes in animals. This part of the topic is introduced by a discussion of cloning and of stem cells; Section 6.2 takes a broader look at the variety of techniques now being developed and some key issues that have arisen. First, some helpful terminology. *In vitro*, normally written in italics, means literally 'in glass' and describes techniques undertaken in artificial conditions outside the body. By contrast, procedures conducted within the body are termed *in vivo*.

6.1 Cloning and the manipulation of stem cells

By now you'll be familiar with the notion of cloning as one form or another of 'genetic copying' of genes or other DNA sequences, as introduced on p. 37. The term has a broader meaning too, which is simply the production of 'more of a like kind' – perhaps cells or indeed whole organisms derived from an original parent. The process you read about in Chapter 3 of producing a colony of genetically identical bacteria is termed **bacterial cloning**. This simple form of asexual reproduction is very distinct from sexual reproduction, which involves the mixing of genetic material from male and female parents and the production of genetically distinct offspring. In recent years – and certainly since 1997 when Dolly the sheep was born – cloning is very commonly used to describe the creation of new organisms that are genetic copies of an adult.

6.1.1 Dolly the sheep and her inheritance

Dolly was the clone of an adult sheep; her birth was such a breakthrough because it was the first time that a genetic copy of an adult mammal had been created by experimental manipulation. (You'll appreciate that the production of identical twins – whether lambs or human babies – is an example of natural forms of cloning.) The creation of Dolly, summarised in Figure 6.1, involved extracting the nucleus from what was highly likely to have been a differentiated (i.e. specialised) cell obtained from the mammary gland (i.e. the udder) of an adult 'donor' sheep. A nucleus from such a differentiated cell (taken from a cell culture grown *in vitro*) was then inserted into the unfertilised egg from another adult sheep in which the nuclear material had been destroyed – a so-called enucleated egg. This reconstituted egg was activated (the details needn't be of concern) and then transferred into the uterus of a 'surrogate' mother – making her pregnant with an offspring of genetic make-up quite distinct from her own – who gave birth to Dolly after the normal pregnancy term of about 155 days. Dolly's genetic make-up was almost entirely identical to that of the adult 'donor' sheep from which the nucleus had been transferred. (Complete genetic identity cannot be claimed, in that some genes are known to lie outside the nucleus – for example, in the mitochondria, which are present in the cytosol. In Dolly's case, the DNA of her mitochondrial genes would have been those of the recipient egg, into which the donor nucleus was inserted.)

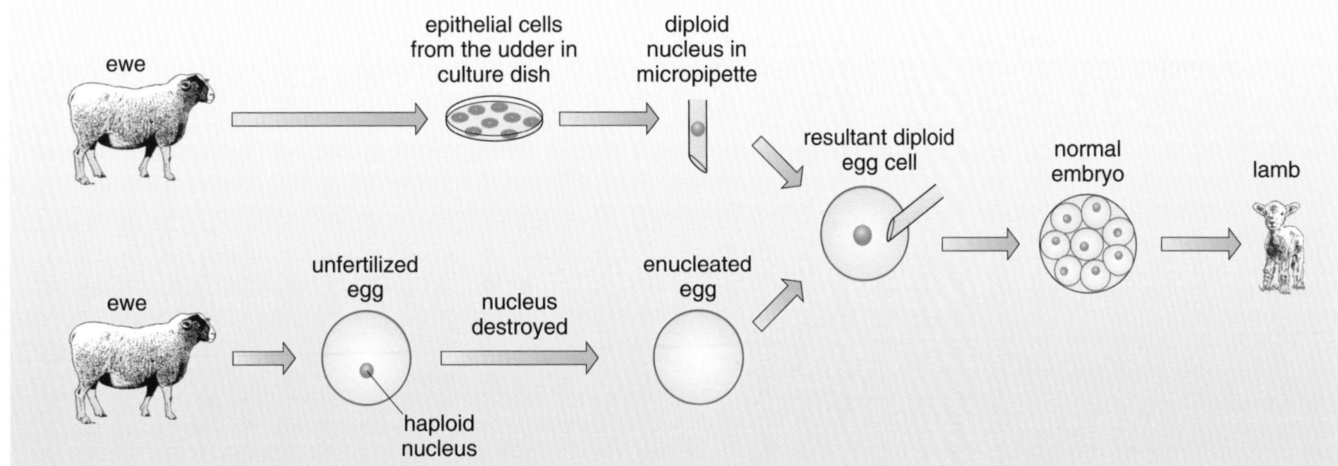

Figure 6.1 The cloning (somatic cell nuclear transfer) procedure using a nucleus from a differentiated cell, as used to create Dolly. An unfertilised immature egg taken from a sheep is subjected to ultraviolet light to destroy the haploid nucleus. A diploid nucleus from a differentiated cell in culture (an epithelial cell from the udder) is then injected into the enucleated egg. The resulting embryo is implanted into a surrogate mother and a live birth can ensue.

The more precise term for this form of cloning is nuclear replacement or **somatic cell nuclear transfer (SCNT),** though in what follows I'll follow the well established convention of using the term 'cloning'.

The birth of Dolly demonstrated the capacity of the nucleus of a differentiated cell to direct the development of a normal offspring. At the time, this was a rather unexpected revelation. You'll be aware that development in a mammal such as a sheep is to a very large degree triggered and guided by the diploid nucleus formed by the coming together of the haploid male sperm and haploid female **ovum** (egg). With just a few exceptions, all the very different cells of our bodies have the same complement of genes – the same could be said for the great majority of plants and animals. During the process of differentiation that takes place as the embryo develops, different genes, or sets of genes, are expressed, as mentioned in Section 2.1, with particular cells becoming fully committed to particular developmental pathways. In general terms, the greater the degree of specialisation of cells – and most cells within the sheep mammary gland are highly differentiated – the greater the proportion of their genes that becomes switched off.

■ With the creation of Dolly in mind, is the switching off of genes in such specialised tissue permanent or can the process be reversed if conditions change?

■ On this evidence, the switching off (and on) of genes can be reversed. Remember that the 'donor' nucleus transferred into the unfertilised egg was removed from a differentiated cell (more than likely) and yet was able to support the development of a whole new individual (i.e. Dolly).

Quite how such switching on and off genes comes about is not fully understood, but the appropriate triggers must come from the particular cell environment in which the genes are located. And the process is far from straightforward; Dolly was born only after many unsuccessful nuclear transfers into surrogate mothers (in all, 277 such transfers were attempted) and only one ended up with the birth of a lamb. Even Dolly developed a number of abnormalities and had to be put down after six and a half years – about half the expected lifespan of her breed.

Where transfers failed, at least part of the explanation must be that the appropriate triggers for gene expressions were lacking and/or that genes were unreceptive to such stimulation. How all such factors proved 'just right' on this one occasion is not known. However, rare though success may prove in practice, that single outcome shows that the transferred nucleus has the capacity to trigger and direct the production of all the many cells types that comprise the adult sheep, e.g. bone, liver, muscle, and red blood cells. You'll be aware that research into animal cloning continues at a great pace, increasing the likelihood of many of the uncertainties we've touched on being resolved. The range of mammals will doubtless continue to extend beyond the present-day (early 2006) list of mice, monkeys, rats, cows, horses, cats and mules, with techniques and approaches somewhat different from that described for Dolly.

Question 6.1

When the birth of Dolly the sheep was announced, some critics claimed that the nucleus transferred might have been from an undifferentiated cell from within the udder of the donor. Why is such a criticism significant?

Question 6.2

In what respect can it be argued that Dolly is not an *exact* genetic copy of the 'donor' sheep used to create her?

6.1.2 What are stem cells?

Stem cells are, to greater or lesser extent, totipotent (a term introduced in Section 4.2.3), i.e. they are uncommitted 'master cells', able to give rise to other specialised cells, usually of a range of different types. Stem cells occur naturally within a whole range of tissue types in adult humans, especially in tissues like skin and blood where normal function depends upon a high rate of replacement of 'worn-out' cells. Adult stem cells have the capacity to differentiate into the cell type – e.g. skin or blood – within which they are located, as particular genes become expressed or repressed (turned-off). The hope is that different cell lines can be used in the treatment of such conditions as Parkinson's disease (replacing nerve cells), Type 1 diabetes (new insulin-producing pancreatic cells), muscular dystrophy (new skeletal muscle cells), macular degeneration (new retinal cells in the eye) and osteoporosis (new bone cells).

Unsurprisingly, stem cells are also located within the fetus growing within the womb, but they are also found in the placenta and the umbilical cord. One especially convenient source of stem cells is the early human embryo; cells derived from such a source are termed **embryonic stem cells** or **ES cells**.

The fertilisation of a human ovum by a sperm normally triggers a series of developmental events that follow a predictable timetable, at first involving not much more than successive divisions of tightly adhering cells (see Figure 6.2). By about 5 days after fertilisation, at which point the embryo consists of as many as 200 cells, the first signs of cell differentiation becomes evident. An inner mass becomes distinct from the outer cells – the latter will contribute to the important tissues that link the fetus with the mother, most obviously the placenta and umbilical cord. The entire embryo at this stage is termed a **blastocyst**, and as you can see in Figure 6.2e, it has an inner fluid-filled cavity. It is at this stage that the embryo would normally become attached to (or 'implanted' into) the wall of the mother's womb, a step that is a necessary prelude to development. In the event of ***in vitro* fertilisation (IVF)**, where for medical reasons, fertilisation is conducted on eggs normally removed from a woman, it is usually the 5-day stage blastocyst that is transferred into the womb after its early *in vitro* development. At this point, normal implantation and development can ensue.

It's the inner cell mass – from which the remaining tissues would normally be derived – that comprises the source of embryonic stem cells. The enveloping cell layer of the blastocyst can be removed, usually by microsurgery, so freeing the inner cell mass, which consists of no more than 30–40 cells at this stage. These embryonic stem cells can then be grown in culture and their differentiation directed along particular lines. Maintaining such a human cell line *in vitro* in a non-differentiated state can be tricky – the cells must not be allowed to aggregate together, for example. Furthermore, they usually have to be kept in dishes that are coated on the inside with mouse embryonic skin cells (fibroblasts), which not only sustain the ES cells nutritionally, but also provides sites for their attachment. Without this layer of 'feeder cells' the ES cells are prone to undergo **apoptosis** (programmed cell death).

There are enormous problems and uncertainties inherent in moving such research on human ES cells from the experimental stage to routine use for patient care. Some such issues are ethical by nature, which we'll return to later, but many are biological problems. For instance, at what precise stage along the road to differentiation should ES cells be used? Will transplanted cells become safely integrated into the tissues of the recipient and adopt a normal function? What's more, given the capacity of undifferentiated stem cells to turn into any one of a number of cell types, what guarantee is there that ES cells will not give rise to 'inappropriate' tissues – tumours in particular? None of these problems is likely to prove wholly insurmountable, given time. For example, although tumours can arise after ES cell transplantation, they seem to arise exclusively from undifferentiated ES cells that may lie amidst a differentiated population; the former would need to be removed. Other researchers are currently investigating the feasibility of transferring 'suicide genes' into ES cells; such genes would become expressed in the event of ES cells becoming cancerous, ensuring that such a tumour could not develop.

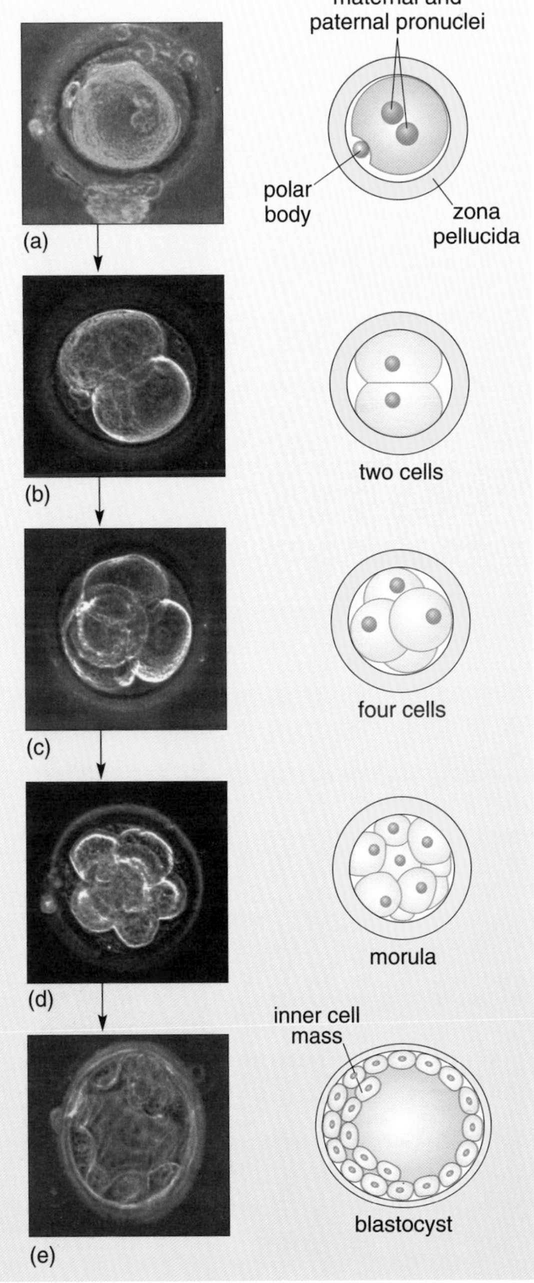

Figure 6.2 Early embryonic development in the human. You need not remember any of the structures shown in (a)–(d) but they are given for completeness. In (a), the maternal (ovum) and paternal (sperm) nuclei are present (as so-called pronuclei) in the fertilised ovum (the zygote), and a polar body is located at the periphery (left). The zygote is enclosed in a membrane called the zona pellucida. Successive cell division produces first a morula (d) and then a blastocyst (e), which contains embryonic stem cells.

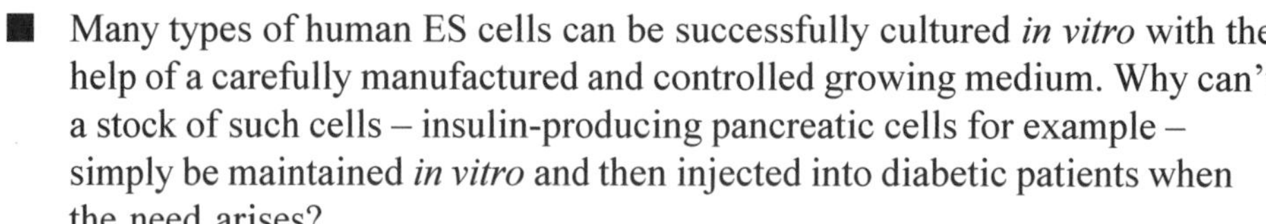

- Many types of human ES cells can be successfully cultured *in vitro* with the help of a carefully manufactured and controlled growing medium. Why can't a stock of such cells – insulin-producing pancreatic cells for example – simply be maintained *in vitro* and then injected into diabetic patients when the need arises?

- 'Off the shelf' replacement tissues of this type are likely to be rejected by the patient's immune system after injection, because they will be genetically dissimilar to the patient's own cells.

Because relatively few studies have been done involving human ES cell transfer, the precise level of risk of rejection is unknown. What is clear is that ES cells, in common with all other cells, have characteristic 'biochemical markers' on their surfaces, of a type that allows the recipient to distinguish between its own cells and those that are foreign. Patients can be treated with drugs that suppress the immunological response, but this leaves the patient vulnerable to a wide range of infections. Perhaps it will eventually prove possible to modify or 'hide' such markers in such a way that they no longer trigger an immune response. But the problem could be avoided altogether if the ES cells to be transferred were genetically identical to those of the recipient. The techniques of cloning already outlined might in time achieve just such an end, as Section 6.1.3 explains. Before addressing that point, it's important to distinguish between two forms of cloning, which differ in purpose.

6.1.3 Reproductive and therapeutic cloning

The production of a new individual in the manner of Dolly is termed **reproductive cloning**, where the offspring is almost entirely genetically identical to one parent. It was this form of cloning that initially prompted so much debate in the aftermath of the creation of Dolly – with headlines that highlighted an increased likelihood of an ability to clone humans. But in the minds of the great majority of scientists who work on nuclear transfer, such techniques have quite a different aim. Here a major goal is to use nuclear transfer to produce replacement cells and tissues, of the type that might substitute for damaged or diseased tissue from human patients suffering from Parkinson's disease or Type 1 diabetes, for example.

The production of replacement cells and tissues that have a genetic identity that matches that of the patient's own cells gets round the problem of rejection just mentioned. **Therapeutic cloning** has the potential to produce a ready source of such 'tailor-made' cells. The example considered here is an attempt to use replacement cells produced by therapeutic cloning as a long-term cure for diabetes, outlined in Figure 6.3. Much the same method of therapeutic cloning has the potential to treat a range of medical conditions.

Therapeutic cloning

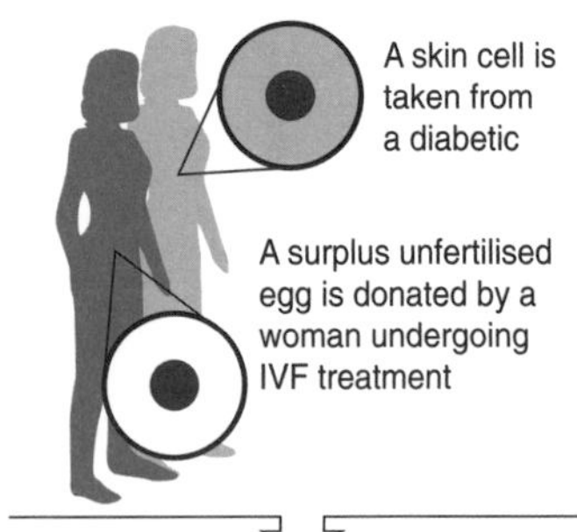
A skin cell is taken from a diabetic
A surplus unfertilised egg is donated by a woman undergoing IVF treatment
(a)

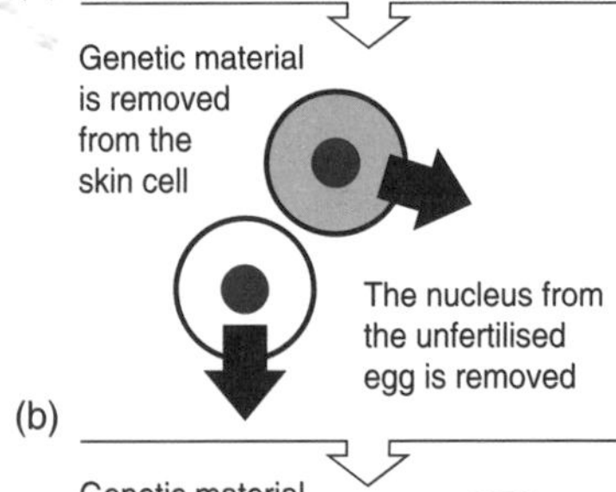
Genetic material is removed from the skin cell
The nucleus from the unfertilised egg is removed
(b)

Genetic material from the skin cell is injected into the egg
(c)

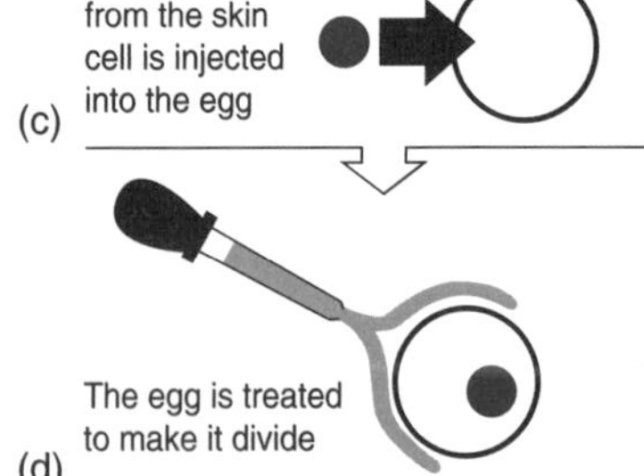
The egg is treated to make it divide
(d)

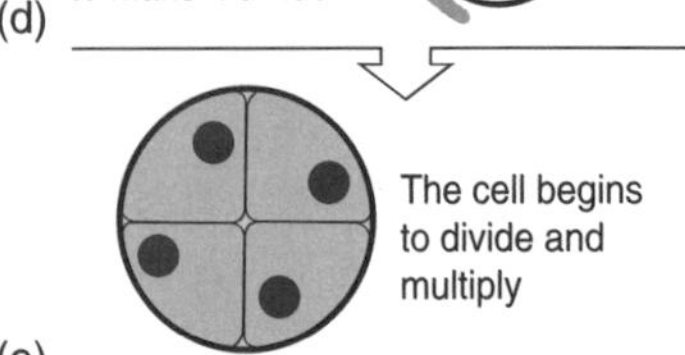
The cell begins to divide and multiply
(e)

The outer cells will develop to become the placenta. The inner cells are known as stem cells and can develop into any of the 300 different cell types that make up the human body
(f)

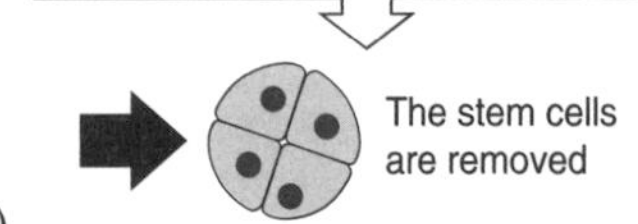
The stem cells are removed
(g)

Researchers plan to turn the stem cells into insulin-producing pancreatic cells

Implanting them into diabetics could cure the condition
(h)

Figure 6.3 Therapeutic cloning, as likely to be used in future for the introduction of modified stem cells into diabetic patients. This is reproduced from an article in the *Guardian,* 17 June 2004.

Suppose a skin cell of a diabetic patient is removed – hopefully, the nucleus of any readily accessible tissue would be just as effective a starting point (Figure 6.3a). This nucleus is to be transferred into an unfertilised, enucleated human egg, probably removed from a woman undergoing IVF treatment. The skin cell nucleus is injected into the enucleated donor egg, step (c), and the egg is then stimulated to divide, as in (d). At the blastocyst stage (f), the inner cell mass can be removed – step (g), and then cultured *in vitro* (h) and, through the action of a range of added 'growth factors', the ES cells become differentiated insulin-producing cells.

- ■ Figure 6.3 is based on an illustration that accompanied a newspaper article reporting an application in the UK to begin this technique. How accurate do you think the information is and how well does it convey information to those who would have limited science background?

- ■ On the whole, the diagram is useful and accurate. It's possible to quibble about a few biological points – for example, the nucleus is shown disproportionately large, the activation of the egg in (d) is more complex than indicated and the blastocyst is shown in a highly stylised way, with no central, fluid-filled cavity of the sort you saw in Figure 6.2e. But very minor modifications of this type and scale are surely unimportant if the diagram is clear and informative.

Because ES cells produced in this way are genetically identical to those of the intended recipient, the two sets of surface markers will be identical and no immune response will therefore be triggered, allowing the insulin-producing cells to adopt a normal function in this diabetic patient. What the technique does is bring together the technology of cloning (in the form of somatic cell nuclear transfer) and the known totipotency of ES cells, to offer a potential treatment, indeed perhaps a cure, for a range of debilitating medical conditions.

- ■ Speculate on some of the uncertainties and risks that would have to be addressed before the use of therapeutic cloning for treating diabetes became routine. Think critically about the problems that might influence the effectiveness (i.e. the efficacy) of such a technique and whether the technique would have proven safety.

- ■ The concerns that spring to mind are whether sufficient ES cells would be transferred, and whether, following transplantation, they would maintain themselves by growth and division and function normally. For example, would they respond in a normal, controlled way to an elevation of blood sugar levels by releasing insulin, in sufficient amounts to have an effect? (It is well known that cells *in vivo* behave differently from their counterparts *in vitro*, so demonstrating such a capacity before transplantation is no guarantee of effectiveness after transfer.) In terms of safety, would such cells remain in their stable, differentiated state, or is there a risk that they would they become diseased or cancerous?

Many people argue that only by undertaking such research on human patients will any such uncertainty be resolved. Doubtless many problems would be exposed in the process, in part reflecting the fact that our knowledge of the cause of diabetes (and to what extent it is genetic in origin) is limited. In the most debilitating form of diabetes (Type 1), the insulin-producing cells of the patient's pancreas have become incapacitated over time by a sustained attack from the body's own immune system – it is one of a range of so-called **auto-immune diseases**. Such gradual loss of function over time could occur with transplanted ES cells, given they are genetically identical to the patient's original pancreatic cells. With many such instances of 'cures' via therapeutic cloning, the effects may be short-lived, suggesting the need for continued periodic replacement.

But the many critics of therapeutic cloning claim that the technique raises such profound ethical issues that further research is inappropriate.

■ Quickly re-read the details of this example of therapeutic cloning. Can you identify why ethical considerations are important here?

■ Because the technique requires a source of unfertilised human eggs which, after nuclear transfer, are encouraged to develop (to the 5-day embryo stage) and then disassembled to extract the inner cell mass.

First, there are concerns about the sources of suitable eggs. In some instances, the female diabetic patient herself might be the source – her ovaries could be triggered by hormone treatment to release eggs. But more often eggs would be required from a donor. IVF treatment, nowadays a widely accepted method for helping infertile couples conceive, generally produces more eggs from the mother-to-be than can be fertilised and implanted. Such 'spare' eggs can be donated for research purposes related to therapeutic cloning. But some critics go a step further and argue that there is no moral justification for creating and subsequently destroying a 5-day-old embryo for a particular purpose – even if such an end involves the alleviation of human suffering. An embryo of such an age certainly represents a potential human life, but does it have the status of a human being?

Those who do take an 'absolutist' line of this type echo the beliefs of the philosopher Immanuel Kant (1724–1804), who argued that it is always morally wrong to use another person entirely as a means to our own ends. When such a Kantian position is combined with the belief that a human embryo, of whatever age, has the same moral status as a human being, then there are presumably no situations where the 'right to life' of the embryo can be violated. Just as the issue of 'rights' is deeply problematic, so is the appealing simplicity of the Kantian view. Here's what the distinguished contemporary ethicist John Harris has to say. (This extract is part of a more developed and complex argument concerning the moral status of the early embryo.)

> The Kantian principle, invoked without any qualification or gloss, is seldom helpful in medical or bioscientific contexts. The argument is that this principle, especially in its simplistic form, would surely outlaw other established medical procedures normally considered ethically unproblematic. Blood transfusions, for instance, involve using the donor as a means to an end of the recipient. Similarly, an abortion performed exclusively to save the life of the mother would also, presumably, be outlawed under this principle. It can therefore be argued that while Kant's principle does have powerful intuitive force, it is so vague and open to

> selective interpretation, and its scope for application is consequently so limited, that its utility as one of the fundamental principles of modern ethical thought is virtually zero.
>
> (Harris, 1998)

Those who support therapeutic cloning take the view that the human embryo at the earliest stages does not have the same moral status as a human being – or that their rights (if such exist) are of a type that can be overridden by the benefits that can accrue to others. Such a philosophical position is in the **'utilitarian' tradition** derived from John Stuart Mill (1806–1873), where relative detriments to some and benefits to others can be weighed on some type of moral scale. Of course, not all acts can be justified on the basis of medical benefit (think of the Nazi's experimentation on human concentration camp victims in World War II) so the process of adjudicating what is or is not acceptable is inevitably contentious.

Other ethical arguments have been raised against therapeutic cloning. Some argue that it represents the beginnings of a 'slippery slope' that will lead to the future use of fetuses (as opposed to considerably younger embryos), or indeed newborn babies, all in the name of the alleviation of suffering. A more compelling slippery slope assertion is that knowledge gained in the development of therapeutic cloning would be directly applicable to the development of human reproductive cloning, leading to the birth of cloned individuals. The counter-argument is that since reproductive cloning is (at least in the great majority of countries) illegal and the overwhelming majority of scientists and ethicists alike remain opposed to its development, no such slippery slope is in prospect. However, for the few 'maverick' scientists that have publicly announced (or indeed claimed success in) their intention of producing a cloned human being, technical knowledge from ES cell work would be invaluable. The traditions of full publication of any such findings in widely distributed journals would ensure instant communication of important 'tricks of the trade'. One of the main practical objections to reproductive cloning at present is that (as already alluded to) in the many species in which this has now been achieved – for example sheep and cattle – there seems to be a high risk of abnormality in the cloned offspring. A related issue (as was evident with Dolly the sheep), is the high 'wastage rate' already referred to. It's possible that work on ES cells for purposes of therapeutic cloning would explain how such abnormalities arise and how they might be avoided. Even if scientific problems of this sort were overcome, strong ethical reservations about human reproductive cloning would remain, but the ethical barriers might be differently perceived if the technique was known to be safe and reliable.

Finally, views about the ethics of cloning have been influenced by the controversy that erupted towards the end of 2005 relating to the work of the South Korean researcher Hwang Woo-Suk. His admitted untruthfulness related in part to the issue of whether or not his female researchers had voluntarily donated eggs for his research. Suspicions deepened when claims were made by fellow workers that he had faked much of the data in his pioneering *Science* paper that claimed the establishment from ES cells of a range of different cell lines of potential therapeutic value. The likely effect is that for the foreseeable future, claims from researchers about the medical value of ES cell work, together with assurances about the sensitivity of scientists to the ethical issues involved, will be treated with extra caution.

Question 6.3

Imagine a scenario of a few years hence where a much-loved pet was suffering from a terminal illness and the owners were seeking to produce a replacement offspring by producing a clone, using existing cloning techniques. Are there likely to be *biological* grounds for urging caution?

6.1.4 Defining your own position

The example that follows should help you work out your own position in relation to this form of therapeutic cloning, focusing on the diabetes example. (The *Guardian* article referred to is available to you on the S250 course website, if you are interested in reading it through in full.)

In a *Guardian* news article of 17 June, 2004 (from which Figure 6.3 was taken), David King of the organisation Human Genetics Alert, is reported as saying the following about an application for research into therapeutic cloning related to diabetes:

> This research is a complete waste of public money, and crosses important ethical lines for the first time. It is very unlikely to produce anything medically useful. We don't believe that embryos are people with rights to life, but neither is it right to create them as raw material for research. It is vital that this receives wide public debate, and that we do not get stuck in the sterile pro-life versus science opposition.

■ Do you think that the research indeed crosses new ethical boundaries? In what other context are embryos created artificially and 'used'?

■ It isn't immediately clear what *new* boundaries are being crossed. Current UK regulations allows research on spare embryos, up until a 14-day limit (or on unfertilised eggs) emerging from IVF treatment.

■ Most of the 'conventional' research now underway on spare embryos aims to improve the reliability of IVF and to improve techniques for the diagnosis of faulty genes. On what ethical grounds (if any) might researchers be denied permission to experiment on embryos younger than 14 days for the purpose of developing therapeutic cloning, while other UK researchers are permitted to undertake IVF-related research on these same embryos ?

■ Speaking personally, I find it difficult to think of any such reason for denying such an opportunity. Neither type of research benefits the embryo but both aim to help people in future. Taking the absolutist's position and according an embryo of this stage moral status, no such research should be permitted, given the embryo's use as a means to an end. A key question is whether an ethical distinction is to be drawn between the use of a *donated* embryos (from IVF treatment) and the use of an embryo specifically *created* for the production of supplying ES cells for therapeutic purposes.

The scientist proposing this particular research (Miodrag Stojkovic, at that time of the University of Newcastle, UK) seems sensitive to just such a concern:

> I completely understand the ethical objections, but we are using eggs that are surplus to IVF treatment, which failed to be fertilised. Instead of being thrown away they have been donated for research. The way I think of it is, why put something in the rubbish bin when it can be used in such a valuable way?

In the same *Guardian* article, David King speculates on the perceived motives behind Stojkovic's move to conduct this research:

> It's very clear that the scientific community is very nervous that the UN could pass a treaty banning so-called therapeutic cloning around the world so they're trying to convince UN delegates that it's worthwhile research by getting some of these research programmes up and running. That way they could say that by introducing a broad ban, the UN would be shutting down something that'll be of great benefit to humanity.

Stojkovic perhaps lends some support to the notion of a political overtone to the research and the promotion of a sense of urgency:

> Our accent is on diabetes. I hope other groups will look at treating other things, such as Parkinson's or Alzheimer's. If you have more and more groups involved in stem cell research, it can only bring benefit.

Whatever Stojkovic's precise motives, it would be naïve to suggest that scientists fail to take account of the political contexts of their work – indeed scientists are frequently encouraged to raise their political sensitivities. (The possible UN embargo mentioned moved a step closer in February 2005, though its influence on the pace of cloning research is likely to be very modest.)

In more general terms, it is understandable that scientists are entirely enthusiastic about the long-term prospects of their work, especially in the competitive culture that currently exists. There is much to be gained by the public promotion of one's own research. The danger here is 'hyping' expectations, something that critics of the field – notably Lord Winston, the IVF research pioneer – have claimed is especially prevalent in ES cell work, perhaps in response to accusations of ethical insensitivity on the part of the researchers involved. This makes a more dispassionate assessment of the likely medical benefit of therapeutic cloning yet more problematic.

A proposal from Dolly's creator, Ian Wilmut, has stoked the controversy yet further. Rather than relying on eggs that are spare from IVF treatment (which can often be of questionable quality) he proposes that healthy women be allowed to donate eggs for cloning research. What is uncertain is whether such eggs would be donated altruistically or whether some kind of payment is envisaged – in recognition of what can be at least an inconvenient, lengthy and sometimes painful medical procedure for women volunteers.

■ Critics say that such a step runs the risk of turning eggs and women into commodities, becoming just a link in a process. Do you agree with such criticisms and how does the issue of whether payment is involved affect your judgement?

- Speaking personally, I find the proposal acceptable; I see no case for preventing the donation of eggs from women who believe that this would hasten the ability of medical science to treat devastating diseases. But the dangers of full-scale commercialisation are such that I would be wary of allowing donors to gain financially.

Activity 6.1 (Part 1, ongoing)

Allow 15 minutes

In about 100 words or so, summarise *your own views* on whether or nor the use of embryos up to 14 days is justified for stem cell research, including your view on egg donation.

In the *Guardian* article, David King asserts that ES cell research is unnecessary in the sense that other techniques offer as much if not more promise of medical benefit. In particular, many researchers are enthusiastic about the prospect of using stem cells from *adult* sources for replacement, so at this point it will be useful to look critically at the merits of this alternative source. The fact that alternatives to ES cell exist may prompt you to look more critically at the piece of writing you have just undertaken.

6.1.5 Adult stem cells – a less controversial way forward?

As hinted already, stem cells are widespread throughout the human body, but most of our knowledge comes from work on such cells in mice. There, they have been located within bone marrow, blood vessels, spinal cord, skeletal muscle, digestive system, retina, liver and pancreas. Such research has revealed that adult stem cells are located in a much wider range of adult human tissues than was initially thought; for example, they also occur in the brain, where the capacity for cell replacement has traditionally thought to be non-existent. Furthermore, it's now known that some types of adult stem cells have the ability to give rise to a range of different types of specialised cell. For example, stem cells within bone marrow, called **haemopoietic** (*pronounced hemo-po-eat-ic*) **stem cells (HSCs)**, are able not only to give rise to the full range of cell types found in blood but also, given appropriate encouragement, to cells that have many of the characteristics of cells normally found in brain tissue.

But many adult stem cells have proved difficult to locate precisely and characterise, let alone extract and utilise. They are often scattered throughout the tissue in which they reside. The brains of adult mice (and probably of all mammals, including humans) certainly contain stem cells, but seemingly of at least three different types, and we have little understanding of their different functions. Adult stem cells are generally rare; probably only 1 in 10 000–15 000 cells in bone marrow is an HSC. More generally, there is much less certainty that adult stem cells identified so far satisfy all the stringent criteria required for success. The most useful adult stem cell type would have a capacity to clone that matches that of ES cells. In other words, a single cell should be able to produce a population of genetically identical cells – capable of following the full range of differentiation pathways to produce all the fully integrated and functional cell and tissue types of interest. At our present level of expertise, with the great difficulties inherent in 'tracking' cell histories during development, it is very difficult to set up animal experiments that test the ability of implanted adult stem cells to do any such thing.

Some proponents of research into adult stem cells accuse colleagues who work on ES cells of a form of 'methodological and/or ethical laziness', for ignoring ethical concerns and going for the 'easy option'. However, there do seem very genuine problems in working with adult stem cells that are likely to contribute to a slower rate of progress than work with ES cells. The renowned scientist Sir Peter Medawar wrote an inspiring book whose title defined science in terms of *The Art of the Possible.* (Medawar, who died in 1987, was a Nobel Laureate for his pioneering work on immunology, and was one of the most inspiring and accomplished scientists of his generation. He was also a wonderfully adept writer about science.) Medawar argued persuasively that scientists generally prefer to work with the practicable tools and sources to hand – to reach for what is attainable. Some critics see this as regrettable conservatism; to others it is an entirely legitimate and defensible working method, in part because it is an approach most likely to reap rewards on a reasonable timescale.

■ Is the case for research on the use of ES cells for the treatment of diabetes (as outlined in Figure 6.3) now redundant, given the potential for working on adult stem cells? What further information would be important before deciding?

■ It would be premature to come to that conclusion on such little information. A key question would be just how readily adult pancreatic stem cells could be identified, purified and their potential for self-renewal and differentiation assessed. (The process is far from easy; not all researchers are convinced that the human pancreas contains extractable stem cells and those who are, don't agree about where such cells are located, or what source is the best to use.)

Activity 6.1 (Part 2)

Allow 10 minutes

Look back now at the piece of writing you undertook on assessing the case for the use of embryonic stem cells (your answer to Part 1 of this activity). Have you shifted your position in view of the information on adult stem cells? Do you see the choice as 'either/or'?

Many critics take the line that the entire notion of a 'choice' between adult and embryonic stem cell research is false. Each particular approach has advantages and drawbacks and there is a clear case for further research in both. Realising the full clinical value of adult stem cells may well depend on the continuation of work on ES cells.

Question 6.4

Some adult stem cells are termed 'pluripotent', in contrast to embryonic stem cells which are generally referred to as 'totipotent'. Thinking in terms of the known differences between the two cells types, what do you think is meant by 'pluripotent'?

Question 6.5

Identify two practical reasons (ignoring ethical issues for now) why *embryonic* stem cells are a more convenient source of stem cells than those derived from adults.

6.2 Genetic manipulation of animals; how and why?

Here I want very swiftly to review the different approaches currently being taken to the genetic manipulation of animals. Having done so, I'll briefly raise some of the emerging ethical questions, which overlap to some degree with the concerns just discussed related to therapeutic cloning of humans.

Four major categories of genetic manipulation can be identified in terms of outcome. It's likely that all four techniques will increasingly rely on the cloning techniques of somatic cell nuclear transfer just outlined, to maintain the new strains created.

1. Many animals are being engineered as 'pharmaceutical factories' – at the time of writing (early 2006), at least 29 different proteins are being produced in this way. For example, **human coagulation factor 1X (F1X)**, essential in the treatment of haemophilia B, is produced in sheep milk. The gene responsible was introduced into fetal sheep cells (in culture) and the resulting nuclei transferred into enucleated eggs. As the construct included a promoter linked with milk protein production, FIX production is limited to just the cells of the mammary gland and significant amounts can conveniently be extracted from the milk.

2. Animals are often used as models for specific diseases, as you'll be aware of from Box 1.2 in Topic 1, and increasingly such animal models are transgenic in origin. Specific DNA sequences representing particular genes are often simply extracted and then injected into a fertilised egg or into an early embryo, as 'naked' DNA. This process of DNA microinjection is a lot more tricky technically than it may sound, and successful integration of the transgene is, in many cases, comparatively rare. Nevertheless, via such techniques, numerous genes implicated in human disease have been introduced into laboratory animals. One early example is the oncomouse, which is used in cancer research and was the first vertebrate to be patented. It reliably develops tumours and generally dies within about three months. In another case, multiple copies of a gene (for example that responsible for the synthesis of growth hormone) can be transferred into mice, leading in this instance to individuals that are double the size of their littermates by 11 weeks of age. There are well over a 100 human conditions, including Alzheimer's and osteoporosis, where a mouse disease model exists. Much of what is known about prion diseases, for example, comes from transgenic

mice, as you read in Box 1.2 of Topic 1. Several thousands strains of mice exist where particular genes have been inactivated (so-called 'knock-out' mice) or replaced by mutated versions, including a number that mimic the cystic fibrosis allele in humans. It's now possible to replace the coding region of one gene by that of another. Many such models allow experiments that would be inappropriate in humans, but you'll be aware that the applicability of any such findings in mice to their human counterparts of these diseases is often problematic.

3. Transgenic animals, especially pigs, are being developed with the intention of using their tissues for transplantation to humans. The aim is to overcome graft rejection. Most such techniques involve the manipulation of genes coding for the cell surface properties that characterise the donor organs. Proteins at the cell surface are especially important in triggering the preliminary phase of rejection of the donor organ via the immune system of the recipient. Modifying those proteins, perhaps into appropriate forms of their human equivalent, should prevent rejection.
4. Farm animals are being developed with the aim of increasing productivity and/or increasing resistance to disease. For example, enhancing wool production in sheep may be possible via genetic manipulation. In the longer term, there is the potential for knocking out particular genes that may, for example, normally limit muscle growth in cattle. Deletion of particular genes may enhance mammary gland growth and increase milk yields. A variety of newly emerging techniques offer a great deal of promise for the future, including a number that apply to sheep.

Currently, there is a lot of interest in using **gene silencing** mechanisms that are known to occur naturally in some animals and a large number of plants. Genes expression can be effectively inactivated via small RNA fragments, called **siRNAs** (short interfering RNAs). These are generally just 19–23 nucleotides long and, as their name implies, are able to inactivate mRNAs that contain base sequences that are complementary to the siRNA sequence.

■ Why would inactivation of mRNA result if part of the base sequence of the targeted mRNA was complementary to that of a particular siRNA?

■ The two RNA portions will combine (hybridise) as the complementary base sequences pair up. These siRNA–mRNA hybrids are then degraded in the cell, with the result that the original mRNA is not available for translation via the ribosomal mechanisms discussed in Section 2.1.

In future, siRNAs of particular base sequence might be constructed to hybridise with RNA of viral origin. If so, it may eventually prove possible to engineer cattle and other farm animals to express sequence-specific siRNAs able to target the transcription products of pathogenic viruses, such as those responsible for foot and mouth disease or swine fever. More generally, a whole range of genes of the host animal involved in susceptibility to microbial pathogens might be engineered. Such genes may have multiple effects, so their inactivation (or enhancement) may lead to unforeseen complications. Furthermore, the technical difficulties are formidable – but so would be the commercial gains from breakthroughs of this type.

The different applications just described are being achieved using a wide variety of ingenious techniques. Figure 6.4 shows some of the methods for producing transgenic mammals in present use or being developed by researchers.

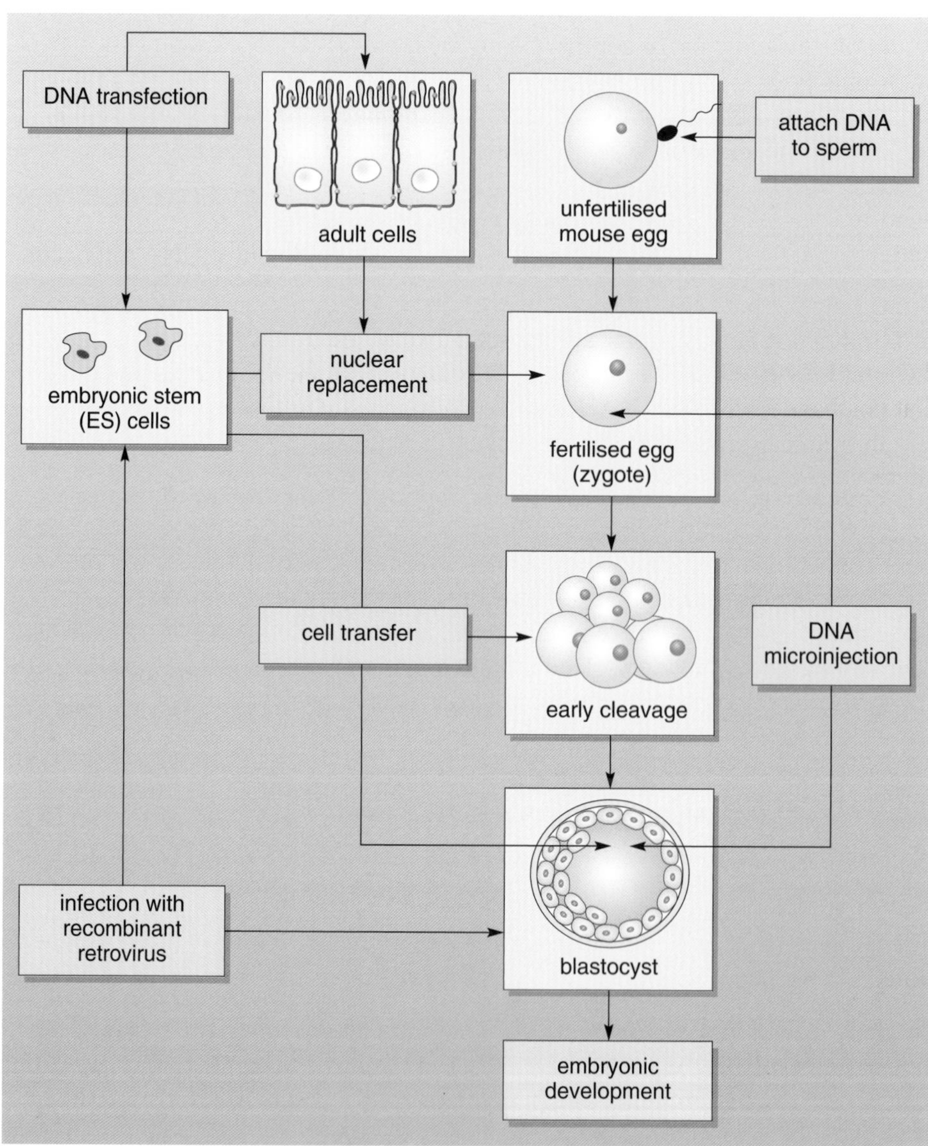

Figure 6.4 Summary of methods used for producing transgenic mammals. Some of the techniques use DNA microinjection; others use the transfer of nuclei or of whole cells. Retroviruses are used extensively, to introduce DNA into the genome, both into embryos and into stem cells.

These techniques all achieve **transfection**, the introduction of novel DNA into another organism. You'll soon learn more about how viruses are often used for this purpose, in which case the process is often called **transduction**, though the two terms are often used interchangeably. But transfection alone is seldom the object of the exercise. Usually the intention is that the introduced DNA becomes fully integrated into the genome, is expressed and perhaps incorporated into the progeny of the transformed cell. The production of new cell lines of this type is far from easy, which explains why such a variety of techniques are being explored.

Occasionally, animal cells in culture can be 'coaxed into' directly taking up foreign DNA, sometimes by the relatively straightforward physical or chemical methods that you read about in Chapter 4 in the context of plant cells. In some instances, DNA is packaged into artificial phospholipid vesicles, which can be taken up with high efficiency; we'll mention this approach again in Chapter 7. You know of biolistics from Section 4.2. The technique called **electroporation** is also being tried; this involves subjecting cells to an electric shock, which often increases uptake. In other instances, as previously mentioned, direct microinjection of naked DNA is possible, into the ovum, the zygote (i.e. the fertilised ovum) or the early embryo; the technique has been used not just in mice, but for example in cattle, pigs and sheep. Efficiency can be low and variable – in one instance, between 5 and 40% of transgenic mice developed from microinjected ova. The site of insertion of the novel DNA into the genome seems random, and numerous deletions and rearrangement of the host DNA can occur.

A great array of different viruses are used to transfer genes, both into animals cells in culture and into living animals. All such viruses are acting as vectors, using the term now to describe any 'vehicle' for DNA transfer, not just the plasmids that you have mainly encountered so far. You know of adenoviruses from Box 2.1; the value of adeno-associated viruses (AAVs) and herpes virus as vectors is also being explored. The use of recombinant retroviruses is common, partly because, although they are often able to introduce only a relatively modest amount of DNA, they usually do so with minimal disruption to the host genome.

Increasingly, DNA is introduced into mice ES cells in culture, via viral transduction for example, and indeed it's now often possible to insert a copy of a gene at a particular location. If such transformed cells are introduced into an embryo – one of the procedures summarised in Figure 6.4 – some of the cells in the developing embryos will contain the transgene and other not. Only if the transgene happens to become incorporated into the genome of a cell of this embryo that will develop into an ovum or sperm does the introduced gene have a chance of being passed on to future generations. One way round this is to introduce the gene very early on in development, perhaps into the zygote, but this is not always possible. Another way round the problem is shown in Figure 6.5, where different strains of animals are used, in this case differing in coat colour, which provides a visible marker that reveals something of the genetic make-up of a particular individual.

First, in Figure 6.5a, the transgene is added to stem cells in culture. The transduced ES cells are introduced into an embryo at the blastocyst stage (b), where they become incorporated into the inner cell mass. If this embryo is then introduced into a surrogate mother, the mouse that is produced is often a **chimera** – containing cells from two distinct strains. The sex cells (ova and sperm) of such a chimera may originate from cells containing the transgene, in which case, crossing such an animal with a normal mouse will produce heterozygous transgenic offspring. Two such heterozygous offspring can then be mated, in which case some of the offspring will be homozygous for the desired transgene. As you see from Figure 6.5, the two strains of mice used here can be distinguished by coat colour. Since the ES cells are derived from mice with a dark coat, the coat of chimeric mice is typically patchworked, while the fully transgenic mouse is also identifiable by its distinctive colouration. Note that, for reasons that are not fully understood, this process works only in mice. Although chimeras can be 'created' in other species, only in mice do the introduced transgenic cells give rise to gametes.

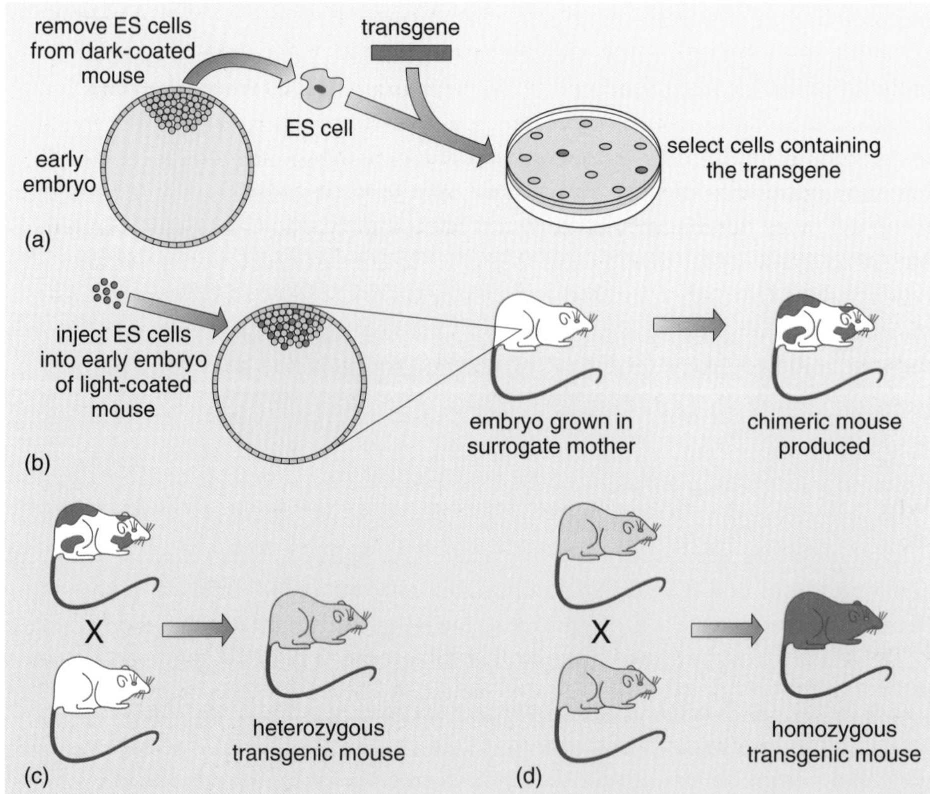

Figure 6.5 One approach to the production of transgenic mice using ES cells, via the production of a chimera. In this instance, the transfected ES cells are derived, as shown in (a), from an embryo from the dark coat colour strain. These transfected cells are injected into embryos from the light coat colour strain, producing chimeras (b). Crossing chimeras with light coat colour mice produces some that are heterozygous transgenics (c); when these are self-crossed, some homozygous transgenics are produced (d), as indicated by their dark coat colouration typical of the strain from transfected ES cells were initially derived.

■ Why can't transgenic mice be produced more simply by conveying the gene into ES cells, and then implanting *in utero*, as indicated in Figure 6.5b?

■ Remember that the aim is to produce an organism where *all* the cells contain copies of the particular transgene. The chimera that results from step (b) has some cells that contain the transgene and others that don't. The object of the next step is to identify those chimeras that produce sex cells containing the transgene, as opposed to its normal counterpart. Once individuals that are heterozygous for the transgene have been identified (by their coat colour), they can be self-crossed to produce 'pure-breeding' offspring, step (d).

Of course, microinjection of DNA into a fertilised egg might achieve the same end and would be a straightforward procedure, but you've seen that this can be a 'hit or miss' affair. The transgene often won't integrate into the host cell genome, which it has to do if is to be replicated by cell division. Some genes are more tricky to transfer than others, which explains why a range of techniques of the types shown in Figures 6.4 have been developed.

This swift survey of techniques and outcomes has done little more than scrape the surface of the approaches now being developed for the genetic manipulation of animals. I've been able to only hint at the complexity of the processes involved and the difficulties to be overcome for stable integration to be achieved. Two brief reminders of previous points may be helpful. First, the expression of genes often seems dependent upon the position in the host DNA at which they become inserted. This seems to result in part from local regulatory genes and DNA sequences having an effect on the transgene – enhancers for example

(Section 2.4). The second complication is that transferred genes can sometimes be naturally silenced, which seems to be linked to an increase in the degree of methylation at the site of incorporation. In those instances where the gene introduced is homologous to an existing one, both genes (i.e. the original and the transgene) can become silenced. Sometimes, silencing occurs at the level of transcription or post-transcription – mRNA can be degraded, for example. There is some evidence that eukaryotic genomes have some capacity to 'scan' foreign DNA sequences and to render them inactive by methylation, reminiscent of the type of protective genomic strategies mentioned in Section 2.3. This is consistent with the fact that prokaryotic sequences within transgenic mice evoke an especially high degree of inactivating methylation. Just how prevalent this phenomenon, and the position effect, are in the human genome is largely unknown.

Question 6.6

Why is it helpful to introduce novel genes into organism in the earliest stages of their development, rather than into particular cells of the adult?

Question 6.7

Some methods of inserting DNA, for example DNA microinjection (Figure 6.4), appear to result in DNA deletions and rearrangement. The point of insertion also appears to be random, though the inserted DNA is stably inherited. How appropriate would such a technique be for human gene manipulation?

Question 6.8

(a) How can novel genes to be introduced into ES cells of mice in culture? (b) Briefly outline the different technique developed in sheep that result in the same outcome, to produce pharmaceutical products for example.

6.2.1 Ethical aspects of using GM animals

■ How do you feel about the text you have just read? For example, does the creation of a variety of animal models (e.g. the oncomouse) raise any ethical concerns in your mind?

■ Speaking for myself, I'm not entirely comfortable with idea of the use of GM for the creation of animal models for disease. The aspect that causes most concern is that these animals are created specifically for the purpose of developing diseases, with perhaps the attendant distress. But on balance I can accept that some compromise to animal welfare is acceptable if medical benefits to humans were likely to accrue.

Such lines of thought reflect a **consequentialist** approach to ethical dilemmas, reminiscent of what was said in the context of therapeutic cloning. Here, the likely benefits that animal GM technology might bring are being measured against the likely distress and pain involved to animals. The aim once more is to distinguish 'good' and 'bad', in ways reminiscent of an accountant's balance sheet – factoring in risks, costs and benefits, for example. By this logic, to my mind, the gain from GM outweighs the harm it causes to animals. Again, this differs markedly from the absolutist's position, which introduces a moral or religious dimension about whether such procedures are good or bad 'in themselves'. Prince Charles adopted just such a stance when commenting on GMOs with his widely reported view (in his 2000 BBC Radio 4 Reith Lectures) that science trespassed into 'God's territory'.

Consequentialist reasoning would be unlikely to find anything inherently wrong with GM technology. Indeed, this is the position adopted by those who undertake GM research and those who have to decide about which approaches are legally permissible and which are not. The following quote captures just such a stance:

> Biotechnology and genetic modification are in themselves morally neutral. It is the uses to which they are put which create dilemmas. The challenge which faces us is to try to achieve an optimal future: one which maximises the benefits of genetic modification and minimises the harm.
>
> (British Medical Association, 1992)

■ Do you agree with this quote? Identify some of the problems likely to be associated with its implementation?

■ I am drawn to the neatness of these sentiments, but I see problems. One stems from the word 'minimises'. Do minimal levels of harm conform to what is acceptable? Another problem is that 'benefits' can only be predicted rather than proven, so they become an immediate subject of dispute. As we've mentioned before, not all medical procedures on animals can be justified on the grounds of potential benefit to humans.

Activity 6.2

Allow 20 minutes

The arguments that follow outline some of the cases that have been made by critics against the creation of GM animals. I've put together the arguments from a variety of different sources, attempting to convey true representations of the anti-GM animals stance. As you read through the three points, assess which of them, if any, influence(s) your overall position.

1. Suffering is the goal of creating GM animal models and can be disproportionate and of no immediate application. This is less excusable than those instances where an animal's welfare is compromised by GM techniques in ways that are incidental and unintentional. As an example of a GM animal model of limited use, transgenic mice have been engineered to develop tumours in the lenses of their eyes, of a type not normally encountered in humans.
2. Producing transgenic animals is inefficient and wasteful. For example, the disruption to the genome that accompanies DNA microinjection leads to a very high incidence of lost embryos, developmental abnormalities and death *in utero*. Numerous cloned and/or transgenic animals, Dolly included, have developed abnormalities, for example in their growth. Animals such as pigs and cattle engineered to maximise their growth suffer a range of deleterious effects, as a consequence of their excessive mass.

3 Animal models have very limited value, as borne out by the fact that many of the modern widely used medicines now thought indispensable – aspirin, penicillin and anti-hypertensive drugs – are ineffective or damaging to animals, and yet were discovered despite rather than because of the results of experiments on animals. The inappropriateness of animal models is also demonstrated by the fact that many thousands of people die each year of adverse reactions to drugs that have been extensively tested for their safety in tests using animal models. In the study of cancer for example, many differences are evident between the way animal and human cancers progress and their underlying causes.

You'll appreciate that ethical debates about GM animals progress well beyond this preliminary exploration of consequentialism, covering ground that we can only touch on here. For example, a follower of deontological ethics stresses the inherent value of all conscious and sentient beings, and tends to ignore any evaluation of potential to contribute to human wellbeing. In its strongest form, such thinking affords animals a range of intrinsic 'rights', of which one might be the right to be free from pain, suffering and premature death. Some argue that animals also have a right not to have violated what some have called their 'genetic integrity', which is variously described as the 'essence, beingness, inherent nature, purpose' – descriptions of such vagueness that they give little clue as to exactly what it is that such procedures may compromise.

Deontological ethics are most usually associated with the philosopher Kant. Effectively, it is a system whereby doing ones duty is essential in order to live a moral life, and the duty is arrived at by rational derivation of absolute moral truths.

Many fundamental questions about GM animals can be reduced to a more direct, yet difficult-to-answer question: do we need GM animals? Here I'm following the well-worn pragmatic path of 'case-by-case' assessment, evaluating each case on the basis of common criteria.

■ Can you suggest what such criteria might be?

■ Factors such as degree of suffering caused, alternative strategies to achieve the same end, safety considerations, likely level of public support and probably economic and social consequences.

For me, the strongest cases can be made in relation to medical need, with a willingness not to expect short-term benefits from such techniques. I cannot see any strong case for not using animals as pharmaceutical factories (as with FIX, Section 6.2), given the limited 'harm' inflicted on the animals and the very substantial benefits gained. The case for improving the productivity of farm animals is less clear; unlike the case for plants (see Section 4.6), the arguments about developing world need are less strong.

Finally, for me, the case for the engineering of farm animals would be strong if, in the UK and beyond, animals can be created with an engineered resistance to disease. In the UK, for example, the damage and distress created by the foot and mouth epidemic of 2001 might prove a thing of the past with such developments. The potential benefits of such technologies to human health would be considerable, given present-day concerns about the spread of disease from domesticated animals such as pigs and chickens to humans.

At the time of writing (early 2006), there are anxieties about the spread of 'bird flu' to the human population, with concerns that such an episode would represent a risk to human health that would match or exceed the 20 million people estimated to have succumbed to the 1918 influenza epidemic.

Summary of Chapter 6

Reproductive cloning, as pioneered with Dolly the sheep, involves transfer of the nucleus of a differentiated adult cell into an enucleated egg, which is transferred into a surrogate (host) mother. The procedure reveals that the nuclei of differentiated cells can be totipotent – an ability to 'rewind' and direct the development of the entire range of adult cells. Of ethical concern is that the incidence of successful birth of clones is modest and numbers of birth and post-birth abnormalities high.

The major purpose of therapeutic cloning is to create a cell line for the purposes of therapy, for tissues and organs damaged by disease or injury, ideally in ways that avoid immunological rejection. Embryonic stem cells can be removed from blastocysts and cultured *in vitro*, and their differentiation triggered into one of a range of cell types. Applications of therapeutic cloning include a potential treatment for diabetes, raising ethical issues of concern – for example, the sources of ova and embryos. Stem cells are widely present in adults, but they are currently a less accessible and less easily manipulated source for experimentation.

GM techniques in animal cells vary from the introduction of novel genes into nuclei for transfer to non-nucleated ova, to harvesting protein products such as FIX and the creation of transgenic animal models to study disease. The genomes of farm animals can be manipulated to improve their commercial usefulness and resistance to disease. More generally, particular genes can be silenced, often by blocking the mRNA they produce. Viral vectors are being increasingly used to introduce novel DNA into ES cells. Homozygous transgenic mice can be manufactured via the creation of chimeras. Gene function can be sensitive to position effects and genomes appear to have protective devices, such as methylation, that prevent novel inserted genes from being expressed.

The value of animal models is disputed, as is the ethical justification for the compromise of animal welfare evident in the creation of animals that model human disease. There are strong arguments to support the notion that medical advances would be slowed if GM animals were not to be created. The same technique has the potential to reduce suffering and risks to the health of humans and farm animals.

Question 6.9

Some scientists stress the potential of nuclear transfer for purposes of conservation. They claim that recently extinct species (e.g. the thylacine or Tasmanian 'tiger') could be 're-created', perhaps using DNA from specimens preserved in alcohol. Another has argued that GM should be used where natural habitats are becoming degraded 'to modify the animals to cope with this new situation'. In your view, are these realistic and ethically acceptable uses of GM?

Chapter 7

Genes in medicine; gene therapy

7.1 A technique of great potential?

Gene therapy offers the hope of avoiding diseases that arise from the presence of defective genes by adding a 'normal' counterpart in the form of a transgene. A great deal of research is currently being undertaken in making vectors that deliver genes safely and reliably, much of it involving viruses. In broad terms, the challenge is to engineer viral genomes to produce recombinant forms that lack disease-causing genes but have an ability to safely invade human cells and convey added therapeutic genes to faulty cells. Disabling the virus is obviously a very important prerequisite for successful gene therapy. Different types of viral vectors have particular advantages and drawbacks; as you know from Box 2.1, retroviruses, for example, are able to infect actively dividing cells and (via reverse transcriptase) can incorporate an introduced gene into the genome of the host cell. However, retroviruses can provoke an immune response in the recipient. Table 7.1 summarises the range of approaches being tried. You'll notice that some of the methods of gene delivery described in the previous chapter are mentioned, such as the microinjection of naked DNA. A variety of non-viral techniques for gene transfer for medical use are also being researched, for example wrapping up DNA in **liposomes** (spheres bounded by an artificial phospholipid membrane), but we shan't pursue these approaches in any detail here.

Table 7.1 Advantages and disadvantages of different approaches to transferring DNA for somatic cell therapy.

	Advantages	**Disadvantages**
Viral vectors		
retroviruses	Stable integration in target cell; infects replicating cells; suitable for *ex vivo* treatment (see Figure 7.1b).	Can activate proto-oncogenes; can provoke an immune response; expression of transgene can diminish over time.
adenoviruses	Infects non-dividing cells; risks of uncontrolled integration are lessened.	Expression of transgene can be transient; can provoke strong immune reaction.
adeno-associated viruses	Non-pathogenic; expression of transgene is long-lasting.	Not proficient at replication so needs 'helper' virus; not able to deliver large transgenes.
Non-viral vectors		
liposomes	Non-immunogenic.	Not able to deliver large transgenes; inefficient compared to viral systems.
lipoplexes*	Non-immunogenic; can carry large DNA molecules.	Inefficient delivery; expression of transgene can be transient.
naked DNA	Non-immunogenic; relatively simple to prepare and administer.	Few cell types can be treated; expression of transgene is often transient; uptake by cells can be very inefficient.

* Lipoplexes are more complex than liposomes, comprising special types of tailor-made lipids that are electrically charged in such a way better suited to containing and then releasing their cargo of DNA.

In some instances, adding the functional 'healthy' transgene may not be enough; the faulty gene already present might continue to produce its faulty protein, with harmful effects. This explains current interest in silencing gene function, of the type already mentioned in the context of the potential application of siRNA technology to farm animals.

- ■ Look back to Section 6.2 and suggest how gene silencing might be used in future on patients.
- ■ What's envisaged is the transfer into affected cells of small RNA sequences (siRNAs) that are complementary to the mRNA known to be transcribed from the faulty gene. The protein product of the faulty gene is unlikely to be produced because translation of its mRNA would now be impossible because the siRNA–mRNA hybrid is formed and then degraded.

The term 'antisense mRNA' is often used to in describing techniques of the type just described, because the key RNA component is complementary (i.e. opposite to) to the 'sense' mRNA transcribed by the faulty gene. Such techniques have great potential but in this instance, achieving delivery of siRNAs to their intended site of action within affected cells is proving very problematic. They tend to be altered or broken down before they have the chance to form the double-stranded RNA hybrid. So, rather more is known at present about more conventional forms of virus-mediated gene transfer, which we shall focus on in what follows.

7.1.1 Types of gene therapy

Two general forms of gene therapy are recognised and, within each, a range of specific applications. The first is **somatic cell gene therapy**. You are familiar already with the therapeutic value of products such as insulin or human coagulation factor IX (FIX) – both examples mentioned earlier. In some circumstances, gene *products* can be injected, to correct for a deficiency resulting from malfunction of the corresponding gene. Somatic cell gene therapy goes a step further; it delivers 'corrected' versions of faulty *genes* into the particular 'target' cells of the body that are most affected by the disease, be they lungs (cystic fibrosis) or muscle (which can be affected by the fatal wasting condition muscular dystrophy). Transferring transgenes of this type presents a formidable technical challenge, in part because some of them are so massive; look back at Table 2.1 and notice the size of the gene responsible for this form of dystrophy.

In contrast, the second type, **germline gene therapy**, involves genetic modification of ova or sperm or the very early embryo. If successful, all the cells of the individual that results are likely to have the altered genetic make-up, including their ova or sperm, such that the inserted genes are passed to subsequent generations. Such a technique depends upon a full and lasting integration of the inserted gene into the genome of the emerging individual; you can appreciate that this raises particularly acute ethical issues, about which I'll say more later.

- Section 6.2 described a number of genetic manipulations of animals. Look back at what was described. Could these best be described as germline or somatic manipulation? (I'm avoiding the word 'therapy' in describing them because none of them is undertaken with the aim of providing a cure for an animal disease.)

- These were all germline modifications. They involve manipulations to the ovum or early embryo that aim at stable integration of the inserted gene into all the cells (including sex cells) and hence transmission of the altered genome to the offspring. For example, sheep that are able to produce human coagulation factor IX (FIX) in their milk are likely to produce offspring that can do so too; clones of such animals would certainly have that capacity.

One approach to somatic cell gene therapy is called ***in vivo* somatic cell gene therapy** (Figure 7.1a), which is the type of therapy used for cystic fibrosis (Section 7.3). This involves the insertion of the transgene into cells that remain in the patient's body – usually because extracting such cells is impractical. The transgene is delivered by non-viral or viral vectors, as indicated in the figure. By contrast, ***ex vivo* somatic cell gene therapy** (see Table 7.1 and Figure 7.1b) involves the removal of affected cells from the patient's body, treating them *in vitro* – which may involve delivering DNA to them via one of a range of vectors – and then, perhaps after a phase of cell culture, re-introducing the altered cells into the patient. Hopes are high that blood disorders can be treated in this way, perhaps by extracting and treating bone marrow stem cells. One promising example of *ex vivo* somatic cell gene therapy will be discussed in Section 7.2.

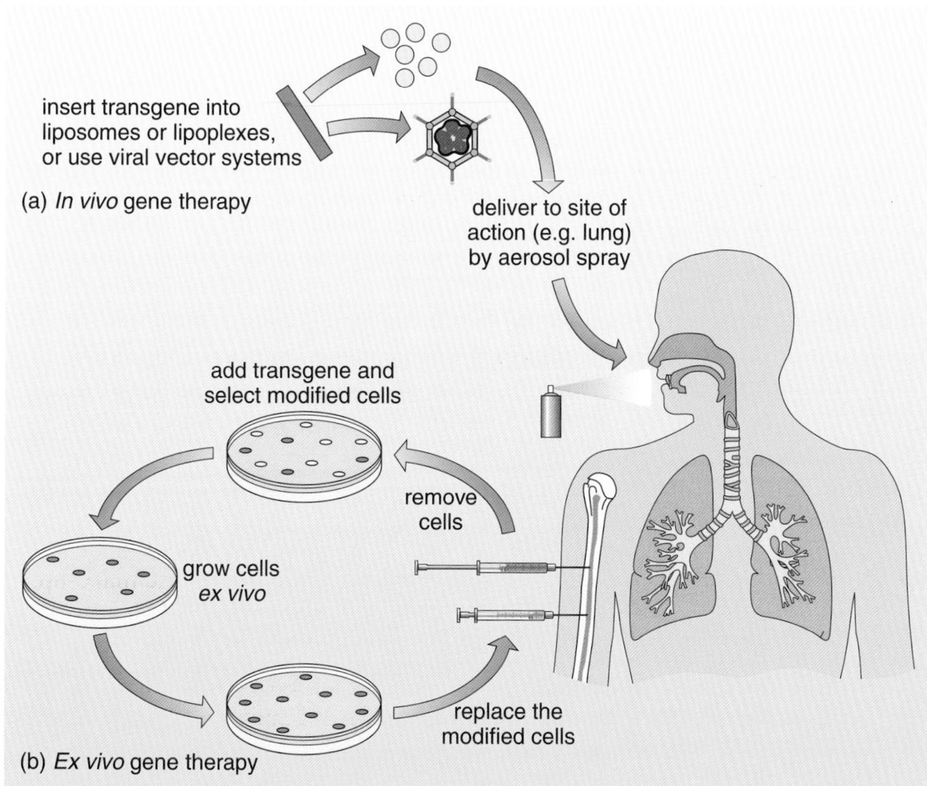
insert transgene into
liposomes or lipoplexes,
or use viral vector systems
(a) In vivo gene therapy
deliver to site of
action (e.g. lung)
by aerosol spray
add transgene and
select modified cells
remove
cells
grow cells
ex vivo
replace the
modified cells
(b) Ex vivo gene therapy

Figure 7.1 *In vivo* and *ex vivo* approaches to somatic cell gene therapy. (a) *In vivo* therapies require direct introduction of the required transgene into cells within the patient's body; the example here involves delivery to the cells lining the lungs, as in cystic fibrosis. (b) *Ex vivo* techniques involve the removal of affected cells from the body (in this case, cells from the bone marrow that give rise to red blood cells), addition of a transgene in culture outside the body, followed by their re-introduction into the patient's body.

Hopes for the effectiveness of gene therapy are perhaps greatest in single-gene disorders, especially those involving one particular type of tissue. But even here, things are not simple. The group of diseases that affect the production and function of haemoglobin is a case in point. Their medical significance is enormous – an estimated 7% of the world's population are thought to be carriers for one or other of these conditions. Topic 1 mentioned sickle-cell anaemia – a disease caused by a point mutation involving a single base pair change (one of the mRNA codons changes from GAG to GUG). There are several different forms of another haemoglobin defect called thalassaemia, involving one or more malfunctions of the family of genes normally responsible for producing the α and β globin polypeptide chains that characterise normal haemoglobin. One complication is that the clusters of genes responsible for α and β globin synthesis depend for their expression on the activity of control regions, in particular a variety of enhancers (Section 2.4), but these are very distant from the sites at which transcription of these genes occur. For example, the enhancer HS40 is more than 60 kb upstream of the two α globin genes it controls. A second set of complications is the fact that one of a huge variety of different mutations can contribute to malfunction of the gene. Sometimes the whole gene appears to be deleted but in other instances, mutations in promoters may prevent transcription or result in nonsense and frameshift mutations (Sections 2.1) and bring about termination of translation. Sometimes RNA processing is affected by mutation at the site of attachment of the poly(A) tail (Section 3.1). So, although such haemoglobin malfunctions of this type are in principle useful targets for somatic cell gene therapy, knowing what new genetic components have to be transferred can be problematic.

In the next two sections, we'll look at two potential applications of somatic gene therapy and the practical problems that have emerged.

7.2 Severe combined immunodeficiency (SCID)–X1 disease

A variety of different forms of **severe combined immunodeficiency (SCID)** exists and what appears to link them is a malfunction of one or other of the genes responsible for producing a functional immune system. About 40% of all instances of SCID are a sex-linked form of the disease, occurring only in boys. This is a lethal condition, carried on the X chromosome. It is properly called SCID-X1 disease, and is commonly known as 'bubble-boy disease'. SCID–X1 is caused by the malfunction of a particular gene (γC) on the X chromosome. This gene is crucial to the normal development of the two types of lymphocyte: T lymphocytes, which are particularly important in killing viruses; and NK, or natural killer lymphocyte cells, which are able to kill cells such as tumour and transplanted cells. The details needn't be of concern, but the polypeptide that this gene produces contributes to the 'signalling' system essential to the development of these two types of lymphocyte cells.

Lymphocytes are one of the two main groups of cells of the immune system. They are responsible for specific recognition of antigens and coordination of the immune response

Because they lack an effective immune system, relatively minor infections can be fatal to these children and they are therefore obliged to live within a sterile environment (hence 'bubble') and often die prematurely. The disease, apparent in about 1 in 100 000 live births, can be treated by bone marrow transplantation;

Section 6.1.5 mentioned that bone marrow contains the stem cells from which the entire range of lymphocytes usually develop. There are obvious difficulties of finding a matching donor when the condition arises – a sibling is the best option. Doctors are often obliged to use unmatched bone marrow, with only limited prospects of success. Apart from the problem of finding a suitable donor, child victims of SCID-X1 may be too ill to withstand bone marrow transplantation, and the associated chemotherapy, which is usually needed to ensure acceptance of the transplant.

The use of gene therapy for treating SCID-X1 has had a chequered history, falling some way short of early expectations. The *ex vivo* approach adopted has involved the removal of bone marrow from the patient and the treatment of the sample with a retrovirus containing a copy of the normal *γC* gene. The aim, of course, is the stable integration of this gene into the genome of a significant proportion of the stem cell population from which the different types of lymphocyte will arise.

■ The cells of the bone marrow are stimulated to divide during their *in vitro* incubation with the engineered retrovirus, but the conditions are such that the stem cells are dissuaded from differentiating. Why should the stem cells be dividing but not differentiating?

■ Right at the beginning of Section 7.1, and in Box 2.1, the point was made that retroviruses infect dividing cells. The trick here is to promote cell division in ways that ensures the cells retain their ability to give rise to the full range of lymphocyte types.

The transformed bone marrow cells are then reintroduced into the patient. Ten months afterwards, both T and NK lymphocytes are detectable in patients. Where tested, the *γC* gene is expressed and such cells were seemingly behaving normally, i.e. they were able to respond to antigens. Of course, what is not known is how many stem cells have been transformed and therefore how long-lived and effective the treatment might prove.

But further uncertainties surround the technique, as first reported in 2003 by the French team that undertook SCID-X1 gene therapy in the way just described. They attempted to transfer the *γC* gene into precursor cells that would normally give rise to lymphocytes using an incapacitated retroviral vector known to be associated with leukaemia in mice. Of the 11 patients involved, nine showed what were deemed clinically significant and long term improvements in their immunological status. But, two of the youngest SCID-X1 patients developed a form of leukaemia relating to their T cell population. These symptoms first became apparent about three years after gene therapy, when tests revealed high rates of proliferation of mature T lymphocytes. Such was the concern that, in 2003, a moratorium was put in place on any further clinical trials.

The risks of such an event were apparent before the human trial. Animal studies had indicated that retroviruses are able to insert into the host genome and affect the transcription of neighbouring genes – a specific example of the type of position effect mentioned earlier, and called **insertional mutagenesis**. For gene therapy, the risks of such an event were thought to be very low; certainly, no such effect had been observed in any previous trial. But the worry remained that retroviral insertion might lead to the activation of genes called **proto-oncogenes** – a type of gene that can be provoked to malfunction in ways that lead to the unregulated cell division typical of cancers. Indeed, gene insertion also carries the potential risk of inactivating genes that have the normal function of suppressing tumours (known, not surprisingly, as **tumour-suppressor genes**) as well as activating proto-oncogenes.

■ Researchers believe that the inactivation of tumour-suppressor genes is clinically less important than the activation of proto-oncogenes. Bearing in mind that both types of gene will nearly always exist in pairs in human cells, can you suggest a reason for this perceived difference in degree of risk?

■ For tumour-suppressor genes to malfunction, both copies (i.e. one on each chromosome) would have to be adversely affected by gene insertion, which is unlikely. Activation of a proto-oncogene is more of a worry because it's likely that only one copy needs to malfunction for tumour formation to begin.

It is estimated that there are about 100 proto-oncogenes in the human genome. It is known that inserted retroviruses can influence the activity of genes that are more than 100 kb distant from the insertion site. Thinking along these lines suggests that if gene insertions were to be a random event, proto-oncogenes might become activated in about 1% of all such retrovirus-mediated inserts. It seems that some unknown properties of human DNA and of the way the retroviruses function means that insertion more often occurs near active genes, rather than in the middle of spacer DNA or within repetitive DNA (recall Section 3.2). Furthermore, given the outcome in two out of the 11 patients, there could be preferential location of the insert close to particular genes. To be precise, the retroviral vector became inserted near the proto-oncogene *LMO2* promoter, which is normally implicated in production of blood cells.

The realisation that such insertion is non-random has both inspired and distressed researchers involved in gene therapy. The risks of overstimulating T lymphocyte production reveals the technique's potential for upsetting normal genome function, as unintended consequences come into play. On this basis, critics of gene therapy advise caution or full cessation of trials. But the more positive interpretation is that this is an early step towards increasing our understanding of the factors that control sites of retroviral insertion, with all the implications that has for understanding the origins of the disease and (ultimately) for more effective and safer methods of gene therapy. By this logic, understanding what 'went wrong' is essential for future improvement. It may be, for example, that in such young patients, the bone marrow extracts have such a large population of stem cells, with such a high capacity for the production of blood cells, that insertional mutagenesis becomes more likely – a proposition that can be tested using animal models. Age-related effects do seem important; recent research has suggested that gene therapy is much less likely to restore normal immune function in older patients.

In 2005, SCID-X1 patients again became the focus of attention with a refinement of previous attempts at gene therapy, so far successful only on affected cells *in vitro*. **Gene editing** utilises naturally occurring 'zinc finger' proteins, which take their name from the characteristic zinc-binding amino acid loops they contain.

The zinc finger 'motif' is commonly found in proteins that bind to DNA (and to RNA). Furthermore, zinc finger proteins of a particular structure are able to bind to specific (mutated) sequences, thereby allowing an attached enzyme to cut the DNA at that point. The cell's own repair system then comes into effect. If the zinc finger protein is first linked with a 'correct' copy of the sequence in question, to act as a template, the correct version of the sequence becomes inserted, at its normal chromosomal location. This opens up the possibility that in future, the precise position of insertion of genes can be controlled, perhaps avoiding the complication associated with positional effects with earlier forms of gene therapy. Some researchers are placing great faith in gene editing for the future, although possible deleterious effects of incorrect insertion remain a worry.

Question 7.1

Suppose a child with SCID-X1 currently faced the prospect of gene therapy, as opposed to an unmatched bone marrow transplant. Outline in general terms the type of risk–benefit analysis that would be appropriate.

7.3 Gene therapy and cystic fibrosis

Cystic fibrosis (CF) is the most common of the fatal genetic conditions to afflict Caucasians – a term loosely synonymous with the racial description 'white'. About 1 in 25 of all Caucasians may carry the defective cystic fibrosis gene, but since this is a recessive gene, they will remain unaffected by its presence. From your earlier studies, you should be aware that there is a one-in-four chance of the offspring of a pair of carriers conceiving a child suffering from CF, where each of the alleles present is of the defective type.

■ If about 1 in 25 of Caucasian male and females is a carrier, what is the likely incidence of CF births in the population?

□ Assuming pairing between carriers occurs at random, then the chances of a partnership between two carriers is

$$\frac{1}{25} \times \frac{1}{25} = \frac{1}{625}$$

If one in four of the offspring of such couples is likely to be affected, then the proportion of births affected by CF will be

$$\frac{1}{4} \times \frac{1}{625} = \frac{1}{2500}$$

i.e. about 1 in 2500 births, which is indeed the approximate incidence of such births in the UK.

No cure for CF is as yet available. Individuals with CF currently seldom live beyond 30 years and usually die from respiratory failure brought about by repeated lung infections. Percussion of the chest in CF patients is routinely undertaken in order to get them to cough up the thick, sticky mucus that is diagnostic of the disease. More generally, pathological changes become evident in a great many 'secretory' glands that produce one form or other of mucus, such as the pancreas, intestine, salivary and sweat glands. It has been known for a considerable time that, in CF patients, the electrolyte content of the secretions from such glands – for example the concentrations of K^+, Na^+ and most noticeably Cl^- – is abnormal. NaCl levels in sweat are three to five times the norm. The pervasive symptoms of CF are now known to be linked to malfunction of electrolyte transport in the epithelial layer that line such secretory organs. In affected tissue, the export of Cl^- that typifies the healthy cell is prevented. Usually an outward flow of water from such cells follows the export of Cl^-, so the mucus produced is non-viscous. In CF patients, the mucus contains less water and so is sticky; this has implications, for instance, for the digestive system because the viscous mucus obstructs the flow of digestive enzymes into the small intestine from the pancreas. Such blockages can cause the destruction of pancreatic tissue, leading to digestive problems together with an increased likelihood of diabetes, as insulin-producing β cells of the pancreas are destroyed. However the tissue most strongly and strikingly affected by CF is the layer of epithelial cells that line the upper surface of the lung. These cells have cilia in their apical surface (facing the lung interior), the beating of which normally helps remove mucus and keep the lungs clear. Lung epithelial cells display only a modest degree of cell division, the significance of which will be apparent later.

The faulty gene responsible for CF has been tracked down to chromosome 7, with the precise position of the gene being established in 1989. Important in such detective work was the use of restriction enzymes in cutting up patients' DNA.

- Recall what do restriction enzymes do.
- They cut up double-stranded DNA into smaller fragments, acting at specific recognitions sequences (see Table 3.1).

The large number of mRNAs isolated from the sweat glands of CF patients and unaffected individuals were used to create a so-called 'library' of distinctive cDNAs, which could then be tested to see which hybridised with particular DNA fragments suspected of containing the CF gene. Comparisons of the cDNA from two different sources (healthy and affected) indicated that three nucleotides were absent in the gene sequences of about 70% of CF patients. The full sequence of the CF gene is now known. As Table 2.1 reveals, it is a large gene. It is about 230 000 base pairs long and includes 27 introns; the mRNA it produces is about 6500 base pairs, which encodes a mature protein 1480 amino acids long. The protein product is called cystic fibrosis transmembrane conductance regulator, which one author has described as 'mercifully' abbreviated to CFTR. This protein product becomes incorporated within the apical membrane of epithelial cells, such as those lining the lung, where they act as channels to conduct Cl^- out of the cell. In CF patients, mutations within the *CFTR* gene often produce proteins that are inappropriately processed or become degraded, often during transit to the membrane, with the result that chloride transport is prevented, resulting in the various manifestations of the disease already mentioned. In fact, the effects of CFTR malfunction are so far-reaching that the protein may well have additional functions, as yet unknown. In the most common form of mutation, the altered CFTR chloride channel becomes established within the apical membrane but the loss of particular amino acids within the CFTR protein affects its capacity to bind the metabolite ATP. (From earlier studies, you may recall ATP as the short-lived energy transfer molecule that can deliver energy to metabolic reactions that require it, as well as 'capture' energy from reactions that generate energy.) This reduced ATP binding capacity seems to reduce the ability of CFTR to open up into an effective channel and to bring about the outward transport of chlorine ions. The key features of the *CFTR* gene and the protein it encodes are shown in Figure 7.2.

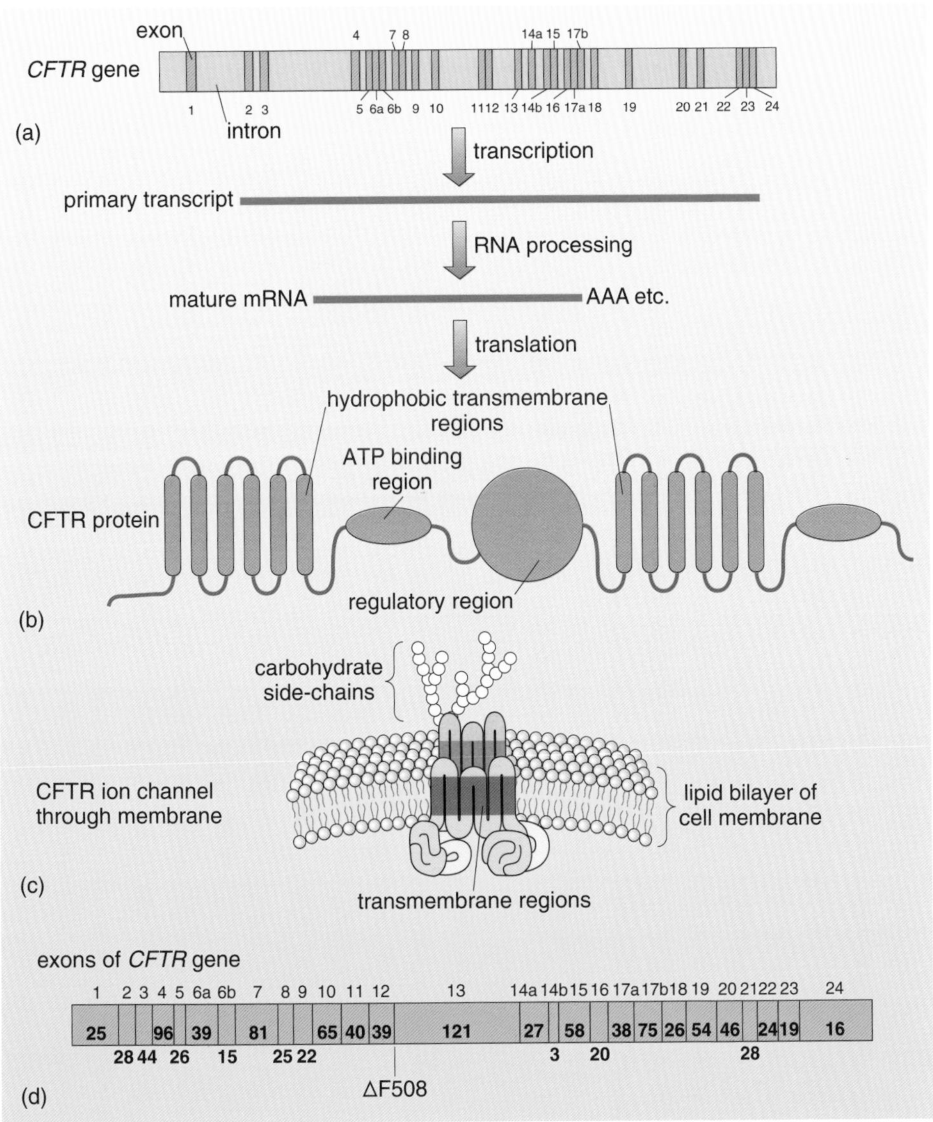

Figure 7.2 The *CFTR* gene and the protein that it codes for. (a) represents the *CFTR* gene, with introns (green) and exons (orange). Only the exons are numbered. The CFTR protein, shown in (b), has a number of distinct regions, notably an ATP binding region and a hydrophobic (i.e. water-hating) region – the transmembrane regions – that spans the apical membrane of the lung cell. (c) shows the folded protein located within the cell membrane. The most striking features of the CFTR protein are the six transmembrane components which form the walls of the pore through which the chloride ions move out of the cell. (d) shows the number of currently known mutations in each exon of the *CFTR* gene; the position of the ΔF508 mutation is also shown.

A great many different *CFTR* gene faults are now known, of which ΔF508 is just one (Figure 7.2d). At the time of writing (early 2006), there are 1415 mutations listed on the website that shows the *CFTR* mutation database. Figure 7.2d shows how the majority of these are distributed over the coding regions of the gene. The mutations are of various types including in-frame deletions, missense, nonsense, frameshift and splicing mutations. As an illustration, Table 7.2 lists the numbers of these different types of mutation for two exons of the *CFTR* gene.

Table 7.2 Numbers of mutations of different types in exons 6b and 18 of the human *CFTR* gene.

Mutation type	Exon 6b	Exon 18
in-frame deletion*	1	2
missense mutation	5	16
nonsense mutation	2	3
frameshift mutation	6	4
splicing mutation†	1	1

* A deletion that has no effect on the reading frame downstream of the mutation point.

† A type of mutation that occurs at DNA sequences where the coding (exons) and non-coding sections (introns) of the gene meet.

■ From your knowledge of CF, identify two or three characteristics of CF that make this a promising area for gene therapy.

■ First, CF occurs very largely through the loss of function of a single gene. Second, the tissue where the effects of CF are most obvious and debilitating is relatively accessible, which means that the degree of invasion required by the vector is relatively modest. The fact that the DNA sequence of the *CFTR* gene is known should in theory make it easier to isolate and clone the *CFTR* gene, for transfer into a vector.

■ Look at Table 7.1. Which of the means of gene transfer identified strikes you as the most promising for CF gene therapy?

■ Remember that the cells lining the lung are generally non-dividing, and that the *CFTR* gene is large, which appears to rule out retroviruses and adeno-associated viruses respectively, suggesting adenoviruses are the best bet.

Recall from Box 2.1 that adenoviruses have a complex, double-stranded DNA genome, the base sequence of which is fully known. They also infect a variety of cell types, can readily be purified and produced in large numbers and are able to infect non-dividing cells.

Introducing the *CFTR* gene itself has proved relatively unproblematic. But silencing or deleting the full range of viral genes responsible for the virus' activation and replication has proved far from straightforward. In a good many cases, gene expression within the recombinant vector has proved short-lived and there is cellular damage at the points of entry within the epithelial cells. This indicates an immune response within the invaded cells, as a consequence of viral proteins being expressed. As a result, administration of the engineered adenovirus in trials had to be suspended. An additional problem is the absence in the apical membrane of the epithelial cells that line the human lung of the type of receptor that these adenoviruses most readily bind to – though such receptors are plentiful in animal models. In mice, the efficiency of infections by adenoviral vectors has been enhanced by simultaneously administering sodium caprate, which makes the lung epithelial cells more 'leaky' to the adenovirus. In these circumstances, expression of the transferred genes was raised more than 25-fold.

Sodium caprate is the sodium salt of the saturated medium-chain fatty acid capric acid, and has also been used as an enhancer for drug absorption.

- ■ Do you think these results with sodium caprate involving mice are sufficiently clear-cut and safe to warrant clinical trials on human patients?
- ■ This is an area of controversy, but the medical consensus is that any such procedure in humans would be premature.

There is no certainty that the increase in *CFTR* gene expression in mice is a consequence of increased adenovirus infection of epithelial cells; some other unknown and perhaps problematic connection between the two may explain the observation. More significantly, making epithelial cells more leaky could have unintended consequences. The mucus of CF patients is especially rich in bacteria, so the lung tissue might be subject of very many unwelcome invasions if the apical membrane is more permeable.

What genetic engineers are trying to achieve is an adenoviral vector that is depleted of all viral genes, so that a cellular immune response would be minimal. But the efficiency of invasion, and likely degree of permanent incorporation of *CFTR* gene, may well still prove too inefficient to be of clinical value. Meanwhile, other research groups favour the development of other viral vectors (see Table 7.1), which are less likely to evoke an immune response and are amenable to repeat administration. If, in future, the actively dividing stem cells from which the majority of cells lining the lung airway are derived can be accessed, the benefits of using retroviral vectors might be more evident.

At present, despite some success with *in vitro* studies and with animal models, the hoped-for correction of the CFTR defect in humans has not been brought about to any significant degree, although many researchers are encouraged by the transient effects observed.

What these problems reveal is just how adept the lining of the human lung has become over time in resisting invasion by natural vectors – a capacity of great benefit in withstanding a wide range of natural bacterial and viral infections but not when we want to use viral vectors for therapy. Indeed, problems of this type explain why some researchers are turning to non-viral vectors (such as liposomes) to deliver DNA, which present technical problems of their own, of the type summarised in Table 7.1.

Question 7.2

Explain why the prospects of successful gene therapy for cystic fibrosis are greater than those for thalassaemias.

Question 7.3

(a) Small genes probes, with base sequences complementary to genes of interest, are now routinely used to test for the mutated version of the *CFTR* gene. Why might their effectiveness in detecting carriers of defective *CFTR* alleles be limited? (b) Carriers produce malfunctional CFTR protein. Why are such individuals not affected by the condition?

Question 7.4

Why is simple replacement therapy, involving the injection of protein into the patient's bloodstream, not an effective remedy for CF?

Question 7.5

In CF, *in vivo* delivery via adenoviruses has resulted in occasional and transitory expression of the *CFTR* gene. Why is it not possible simply to increase the dose of the virus in order to increase its effectiveness?

7.4 Genes and cancer

Cancer is sometimes called, with some exaggeration, a 'disease of DNA'. Indeed, the first suspicions that cancers arise as a result of genetic changes in cells were voiced about 100 years ago.

There are two main lines of evidence to support this conclusion. Once a cell has become cancerous, it will divide to produce other cancerous cells, implying that the changes that have caused the cell to become cancerous can be passed on. Cell biologists refer to the process by which a cell becomes cancerous as **transformation** and a cancerous cell is described as 'transformed' – a terminology adopted here from now on. Such cells can often be grown in tissue culture outside the body indefinitely, unlike normal cells which have a definite 'life'. For example, normal fibroblasts (the principal cells found in connective tissue) can undergo up to only about 50 divisions outside the body before they stop dividing and die. There are, however, many examples of cells originally taken from cancers that have been kept growing for many decades. Perhaps the most famous of these is the HeLa cell line which was originally derived in 1953 from the cervical cancer of a woman called Henrietta Lacks, after whom it is named.

Be careful not to confuse this meaning of the term 'transformation' with transformation of cells via receipt of a vector (Section 3.2).

The second piece of evidence that cancer has a genetic origin is that some types of cancer appear to run in families. One example is retinoblastoma, a rare childhood tumour affecting the retina of the eye. Research in the early 1970s revealed something of the factors that account for this condition; it arises as a consequence of changes in two classes of gene, now known to be widely distributed. The first was mentioned in Section 7.2; these are tumour-suppressor genes. Normally these would suppress the extensive cell growth and cell division typical of transformation. However, if such genes mutate, cancer may develop.

■ The mutant allele of the tumour-suppressor genes is recessive to the normal allele of the gene. In order for transformation to occur, would one or both copies of the normal allele have to mutate?

■ You may well recall much the same point from p. 136. Because the mutant allele is recessive both copies of the normal allele would have to mutate to set the cell on the road to transformation.

A second class of gene implicated in cancer are **oncogenes**; their expression enhances cell transformation. There'll be more to say soon about how these genes become switched on. When changes occur in both these types of gene, cancer generally develops. This relationship was first put forward in the early 1970s as the **'two hits' hypothesis**, to explain the onset of retinoblastoma. The idea is now known to have wider applicability; indeed, most cancers seem to originate from multiple mutations.

Somatic mutations can occur naturally, usually as a result of mistakes in DNA replication, as was discussed in Section 2.2. Most of these are eliminated by cellular repair mechanisms, brought about by DNA repair enzymes that are themselves produced by genes that can mutate. In that event, because DNA repair enzyme production ceases or is impaired, cancer becomes all the more likely. As you know from Section 2.2, mutation rates – and thus the likelihood of a tumour developing – can be increased by exposure to ionising radiations or chemical mutagens.

In what follows, bear in mind these two gene types just described. Tumour-suppressor genes prevent transformation of cells. Such genes oppose the action of oncogenes, which can directly bring about transformation. Also note the importance of DNA repair enzymes.

Let's now look in a little more detail at how these genes act.

7.4.1 Controlling the cell cycle

As we have seen, one of the ways in which a cancer cell differs from a normal cell is that it can keep dividing indefinitely. All types of normal, growing cells pass though a defined sequence of stages called the cell cycle, illustrated in Figure 7.3.

You may already know about the stages of cell division, or mitosis, in which the chromosomes become visible under the microscope and separate into two new cells. However, the stages we are concerned with here occur between successive cell divisions, in interphase. As you can see from Figure 7.3, in an actively dividing cell, interphase is divided into three episodes, called G1, S and G2. G1 represents the stage between the end of mitosis and the beginning of the next phase of DNA replication; S phase is the period of DNA replication, in preparation for the next cell division. G2 is the phase between DNA replication and the beginning of mitosis. If a cell has finished dividing, because it is

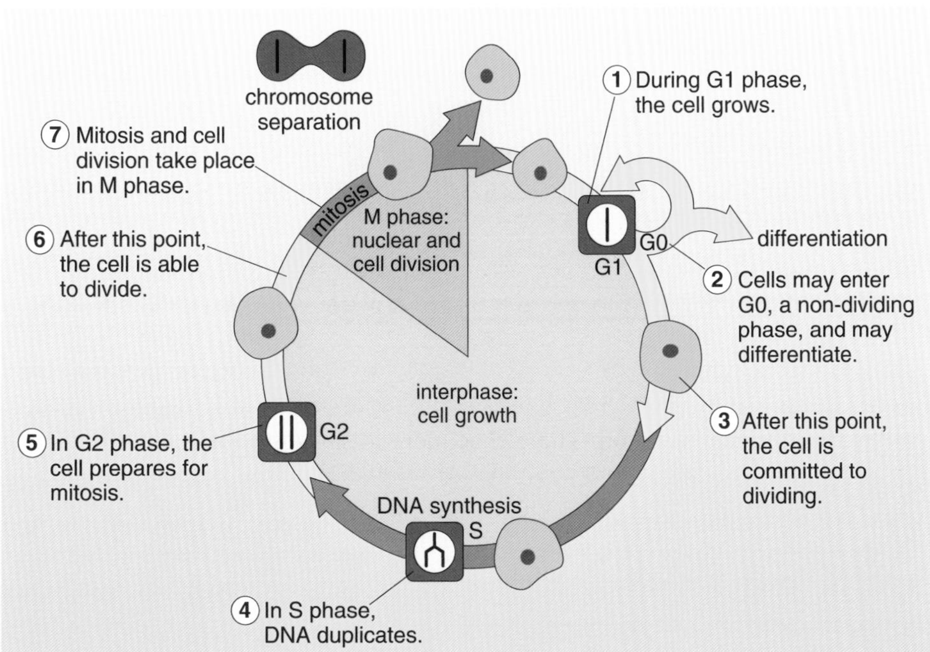

Figure 7.3 The eukaryotic cell cycle. Interphase, the period between cell division is divided into G1, S and G2. The following phase, M, consists of nuclear, followed by cell division. The appearance of one chromosome is also indicated. If you are familiar with mitosis you may recall that the chromosomes first become visible in late interphase, as pairs of chromatids, well before cell division begins.

differentiating into a normal mature cell, the process is halted before the end of G1 and the cell is then said to enter G0. There is an additional possibility: the cell can start to undergo programmed self-destruction, i.e. apoptosis.

Apoptosis is quite distinct from accidental or necrotic cell death following injury or the action of toxins. It is an active process in which specific genes are turned on in sequence. Apoptotic cells are recognised and destroyed by cells of the immune system before they disintegrate, so there are no cell fragments left to cause inflammation. (Inflammation is associated with the cellular breakdown that follows necrotic, unprogrammed, cell death.) Apoptosis occurs throughout the life of an organism and is particularly important during embryonic development. Examples of apoptosis that occur during development include the disappearance of the tadpole's tail as the tadpole metamorphoses into a frog and the elimination of cells that initially exist between the developing fingers of the human hand.

What factors decide whether a cell continues to divide, stops dividing and differentiates, or undergoes apoptosis? Normal cells receive their cues from their environment and such cues consist of chemical stimuli or contact with other cells. On the surface of each cell, specialised receptor proteins detect various stimuli from the environment, by binding to molecules in solution or on the surfaces of adjacent cells. When this binding occurs, a complex chain of interactions is initiated that ultimately results in appropriate genes being expressed. The products of these genes determine whether the cell progresses to another round of division, stops dividing and differentiates, or undergoes apoptosis. Any disruption of this mechanism can lead to a cell becoming transformed.

■ In the light of this discussion, what roles do you think oncogenes and tumour-suppressor genes might play in these control pathways?

■ An oncogene might be expected to code for a protein that stimulates a cell to divide, whilst a tumour-suppressor gene might be expected to code for one that causes a cell to stop dividing and differentiate or to undergo apoptosis.

Since all cells undergo normal division for part of their lives, they must all contain genes that stimulate cell division. The problem occurs when these genes continue to be expressed inappropriately. It is at this point that they are said to become oncogenes. The same gene, normally expressed, in an unmutated form, is generally termed a proto-oncogene, which you know of already from Section 7.2.

Figure 7.4 summarises what has been said so far about the role of oncogenes and of tumour-suppressor genes and their role in cancer. One question that remains is: how do proto-oncogenes become oncogenes?

The conversion can occur by several mechanisms. For example, proto-oncogenes can undergo mutations that alter the structure of their protein product. As a result, instead of being converted to an inactive form when it is no longer needed, the product remains active and continues to stimulate cell division. A good example is the *ras* gene, which produces a membrane-bound receptor protein, Ras, that is sensitive to incoming signals of the type that can trigger cell division. The functioning of Ras depends on a change in its shape. In response to signals, it switches between an active form, which can trigger cell division, and an inactive form, which does not stimulate cell division. The likelihood of cell division therefore depends on the balance between these two forms, as Figure 7.5a

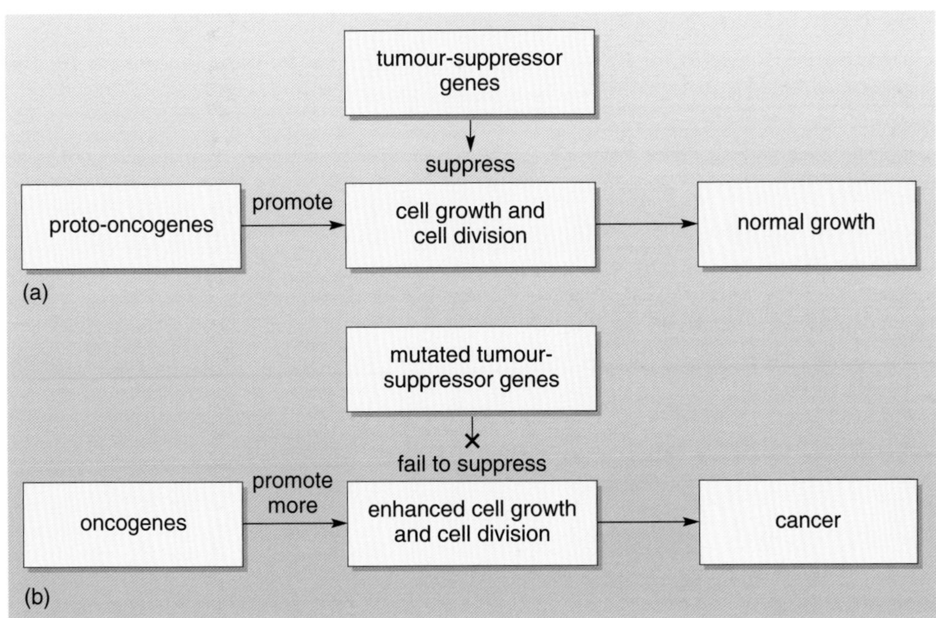

Figure 7.4 The role of oncogenes and tumour-suppressor genes. (a) Normal cell growth is controlled by the products of proto-oncogenes and tumour-suppressor genes. (b) Cancer can result from mutations in either type of gene.

indicates. However, a single point mutation, responsible for substituting just one amino acid, can change the protein into a mutant version that is stuck permanently in an active form.

■ What effect would this mutation have on cell division?

■ The abnormal Ras protein would be active all the time, and stimulate cell division, irrespective of whether appropriate signals were being received to do so, see Figure 7.5b.

Other mutations can result in genes responsible for stimulating cell division being copied to different parts of the genome. Because there are then many copies of the gene, it will produce much more of its product than in normal cells.

A gene may also be copied to a part of the genome that is close to a control sequence associated with an entirely different gene. An example of this is the *myc* oncogene, which is implicated in Burkitt's lymphoma, as well as some other tumours. *myc* codes for the protein p62, which prevents the cell from exiting from the cell cycle into G0, and causes it to continue dividing. In 80% of cases of

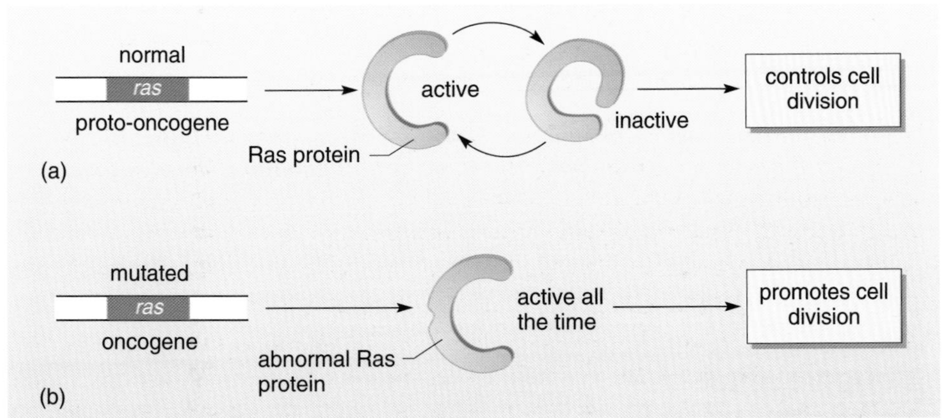

Figure 7.5 The *ras* gene and its protein product, Ras, in (a) a normal cell and (b) a cancer cell.

Burkitt's lymphoma, copies of *myc* oncogene, which is normally located on chromosome 8, are found on chromosome 14, close to the gene that codes for the immunoglobulin heavy chain. The immunoglobulin heavy chain is one of the polypeptide chains that make up antibody proteins.

■ What effect is the presence of *myc* close to the control sequence for an immunoglobulin likely to have on the expression of *myc*?

■ When these cells are stimulated to express the immunoglobulin, they will also express the *myc* gene product, p62.

Since Burkitt's lymphoma is a cancer of B lymphocytes (whose function in the body is to produce antibodies), these cells will produce p62 in large quantities and hence be stimulated to continue dividing.

7.4.2 Gene therapy of cancer

■ In the light of the previous discussion, suggest two gene therapy approaches that researchers might use to reverse the genetic changes leading to the transformation of cells.

■ An attempt to control cancer by gene therapy could either (a) replace an inactive tumour-suppressor gene with an active version or (b) try to inhibit the expression of an oncogene.

Both approaches have been attempted with a number of different genes, but perhaps most research effort has been put into replacing defective versions of the tumour-suppressor gene ***p53***.

The *p53* gene is expressed in all normal cells so far investigated. The protein it produces is known to be able to halt the cell cycle at three different points, one towards the end of G1, at another point near the beginning of the S phase and at a third at the end of G2 phase, just before the cell goes into mitosis. A major function of p53 protein is to block the cell cycle if the process of DNA replication is incomplete or if errors during replication are not repaired. The cell cycle then normally resumes once DNA damage has been repaired; indeed, one effect of p53 protein is to stimulate DNA repair, by activating a repair protein. *p53* is also one of the genes involved in the control of apoptosis; in particular, *p53* can induce apoptosis in response to DNA and cellular damage caused by, for example, the cytotoxic drugs used to kill cancer cells. In general then, *p53* offers some protection from cancer-causing effects of DNA error or damage.

■ *p53* has been shown to be inactive in many different types of tumour cell. What might be the effect on cell growth of the absence of active *p53*?

■ First, the control points in the cell cycle would be removed. So cells would be able to replicate their DNA and undergo mitosis irrespective of any errors accumulated in the DNA. Successive rounds of cell division could then take place unchecked, i.e. growth would be out of control.

Secondly, if mistakes in DNA replication occurred leading to mutations, those mutations would be passed on to the daughter cells. For example if the *ras* proto-oncogene became converted to the *ras* oncogene due to a mistake in replication and the damage was not repaired, the cell would still be able to divide, ensuring that the two daughter cells and all of those arising from them carried the *ras* oncogene. For this reason, in the absence of p53 protein, mutations are much more likely to survive and be transmitted. Lack of *p53* activity is therefore also associated with genomic instability in tumours.

Thirdly, the cell would become more resistant to the cytotoxic drugs used to treat cancer.

The issue of drug resistance is important in the clinical treatment of cancer. Most cancer drugs act by killing cells, but as they develop, many tumours become resistant to such drugs. One of the reasons they do so is because the tendency for damaged cells to undergo apoptosis is inhibited. If the damage is not sufficient to kill the cell outright, the damaged cell may survive and continue to divide. Radiation therapy and some cytotoxic drugs act by damaging DNA or interfering with replication, and it is even possible that administering such treatments to resistant cells could introduce further mutations, which would be passed on to daughter cells. As a result, overcoming the drug resistance of tumours has been as much an aim of gene therapy as restoring the normal cell cycle controls.

p53 would therefore seem to be a particularly suitable target for gene therapy, especially as a lack of active *p53* is a hallmark of a very wide range of tumours. For example, mutations of *p53* have been found in 60–65% of lung and colon cancers, 40–45% of stomach, oesophageal, and bladder cancers, 25–30% of breast, liver and prostate cancers and 10–15% of leukaemias. Overall, about 45–50% of human cancers have a defective *p53* gene.

If a functional copy of the normal *p53* gene is to be introduced into a cell, it of course requires a suitable vector. For *p53* gene therapy, the most commonly used vector is an adenovirus. The *p53* gene is spliced into the genome of the adenovirus close to a promoter that will ensure expression. At the same time, as with the adenovirus developed for cystic fibrosis gene therapy, a gene that is necessary for viral replication is spliced out/inactivated, in order to reduce the virus's infectivity.

Adenoviruses modified in such a way are an effective method of inserting the *p53* gene into cells and perhaps incorporating it into the cell's genome. They are normally administered by injection directly into the tumour, thereby ensuring that a sufficiently high dose is received by the transformed cells. This also reduces the likelihood of the virus being recognised by the immune system and being eliminated by it. As a result, the method has been used mainly as a means of treating solid tumours that are reasonably accessible, such as tumours of the head and neck. Tumours so treated show that the expression of *p53* can be restored, but because the material is injected into solid tumours, the effect tends to be limited to within about 1 cm of the site of injection site. Nevertheless, early trials showed some success in preventing the regrowth of tumours that had been surgically removed and also some tumour regression when the method was combined with cytotoxic drugs or radiotherapy. Unlike most conventional cancer treatments, there appear to be few side-effects.

A further strategy based on *p53* involves the manufacture of a rather different type of modified adenovirus. This approach exploits the fact that *p53* also acts as one of the main cellular defences against viral infection. In a normal cell that has been infected by a virus, the replication of viral DNA is recognised by the cell as abnormal and instead of continuing to reproduce, the cell undergoes p53-induced apoptosis. In order to protect itself, the normal virus contains a gene for a protein inhibitor of the *p53* gene called E1B. It therefore follows that an adenovirus that cannot make E1B will not be able to reproduce in normal cells which contain the p53 protein, but could do so in cells deficient in p53.

■ Why might such a virus be an effective anti-cancer therapy?

■ When viruses reproduce in cells, they eventually kill them. A virus that was unable to make E1B would be able to reproduce only in cells that had no p53. Since normal cells have p53, they would be unaffected, whilst tumour cells deficient in p53 would be killed.

Such a virus, ONYX-015, has been produced and is, at the time of writing (early 2006), in clinical trials against a variety of different tumours. Early results suggest that this approach has some promise.

Whilst the effects of a defective tumour-suppressor gene can be overcome by supplementing it with a functional copy, a rather different approach is needed to counteract the effects of an oncogene. Whilst *p53* can act as a tumour-suppressor gene by inducing cells with damaged DNA to undergo apoptosis, other genes produce proteins that suppress apoptosis and thus enable such cells to survive. If such a gene came to be inappropriately expressed, it would become an oncogene. One gene of this type is called *Bcl-2* whose product inhibits the action of *p53*. Like *myc*, *Bcl-2* can become translocated from one chromosome to another, in this case from chromosome 18 to chromosome 14. Like *myc*, it can also become associated with the immunoglobulin heavy chain gene and hence be produced in large quantities in lymphocytes.

One way of tackling this problem is to use antisense therapy, of the type mentioned in Section 6.2 and the opening paragraphs of Section 7.1: siRNAs (short interfering RNAs) could be used, complementary to the single-stranded mRNA produced by transcription of the gene in question, so blocking translation.

■ Why is this approach not as straightforward as its sounds?

■ Section 7.1 mentioned that siRNAs are broken down rapidly in the body, which implies that large quantities would have to be used to have any measurable effect on tumour growth.

One of the ways around this is to modify the backbone of the antisense RNA to make it resistant to breakdown. This can be done in a number of ways, but the most satisfactory involves the replacement of one of the oxygen atoms in the phosphate bridge between each nucleotide with a sulfur atom. Short nucleotide sequences that have been modified in this way are called phosphothiorate oligonucleotides.

The pharmaceutical firm Genta has produced an antisense phosphothiorate oligonucleotide called G3139 or 'Genasense', consisting of just 18 nucleotides complementary to short stretch of *Bcl-2* mRNA. At the time of writing, this compound is in clinical trial against a number of different cancers including leukaemia, non-Hodgkin's lymphoma, prostatic carcinoma, breast carcinoma and melanoma. It is normally given to the patient by infusion and in combination with a cytotoxic drug. It has been shown to overcome the resistance to cytotoxic drugs shown by many tumours, particularly melanoma.

■ Why might an antisense oligonucleotide that blocked Bcl-2 protein synthesis be expected to overcome resistance to cytotoxic drugs?

■ Cytotoxic drugs interfere with DNA synthesis or the process of mitosis. The normal response of a cell to this type of damage is to go into apoptosis. If the *Bcl-2* gene is overexpressed, then because the Bcl-2 protein inhibits apoptosis, these damaged cells will survive. Inhibition of Bcl-2 synthesis will therefore restore the normal response to damage and the cells will undergo apoptosis.

Two new cytotoxic drugs, Docetaxel and Irenotecan have been shown to be particularly effective in combination with Genasense. These drugs are manufactured by another pharmaceutical company, Aventis, which has formed a partnership with Genta to promote this treatment.

As you may have gathered, the interplay of the various mechanisms that cause a cell to become transformed is very complicated and there has been space here to mention only a few approaches. There are, however, several other points in the mechanisms controlling the cell cycle and apoptosis where intervention is being investigated. Other possibilities include modifying cell surface receptors and the pathways by which these receptors communicate with the rest of the cell, interfering with the mechanism by which cancer cells are able to resist ageing, and disrupting the process by which a growing tumour develops a blood supply. All these approaches have their advocates and it will be fascinating to see how the field develops during the lifetime of this course. But it is worth bearing in mind that the techniques of somatic cell gene therapy have suffered a number of setbacks too, so progress is far from assured. In particular, the death of the American teenager James (or Jesse) Gelsinger in 1999 had a particularly devastating effect on many hitherto enthusiastic supporters of the technique. His adenovirus-based gene therapy was designed to treat a condition involving deficiency of the liver enzyme ornithine transcarbamylase (OTC) and the viral genes thought to be responsible for inducing an immune response had been removed. Nevertheless, this pioneering therapy provoked a strong reaction in Gelsinger's immune system, producing a very strong inflammatory response that caused most of his vital organs to fail. The case brought the ethics of gene therapy into sharp focus, and it is with this aspect that I want to finish the chapter.

Question 7.6

Name a gene whose product is able to halt cell division and also cause cells with damaged DNA to go into apoptosis.

Question 7.7

Do you think it likely that individuals heterozygous for a defective copy of *p53* will be more or less susceptible to cancer, compared to individuals who are homozygous for the defective gene?

Question 7.8

Name an oncogene that inhibits the action of *p53*. How can the activity of this oncogene be blocked and how is it implicated in the resistance of tumours to cytotoxic drugs?

7.5 The ethics of gene therapy

Does gene therapy represent a new departure for medical practice, with novel ethical concerns? Lung transplantation for example, offers the potential for a cure for CF but the procedure is both expensive and risky, in part because of the continuing need for immunosuppression to guard against rejection, with all the associated vulnerability to infection. Is implanting a gene different in kind to the transfer of an organ, or just different in scale? One type of SCID (severe combined immunodeficiency, Section 7.2) occurs because of a deficiency of an enzyme ADA (adenosine deaminase). Need an ethical distinction be made between giving affected individuals the enzyme (an expensive product, to be taken frequently) and transplanting the ADA gene (which is currently being attempted in the UK via gene therapy)?

The most commonly held view at present is that the type of gene therapy discussed so far poses no great new ethical challenges. Thus, in the UK, the Clothier Committee reported in 1992:

> We conclude that the development and introduction of safe and effective means of somatic cell gene modification, directed to alleviating disease in individual patients, is a proper goal for medical science. Somatic cell gene therapy should be regarded, at first, as research involving human subjects and we recommend that its use be conditional upon scientific, medical and ethical review. Although the prospect of this new therapy heightens the familiar ethical concerns which attend the introduction of any new treatment, we conclude that it poses no new ethical problems.

The classification of somatic cell gene therapy as *research* is intriguing. In medical contexts, assessment of levels of risk tends to be different from the norm. Individuals opting for gene therapy are often very ill, as with the cancers just described, and more conventional treatments have inherent risks and may be of limited effectiveness. But does research always prioritise the interests of the patient, as opposed to the researcher's need to 'find out more'? The ethical concerns that arise for doctors are perhaps not different in kind from those decisions associated with any emerging technology. But you'll have noticed the Committee's emphasis on *somatic* cell gene therapy. The ethical debate surrounding germline therapy is more distinct, in part because such genetic changes are likely to be long-term.

- Critics of germline therapy often assume that the results of germline therapy are irrevocable. Do you think this will be so?
- Not necessarily. It is likely that once techniques are developed for the effective replacement of particular genes, the same techniques are likely to permit the excision of the normal version and re-insertion of the faulty version, if such a step was ever desirable.

Germline therapy is not only much more controversial than somatic cell therapy, it is technically more difficult. Stable and permanent integration of the transferred gene is a prerequisite, together with normal gene expression. To be most effective, the abnormal gene would need to be either repaired or excised from the chromosome and replaced with the normal allele. Such genetic techniques are not routinely available at present, nor are scientists able to guard against associated risks such as insertional mutagenesis; some see the techniques of gene editing outlined in Section 7.2 as showing the way forward. At present, the general view is that the technique is too risky to be applied to humans, though using the technique for animal research is regarded as acceptable. In ethical terms, exposing ill patients to risky procedures, with their full consent, might be acceptable; genetic manipulation of human early embryos is much less so, in part because safety cannot be assured. But if (and many would say 'when') in future, germline therapy is reliably safe and effective, what ethical quandaries might it present?

- Do you hold the view that germline therapy is *unnecessary*? To guide your thinking, look back at whether the development of somatic cell gene therapies, such as for CF, could be deemed 'necessary'.
- Deciding something as *necessary* is no easy matter, as the author Michael Reiss has pointed out in this context. He urges his readers to reflect whether parliaments, cycles, domestic pets (perhaps even The Open University) are strictly 'necessary'. CF can be treated in other ways besides gene therapy, using methods that, while less effective and non-curative, are 'tried and tested'. Some people argue that 'unnecessary' but glamorous cures such as gene therapy draw attention and resources away from other potentially useful treatments, such as drugs, to reduce lung infection.

Perhaps in future, germline therapy will bring benefits not offered by other forms of cure or treatment. With CF, germline therapy carries advantages; in principle, it would ensure the presence of a functional gene in all otherwise susceptible cells (those of the pancreas, for example), not just those currently targeted by somatic cell gene therapy. Imagine a future scenario where partners who are both CF carriers take the view that germline therapy would be the best way of ensuring their offspring would be free of the risks of transmitting their faulty genes.

- What procedures would such couple have to undergo at present in order to be sure that their offspring did not inherit the faulty CF gene?
- The practical and emotional demands of IVF treatment, genetic screening and implantation of embryos with the normal CF gene – procedures that, inconvenience apart, are not 100% effective.

Should a carrier couple's wish that (at some future time) their descendants be free of such complication be denied? By many measures, it is more convenient and less costly to eradicate a disease 'once and for all' within the present generation than to treat the disease on each occasion it arises in progeny to come. In most medical contexts, prevention of disease has a greater social value than treatment, and genetic intervention via germline therapy may be one of the few opportunities for permanent prevention. The philosopher John Harris comes close to arguing that a moral duty exists to eradicate such suffering. He points to a clear dilemma:

> On the one hand, we must not make changes to the genetic structure of persons which will adversely affect their descendants. On the other hand, we must not fail to remove genetic damage that we could remove and that, if left in place, would cause harm to future generations.
>
> (Harris, 1992)

Supporters of gene therapy would argue that such a need is especially strong in the case of conditions such as retinoblastoma (Section 7.4), occurring in a tissue unlikely to be amenable to somatic cell gene therapy. Many cases of this disease arise because of somatic mutations that occur after birth that allow the oncogene responsible to transform retinal cells – recall the 'two hit' hypothesis. In this case – and for many other cancers where multiple factors are at work – germline therapy may be the *only* fully effective mode of prevention, protecting *all* vulnerable cells.

But has one generation the right to decide what is best for later generations? The philosopher John Mackie points out the dangers in doing so, arguing that 'if the Victorians had been able to use genetic engineering, they would have aimed to make us more pious and patriotic'. Indeed, issues of necessity apart, many philosophers and theologians counter-argue that germline therapy is intrinsically wrong, some arguing that 'interference' to a presumed natural order is morally unacceptable or, more pragmatically, that the procedure is open to abuse and/or has unforeseen consequences. Some argue that germline gene therapy will pose biological dangers in terms of reducing human variation and thereby compromising future human evolution. You'll appreciate that genetic variation indeed provides the drive behind evolutionary change.

■ Do you find this objection credible? Think of the likely scale of future germline gene therapy and of how genetic variation might be affected.

■ First, it's difficult to see, at least in the foreseeable future, how genetic variation would be compromised on a sizeable scale. Secondly, there is no logical reason to believe that germline therapy would inevitably lead to a reduction in genetic variation; in fact, the opposite may be true. Finally, the assertion that genetic variation is useful is not convincing in the case of seemingly damaging mutations such as CF.

But one concern is that some seemingly disadvantageous alleles occur in populations in frequencies higher than might be expected. The best understood example is the mutation that causes sickle-cell anaemia; those heterozygous for this condition enjoy an advantage in terms of increasing resistance to malaria.

More recent evidence suggests that the heterozygous individuals carrying the faulty CF gene are more resistant to the damaging physiological effects of cholera, a disease typified by electrolyte imbalance; remember that the function of the CFTR protein is to control electrolyte balance. Some people have argued that a whole range of 'faulty genes' might confer advantages at present unknown and that the eradication of such genes from the population at large would therefore be a mixed blessing.

Those whom others presume have most to gain from gene therapy are sometimes far from unreservedly enthusiastic about what it offers. Some feel gene therapy 'stigmatises' genetically based diseases, some extending the argument that CF patients are being ethically misused, as 'research fodder' within 'arduous if not painful experiments on human subjects'. One patient argues as follows:

> The process has reduced the desires and the needs of people with CF to a cure at all costs. This suggests a lack of understanding of the way in which people live with and experience the disease. The Cystic Fibrosis Foundation's choice to focus research on a 'cure' has meant that the many other potentially competing needs of people with CF and their families, such as CF education, social support, and age-appropriate care, have been marginalised.

Another patient argues that:

> A concentration on gene therapy cannot but construct people with genetic impairment as those impairments, so legitimising the medical model of disability and all the negative effects that follow in its wake. The paradox is that attempts to devise therapies that researchers claim may lead to people enjoying a better quality of life in the long term can have entirely the opposite effect in the short and medium term.

A fundamental concern about germline therapy is that in future it will doubtless be used not only for the repair of faulty genes of clear medical significance but for (supposed) enhancement of the human condition, given that the technology required for these two facets is identical. Safety reasons apart, the present-day prohibition of germline gene therapy reflects the common assumption that this is, or could readily become, a eugenic pursuit. If it were possible to safely transfer genes to modify intelligence, athleticism, height, aggressiveness, etc. in more favourable directions, oughtn't such laudable changes be permissible? One problem with this line of thinking is that it greatly underestimates the complexity of the factors that influence such traits. Hugely influential though genes can be, environmental factors have a crucial influence on human characteristics such as these, as do interactions between suites of genes and their controlling promoters and regulatory genes. None, of course, is determined on the basis of singe-gene effects.

Even if such manipulations were possible, say for intelligence, benefits are by no means assured. For example, Michael Reiss draws our attention to the downside of producing the human equivalent of an engineered strain of the fruit-fly *Drosophila* that learns ten times faster than its normal counterpart:

> Improved learning implies improved memory and if you have a far superior memory you will forget less. Most of us have experienced unpleasant happenings that we are only too grateful to forget. Furthermore, there is anecdotal evidence that the handful of people who have total recall or perfect photographic memories find life difficult.

Biologically speaking then, improving human nature seems impractical, as well as inadvisable.

Much the same could be said of concerns that 'superior' humans could be created in a form of societal engineering – perhaps more compliant or fiercely nationalistic. Even in the unlikely event that such genes could be identified, it seems unlikely that dictators would turn to such problematic strategies. As Reiss points out, recent history has testified to the fact that there are other, psychological, social and political means of exerting power over society at large which don't involve biological interference. Altogether, the arguments of this type that germline therapy should be banned are different expressions of the 'slippery slope' form of reasoning, which argues against innovation – however beneficial and well-intended – for fear of where it may lead. This notion is much discussed by philosophers and theologians, and for most, slippery slope arguments alone are generally viewed as insufficiently strong to prohibit germline therapy in humans, assuming such a technique could in time be both safe and efficacious. Those uncomfortable with this position often counter by referring to past experience of slippery slopes and scientific innovations, pointing out 'that the road to hell is paved with good intentions'.

Activity 7.1

Allow 15 minutes

To help sharpen your own views on whether germline gene therapy is ethically acceptable, write down three arguments in favour of the technique and three arguments against.

At present, germline gene therapy is such an unsafe and unexplored procedure that ethical debates geared largely towards 'designer babies' have a rather contrived and premature ring to them, ignoring the huge biological complications and uncertainties we have touched on. Nevertheless, in an unknown number of years to come, some such procedures will be sufficiently safe and reliable to be within reach, in which case these dilemmas will take on a more preoccupying urgency.

Summary of Chapter 7

Somatic gene cell therapy aims to rectify the effects of a 'faulty' gene, via the introduction of a transgene into affected body cells. Germline gene therapy targets reproductive cells or cells of the early embryo. *In vivo* entry routes, as with cystic fibrosis treatment, involve inserting transgenes into cells *in situ*; *ex vivo* procedures require extraction of cells (e.g. blood, bone marrow), genetic modification in culture and subsequent re-introduction.

Vectors used are similar to those associated with cloning procedures (Section 6.2); use of both retroviruses (as with treatment of SCID-X1) and adenoviruses (for cystic fibrosis gene therapy) is problematic. Production of infective viral particles must be avoided. Non-viral vectors (e.g. liposomes) offer promise, as does the microinjection of naked DNA. With SCID-X1, cures were effected after transgene insertion, but for some, leukaemia was a complication, possibly through non-random genome insertion. For cystic fibrosis, *CFTR* malfunction can be rectified *in vitro* via recombinant adenoviruses, but clinical signs of alleviation after aerosol delivery are hard to achieve, partly through difficulties of cell targeting.

Many cancers, perhaps most, have a genetic basis. Tumour-suppressor genes, such as *p53*, are inhibitory; oncogenes are stimulatory. Defects in the repair mechanisms of cells underlie many cancers. The conversion of proto-oncogenes to oncogenes can occur by one of several mechanisms, resulting in the stimulation of inappropriate cell division. *p53* is inactive in a wide range of tumours; gene therapy seeks to replace inactive *p53*, such that oncogenic damage can be effectively opposed. The *p53* gene can be introduced via adenoviral vectors. Antisense techniques are being developed to block the products of the oncogene *Bcl-2*, which inhibit the action of *p53*.

Somatic cell gene therapy is generally thought not to raise novel ethical concerns, though at present it represents a research activity rather than safe and effective therapy. Gene therapy is seen by some as reinforcing negative perceptions of disease and disability. Germline therapy is widely considered ethically unacceptable, mainly because it is non-consensual; it is also technically very ambitious. Gene editing, if refined, may avoid the consequences of inappropriate insertion into chromosomes. But the feasibility of any such gene therapy technique to enhance complex human characteristics, such as memory, is doubtful.

Question 7.9

Which of the statements (a)–(c) relating to somatic cell and germline gene therapy are correct? Give reasons.

(a) Effective somatic cell gene therapy would involve delivering DNA into each of the affected cell populations, e.g. for CF, both pancreas and lung cells; in contrast, with germline gene therapy, only the small cell population in the early embryo would need to be targeted.

(b) Germline therapy places greater emphasis than does somatic cell line therapy on the *replacement* of a malfunctional gene with a 'healthy' version and the safe integration into the genome; with somatic cell therapy, an effect – albeit temporary – will be achieved simply by adding the functional gene.

(c) For a 'carrier' couple, germline therapy would nowadays offer a more convenient, effective and safe means of avoiding a child inheriting the condition than would testing of any embryo prior to implantation.

Question 7.10

The first two, (1) and (2), of the arguments that follow are often advanced to support the case for germline gene therapy; arguments (3) and (4) are used as in opposition. Which, if any, of (1) to (4) do you find credible?

(1) Germline gene therapy offers a more efficient, 'once and for all' intervention than does repeated episodes of somatic cell gene therapy.

(2) Researchers ought to be allowed the freedom to investigate new ways of treating disease, and be allowed to choose the best forms of treatment for their future patients.

(3) If the techniques have unforeseen complications, then not only are the immediate progeny affected, but also all their descendants.

(4) Because germline gene therapy will prove of little benefit in the effective eradication of disease, there will be pressure to apply the technique for genetic enhancement, e.g. for 'trivial' aspects, such as appearance.

Chapter 8

Final thoughts

This topic has encouraged you to explore a wide range of different aspects of genetic manipulation. The approach adopted combined an account of some of the scientific developments that heralded progress in this field, with an emphasis on those areas that exemplify themes of particular concern to the course. For example, an assessment of risk is at the very heart of the issue of genetic manipulation, as is the notion of uncertainty. To what extent can risk of a particular quality be measured and how is the presumed level of risk interpreted and communicated by others? How might conflicting opinions on risk best be represented in policy meant to reflect the interests of society as a whole? We've seen that ethical quandaries in this area revolve around dilemmas of choice. While pragmatists may incline to a case-by-case evaluation of the worth of particular innovations in GM, there are plenty of voices that express a more deep-seated and all-embracing distaste for the GM enterprise:

> What kind of understanding of suffering is yielded by the creation of animals that are genetically programmed to suffer, and by the hardening of human sensibilities which this scientific exercise requires? The knowledge pursued by the indefatigable advocates of genetic engineering does not promote pleasure or well-being by revealing previously unappreciated qualities of a desirable object. Instead it is aimed at uncovering foreign objects – the clone, the redesigned baby, the legless mouse or monkey that glows in the dark – in order to temporarily satisfy the itch of curiosity.
>
> (Bowring, 2003)

Few perhaps would go as far as to impute the motivations of scientists as no more than the casual satisfying of the 'itch of curiosity'. But the notion of some intrinsic ethical objection to genetic manipulation is widespread, whereas what is natural is lauded. And such sentiments need not derive from the absolutist frames of thought mentioned earlier. Here is the scientist Colin Tudge on the subject:

> What of the kind of objection that Prince Charles has raised, that this is 'God's territory'? If we reject the idea of God, as is common in this secular age, does such an objection make any sense? I suggest that it does. Again, I feel that we would do well to be cautious on absolutist grounds, to cultivate the feeling that such interventions really are beyond the pale. But again, this point can be made simply by consequentialist arguments.
>
> For consider the point made earlier: that we can never, for inescapable reasons of logic, understand biological systems exhaustively. We may develop wonderful theories that seem to explain the observed facts beautifully and, indeed, we already have many such theories. But we can never know that we have taken all possible factors into account.
>
> (Tudge, 2000)

It may be of little comfort that, despite the wealth of scientific information presented in this topic, the magnitude of the scientific uncertainties threaten to overwhelm the argument. Ignorance of science is commonly portrayed as the main reason why genetic engineering is so frequently opposed; if only 'people' knew about the science involved, the more supportive they would be of the technology, the argument runs. Now, science's inevitable ignorance of biological systems is presented as a reason for precaution. Critics of GM are fond of quoting the many recent instances of 'surprises' that often went against the grain of belief at the time. Examples range from the discovery of introns, the role of reverse transcriptase, the influence of retrotransposons. But should the possibility of surprises inhibit scientific developments? If the rewards of GM technology are as significant as many argue, then the key task is surely to undertake the kind of 'cost–benefit' analysis that we have touched on, imperfect though the art of scientific prediction is known to be. Such analysis needs to include facts that are beyond the realm of science itself – it needs to take account of how non-experts 'feel' about the acceptability of particular innovations, about who is likely to gain most from particular innovations.

What we hope your study of this topic has achieved is a continuing openness to a wide range of arguments and a few useful thinking strategies relevant to the challenges and dilemmas that GM poses. It certainly hasn't been our intention to offer any answers, or to sway you into one way of thought or the other, even if it may have seemed so at times. As scientists, we warm to the principle of evaluating the evidence in as reasoned and dispassionate a way as possible. But what is apparent is that no evaluation of the rights and wrongs of GM can stand or fall using scientific criteria alone. 'Feelings' about what is right or wrong have a legitimacy too. Indeed the distinguished Scottish philosopher David Hume (1711–1776) took the view that all ethical statements are rooted in feelings. For us, and hopefully for you, this is all the more reason to find issues relating to genetic manipulation so compelling. The topic has a bearing on so many fundamental problems, such as what sort of society is wanted and how science can best be used for the greater benefit of society as a whole.

Learning Outcomes for Topic 6

S250's Learning Outcomes are listed in the Study Guide under three categories: Knowledge and understanding (Kn1–Kn6), Cognitive skills (C1–C5) and Key skills, (Ky1–Ky6). Here, we outline how these overall learning outcomes have been treated in the context of Topic 6 Genetic manipulation.

You have learnt a good deal about the science that underlies the development of GMOs, including not only how gene transfer is sometimes brought about but also the underlying biological knowledge that these techniques build upon (Kn1). The importance of the inherent uncertainty of such procedures was emphasised (Kn2), though it is also clear (as from Chapters 3 and 4 for example) how such developments reflect the ingenuity and enterprise of scientists. How ideas and findings are communicated to the public (Kn3) has been stressed, together with the difficulties of effective policy-making (Kn6). Assessing issues such as the impacts of GMOs on human health and the environment have traditionally centred around risk assessment (Kn4). Ethical issues have been highlighted throughout the topic (Kn5). You'll appreciate that many of the factors that influence decision making about GMOs are non-scientific, e.g. economic and personal value systems (Kn6).

Having studied Topic 6, you'll be aware that our present understanding of GMOs falls short of what is required to be confident of safety (C1). Such a shortfall can increase ethical anxieties (C2); at several points in the topic you have been encouraged to formulate your own judgement about contentious issues (e.g. Golden Rice, stem cell research), increasing your awareness of the importance of scientific thinking and knowledge, but also of some of science's limitations (C4). You should now have a greater ability to understand and interpret unfamiliar aspects of the GM, as new opportunities arise (C5).

While studying Topic 6, you were expected to receive, respond to, select and use relevant information from printed course material. However, other learning sources, notably electronic media, were important too, especially in relation to assessment (Ky1). Issues that you have encountered have been both quantitative (e.g. Chapter 4) and qualitative (Section 7.5) in nature (Ky2 and Ky3), although the emphasis on mathematical skills in Topic 6 has been less than in some of the other topics. The importance of sensitivity to audience in communication has been emphasised, e.g. in Chapters 2 and 5 (Ky4). You have had the chance to develop your skills of communicating via imparting and receiving information and opinions from others, perhaps through electronic media (Ky5). You have also had the opportunity to plan, monitor and develop strategies for more effective learning (Ky6).

Answers to questions

Question 2.1

(a) Where the two copies of a particular gene exist in different forms (i.e. as different alleles), the individual is heterozygous with respect to that gene; if the two copies of the gene are identical, this represents the homozygous state. You were reminded of these terms in Section 2.1; they were also mentioned in Box 1.6 of Topic 1. (That box also reminded you of the terms phenotype (i.e. appearance) and genotype (genetic make-up) which are relevant to this topic.)

(b) Within the split genes of eukaryotes, introns are non-coding (remember these are the *in*tervening sections), while exons are represented within mature RNA and therefore *ex*pressed (see point 5 in Section 2.1).

(c) DNA is double-stranded and its nucleotide bases are A, T, C and G. mRNA is single-stranded and the T in DNA is replaced by U (uracil). (The sugar component of DNA is called deoxyribose and that of RNA is ribose.)

(d) Transcription is the process of mRNA synthesis from its constituent nucleotide monomers, with the sequence of RNA bases determined by that of the template DNA strand. Translation results in the production of a polypeptide chain, via the assembly of amino acids in a particular sequence determined by the sequence of bases in the RNA template.

(e) RNA polymerase synthesises mRNA via transcription, linking RNA nucleotides together. (There are, in fact, different types of RNA polymerase in eukaryotes, each transcribing different types of RNA, i.e. mRNA, tRNA, rRNA.)

(f) The genetic code is redundant in the sense that some amino acids are specified by more than one codon. The example given in the text is proline, encoded by any one of four codons. (The term 'degenerate' is sometimes used to describe the same feature.)

(g) The most obvious examples are introns within split genes, and spacer DNA that exists between split genes. Nearly all of the DNA that is moderately or highly repetitive is also non-coding.

(h) Chromosomal mutations refer to alterations in the number and structure of chromosomes. Base substitution (Figure 2.5) involve the alteration of a single nucleotide (and hence, through replication, in the matching nucleotide in the complementary DNA strand), or perhaps the deletion or addition of a single nucleotide pair.

Question 2.2

(a) Bacterial genomes are relatively small, with genes often grouped together as operons, transcription and translation are closely associated and there is no mRNA splicing. Eukaryotic genomes are much larger, contain split genes, and transcription and translation are separated in space and time, with transcription occurring in the nucleus and translation in the cytoplasm.

(b) One gene can produce more than one type of protein via the very significant process of alternative splicing, characteristic of 'smart' genes; the same primary mRNA transcript is produced, but cut and sealed at different points, so producing a range of different mature mRNAs comprising different combinations of exons.

(c) The two numbers differ for a number of reasons. Since genes exist in pairs, each of the pair will produce the same protein type, at least in the homozygous state. Alternative splicing would lead to many more types of protein being produced by any one gene. Also, the numbers of genes that are expressed in any one cell, i.e. producing protein, is likely to be a small fraction of those present. Finally, you'll know (from Section 2.3) that a considerable number of genes code for a variety of tRNAs and rRNAs.

Question 2.3

'Junk' DNA is used to refer in an imprecise way to the non-coding parts of the genome, or to those DNA sequences that have no known function. The great majority of moderately and highly repetitive DNA could be so described. Spacer DNA is also of this type, as is the DNA that makes up introns. The term is rather misleading in that although some such DNA may be relics of the past, with no likely function, the function of other sections is more appropriately describe as 'not yet known', in which case, the term 'junk' is inappropriate.

Question 2.4

In the appropriate space, I'd include the key points about the characteristics of eukaryotic DNA and gene structure/function covered in Section 2.3, with terms such as split genes, gene families, moderately and highly repetitive DNA, promoters, enhancers, transcription factors, alternative splicing, post-translational control.

Question 2.5

The analogy presented in Figure 2.4 has some limitations. First, the 'tape' of DNA is in reality almost entirely 'silent' – remember only about 1% of the information in the genome codes for protein. Thus the gaps between 'songs' are very prolonged – containing, amongst other 'junk', largely inaudible fragments of songs from now dead singers! Some of the complexities of gene expression (of 'singing') cannot be represented – the genome has the capacity to put different 'verses' together from the same raw material on the 'tape', by alternative splicing – perhaps entirely different 'songs'! In the genome, the 'tape' may sound quite different on successive 'plays'.

Question 3.1

(a) By passing a mixture through a column with multiple (i.e. poly) thymine sequences, where the poly(A) tail of the mRNAs become bound. (b) By gel electrophoresis, involving the separation of gel-embedded RNAs on the basis of differences in their size.

Question 3.2

This fortuitous arrangement means that bacteria (and their progeny) that take up plasmids of this type can be identified; those that are able to grow as colonies in the presence of the antibiotic have taken up at least one such plasmid.

Question 3.3

Both the recombinant and non-recombinant plasmids will contain the genes for antibiotic resistance, so growth in the presence of antibiotic can't be a useful means of distinguishing them. Rather, it is the absence of a functional β-galactosidase gene that is key. If the different bacterial colonies are grown on X-Gal plates (plus antibiotic), those that do *not* produce a blue colour are the ones that lack the β-galactosidase gene, i.e. they contain the unwanted, non-recombinant plasmid.

Question 3.4

By growing colonies on X-Gal plates, as before. Because the insulin gene inserts into the β-galactosidase gene, the latter will no longer be functional, so no β-galactosidase will be produced. Therefore colonies of bacteria that contain such a plasmid will not produce a blue colour on X-Gal plates, i.e. the corresponding areas on the plates do not become blue. Those bacteria that contain plasmids without the insulin gene insert would be able produce β-galactosidase, which would produce the blue colouration – the converse of the test procedure shown in Figure 3.7.

Question 3.5

(a) Because the mRNA initially transcribed (the primary mRNA transcript) contains the coding and non-coding sequences, corresponding to the exons and introns respectively. For recombinant protein production within *E. coli*, what is needed is the mature mRNA product, so that the cDNA produced lacks all the intron-derived sequences. (Since mRNA is normally extracted from cell cytoplasm, this is the type of mRNA routinely used for cDNA production; the primary mRNA transcript is confined to the nucleus.) (b) Recall the 'redundancy' of the genetic code; a variety of DNA sequences (and hence corresponding mRNA sequences) can code for a particular amino acid in a polypeptide chain, such as the insulin chain A or B. (The full base sequence of the insulin A and B chain genes is now available, but was not known at the time of the work described.)

Question 4.1

(a) The two plasmids are the artificial Ti plasmid and the disarmed Ti plasmid or helper vector:

- The artificial Ti plasmid carries the foreign DNA that is to be transferred, a selectable marker sequence (these are both inserted between the left and right border sequences, and form the artificial T-DNA sequence) and origins of replication (ORIs) which allow it to be replicated in both *A. tumefaciens* and *E. coli*. This plasmid incorporates the genes that are to be transferred into the plant cell.
- The disarmed Ti plasmid (helper vector) contains the virulence region and an ORI that allows replication in *A. tumefaciens*. The virulence region codes for the proteins that are necessary to effect transfer of the T-DNA sequence, i.e. this plasmid facilitates transfer of T-DNA into the plant cell and its integration into the nuclear genome.

(b) Only the T-DNA sequence is actually incorporated into the plant cell's genome, i.e. the foreign DNA, the selectable marker sequence, and anything else between the left and right border of the T-DNA sequence.

Question 4.2

(a) The protein produced by *Bacillus thuringiensis* is a protoxin – when converted into its active form it becomes incorporated into the membranes of the cells lining the insect's gut. A chain of processes is initiated that cause the cells to die. The insect can no longer absorb food or water, and quickly dies from dehydration.

(b) The protoxin is converted into the active toxin only in alkaline conditions and in the presence of specific proteases. Humans and other vertebrates lack these specific proteases. In humans, the protoxin is likely to be destroyed by other proteases and the acid conditions in the stomach.

Question 4.3

(a) Glyphosate inhibits the enzyme EPSP synthase and prevents the synthesis of aromatic amino acids via the shikimic acid pathway. Without these amino acids, the plants die.

(b) The two methods attempted to genetically modify plants to tolerate glyphosate were to engineer the plants so that they produced:

- massive amounts of normal EPSP synthase.
- normal amounts of an EPSP synthase that remains active in the presence of glyphosate.

Question 4.4

Golden Rice differed scientifically in that its production was more complex – it involved the introduction of more than one new gene. The social issues surrounding it were different too. Glyphosate-tolerant and Bt crops obviously benefited large multinationals, but Golden Rice appeared to address an urgent humanitarian need – vitamin A deficiency in developing countries.

Question 5.1

(a) If a new technology is to be introduced in a just way, decision makers might need to consider whether the benefits and any problems associated with it will be shared fairly by those affected, and might try to direct the benefits to those who need them most.

(b) It is relatively easy to define a just approach, but much harder to enact one. Scientists, decision makers and the public may all reach different conclusions about the possible benefits and problems. They may differ in their assessment of how to strike a balance between the competing interests of individuals, groups, industry and the State. Fundamentally, they may differ in their ethical stances – leading them to quite different conclusions.

Question 5.2

(a) Press releases, interviews, direct postings to websites and so on, are not subject to the rigours of peer review and therefore have not been assessed as to their scientific merit, or otherwise.

(b) Whatever the problems with direct communication of scientific results to the media, it is surely unrealistic to expect scientists not to communicate in this way. The highly competitive atmosphere in which much prominent science is conducted means that scientists are under pressure to release interesting results prior to publication – to enhance their own standing, to establish precedence, and to satisfy the desire of the media for a good story.

Question 5.3

(a) The principle of substantial equivalence is that if a new food substance can be shown to be 'substantially equivalent' to an existing food substance, it can be treated as being safe for human consumption.

(b) Campaigners opposed to GM food argued that the principle was poorly defined and amounted to an excuse not to expose GM products to rigorous safety testing.

Question 5.4

It may be that some of the participants were broadly opposed to science, but the evidence is that the opposition of the majority was based on a range of social and political considerations. In particular, the participants showed a marked distrust of Governments and multinational corporations. If anything, the respondents wanted to see more scientific research into the possible risks of the technology, but they were keen that this research was carried out independently.

Question 6.1

Because such a result would not support the claim that the nuclei of *differentiated* cells could be 'reversed' in ways that enabled then to recapture powers of totipotency. The fact that undifferentiated cells can support the full range of developmental options is well known, so Dolly's derivation from such a cell nucleus would not have been surprising. (However, there is now strong evidence that the nucleus was in fact derived from a fully differentiated cell.)

Question 6.2

Recall that Dolly is an exact copy only in relation to the nuclear DNA of the donor sheep. There are genes within the mitochondria of the cytoplasm of the egg from which Dolly developed – and these are derived from those present in the recipient egg from which the original nucleus had been removed.

Question 6.3

Ethical concerns apart, the biological grounds for urging caution relate to the reliability of current procedures. You may recall the large number of attempts at the procedure that had to be undertaken with Dolly before success was achieved. The related concern is that a relatively high proportion of cloned offspring seem to have some form of abnormality. (A common finding is that cloned offspring are exceptionally large, which suggests that some aspects of gene expression in the cloned embryo may be abnormal.) Thus in these circumstances, the chances of a successful outcome with a healthy offspring are limited. Note too that clones are unlikely to be identical to the originals in every sense. Their different experience in early life, within the surrogate womb and then in the distinct environment of the outside world, would contribute to their unique individuality. The fact that a clone is not genetically identical to the donor animal in every respect (see Section 6.1.1) is also pertinent.

Question 6.4

As should be evident from Section 6.1, pluripotency describes a condition where a cell is not yet differentiated but has the ability to change into one of a narrower range of cell types than can genuinely totipotent cells, of which ESC are the best example. For example, stem cells within bone marrow (HSCs) can change into many types of blood cells, and some types of brain cell, but there are cell types that (according to current evidence) they cannot differentiate into.

Question 6.5

The main reason why ES cells are so convenient is that they are totipotent and represent an accessible source of supply, though the supply of eggs raises problems. By contrast, adult stem cells are often dispersed through adult tissue, difficult to access in large numbers and unlikely to be totipotent.

Question 6.6

The advantage of modifying genetic make-up during the earliest stages of development is that all the cells that are produced as the embryo, and subsequently the fetus, develops will contain the introduced gene. Furthermore, if the gene becomes stably integrated into the genome of the reproductive cells, then that individual's offspring will also contain that gene.

Question 6.7

These effects illustrate just how problematic it is to apply such techniques to the manipulation of genes in humans. Stable incorporation seems to be achieved by these techniques, but the degree of disruption would raise concerns over safety and reliability. Even though a large proportion of the human genome could be altered without any obvious effect (i.e. within repetitive, non-coding regions), the fact that insertion is random means that the degree of uncertainty is unacceptably high.

Question 6.8

(a) There are many techniques described in the text, implying that mice (especially) are very amenable to genetic manipulation. The production of chimeric mice is just one, in which the genetically engineered stem cells are introduced into a blastocyst. Figure 6.4 shows a variety of other techniques, including use of retroviruses.

(b) With sheep, the comparable technique is somatic cell nuclear transfer, or SCNT, where a modified nucleus is introduced into an enucleated egg, which is then introduced into a surrogate mother. (The reason why ES cells are not used in sheep is that the technique, so appropriate for mice, for some reason does not work with other species. So far, ES cells line have been extracted from mice, and there has been limited success with attempts to produce chicken ES cell lines.)

Question 6.9

First, are such hopes realistic? There must surely be doubt about the biological feasibility of such procedures – you'll recall that the success rate following nuclear transfer is very low – and the integrity of long-preserved DNA is by no means assured. There are ethical concerns about modifying animals to 'cope' with these new circumstances. Even if such gene manipulations were feasible (remember the warning in Chapter 2 about genetic determinism) there is surely a worry that such steps would legitimise and perhaps encourage, habitat degradation.

Question 7.1

The *benefit* is that gene therapy offers the prospect of a cure, as opposed to alleviation of the symptoms. The *risks* include that of developing leukaemia, as with two of the trial participants. But the alternative treatment (unmatched bone marrow transplantation) is not without risk either. (The procedure has proved fatal for about one-third of patients.) Also, there is a risk if patients continue with the disease unchecked. It is relevant too that the leukaemia that developed after therapy has proved fully treatable.

Question 7.2

The various types of thalassaemias are complex conditions, where a variety of abnormalities of the α and β globin genes is evident. CF involves a single gene, though a great variety of mutations are evident. (There are additional points to consider such as the ease of access – consider lung tissue v. bone marrow – and knowledge of the biology/genetics of the two conditions, probably greater in the case of CF.)

Question 7.3

(a) Many gene probes rely on exact matching with the gene in question. Given that so many different mutations are apparent (Figure 7.2), only the most common mutations (notably ΔF508-*CFTR*) are likely to be picked up. The accuracy of tests is therefore limited (to about 90%). (b) CF carriers (i.e. heterozygotes) are not affected because, as is generally the case with recessive conditions, the 'healthy' version of the gene (in this case, *CFTR*) presumably produces enough of the fully functional product.

Question 7.4

The protein (CFTR) is membrane-bound. Even if after injection it was to remain viable, it is very unlikely to become integrated within the membrane in a functional state, given that CFTR is normally produced and processed within the appropriate (i.e. epithelial) cells. Remember too that in the unlikely event of the protein working *in situ*, additional injections would be needed to ensure continued functioning.

Question 7.5

This is a problem central to the use of viral vectors; increasing the dose of the virus would increase the likelihood of infection. With adenoviruses in general, an excessive dose is likely to lead to a more marked immune response, with fever and inflammation (see Table 7.1).

Question 7.6

This describes the role of the tumour-suppressor gene, *p53*, which can have the effects of blocking the cell cycle at one of three points. Recall too that the protein product of *p53* can trigger apoptosis, in response to DNA damage.

Question 7.7

Less so. Recall that the 'healthy' version of *p53* is protective against cancer, so a heterozygous individual will produce some (presumably half the normal) tumour-suppressor gene product, whereas those with two copies of the defective gene will not have even this degree of protection. (This is not always the case – sometimes, for reasons that are unclear, loss of one normal allele is sufficient to eliminate all protection.)

Question 7.8

Bcl-2, the effect of which can be blocked by 'antisense' techniques, i.e. adding a single-stranded oligonucleotide sequence that is complementary to *Bcl-2* mRNA. As an oncogene, inhibiting apoptosis, *Bcl-2* would allow cells damaged by cytotoxic drugs to survive; if *Bcl-2* expression is blocked, apoptosis would be triggered.

Question 7.9

(a) True; this is indeed an advantage of germline gene therapy. (A related point is that with somatic cell gene therapy, a range of specific delivery issues would have to be resolved with each disease; with germline therapy, the prospects for a developing a standard approach to a range of diseases are much better.)

(b) True; it is this aspect that makes germline therapy the more tricky procedure – integration is essential if the transgene is to be inherited. Problems of integration of the transgene are evident too in somatic gene cell therapy, as shown by SCID-X1.

(c) Not true; this cannot be claimed at present – certainly the effectiveness and safety of the procedure is unproven. As for 'convenience', germline cell therapy would be a demanding and stressful procedure for the carrier couple, as is pre-implantation diagnosis, but their offspring's descendants would be relieved of such a burden.

Question 7.10

Here, I can offer my own thoughts; yours may well differ.

1 In my view, this is a credible argument. Although not true at present, it points to the long-term prospect for germline gene therapy and I find arguments for preventing disease in this way persuasive.

2 This is not a credible argument. The notion that researchers should have complete freedom, irrespective of societal concerns, is not persuasive.

3 This is a credible argument in opposition to germline cell therapy, though that view does presuppose that changes engineered in this way are irreversible, which some researchers dispute.

4 This is not a credible argument. This is not to deny the possibility of 'slippery slope' arguments, but to my mind they are not of themselves sufficiently strong to prohibit future genuine medical application of germline therapy.

Comments on activities

Activity 2.1

The label 'A gene' in the diagram of the double helix in Figure 2.4 is misleading in that it refers to a length of DNA that is just about 10 nucleotide base pairs long, which corresponds to just one turn of the helix. As Table 2.1 makes clear, human genes are much bigger!

For me, the analogy is a useful one, as it draws attention to the difference between coding and non-coding parts of the gene. In a diagram of this type, using technical terms generally isn't appropriate. It's noticeable that the introns are portrayed as equivalent to the 'silence' between the 'verses' of 'songs', as distinct from the much more substantial 'silences' between 'tracks'. The figure also does well to highlight the importance of control points (= 'dubbing cues'), which as we'll see later are important aspects.

Activity 4.1

(a) Feedback on this part of the activity will be given on the S250 course website.

(b) Seventeen countries grew GM crops, and four types of crops were grown. Were you surprised to learn that in 2004, after nine years of commercial cultivation, there were only four types of GM crop grown globally in significant amounts? These crops were modified to show either herbicide tolerance, insect resistance, or both these traits. (We will examine in Sections 4.2 and 4.3 how the traits are introduced and how they work.)

(i) The top five GM crop-growing countries are, in order, the USA, Argentina, Canada, Brazil and China. It is significant that three of these five are in the developing world. These countries had a total area of 77.9 million hectares of GM crops, forming 96% of the 81.0 million hectares sown globally.

(ii) These 81.0 million hectares used to grow GM crops covered just under 6% of the world's cultivated land. Nevertheless, this is a very large area, over three times the land area of the UK.

(iii) In 2004, 53.4 million hectares in developed countries were used to grow GM crops, compared to 27.6 million hectares in developing countries. Significantly, these represent annual increases of 13% and 35% respectively. It appears that GM crops are being taken up in developing countries far more quickly than in developed ones. (This is explored further in Section 4.3.)

(iv) I would summarise the global position of GM crops in 2004 as follows:

The area of land sown with GM crops has grown extremely quickly in the nine years since they were first grown commercially, in 2004 forming 6% of the global area of cultivated land. However, take-up has been limited to 17 countries, and five of these cultivate over 96% of the area sown. The types of GM crops grown were also limited; in 2004 only four different GM crops were grown, modified to show herbicide tolerance or insect resistance or both traits.

Activity 4.2

I think she is making three key points:

- Previous work on genetic modification has been shaped by the need of Western agrochemical multinationals to make a profit.

- Public and charitable funding means this work may be made freely available to the most needy.
- This breakthrough may help to persuade more people that GM crops are acceptable.

Activity 4.3

(a) Potrykus' goal is 2 μg of provitamin A per gram of rice, which is equivalent to 200 μg per 100 g. Shiva refers to 33.3 μg of vitamin A per 100 g of rice. The *Science* paper refers to provitamin A, whilst Shiva refers to vitamin A itself. Shiva has divided by a factor of 6, in order to take into account the idea of retinol equivalents. Given that Shiva's audience is not a scientific one, you might argue that this is perfectly justified.

(b) I think Shiva's main points might be summarised as:

- She disputes whether the rice can provide enough provitamin A.
- She argues that other dietary sources would provide an adequate supply, if diets could be changed.
- She dismisses it as a technological quick fix, arguing that earlier technological solutions (e.g. the Green Revolution) made matters worse, not better.

Activity 4.4

The Golden Rice case study involved various forms of communication. The scientists published in a prestigious peer-reviewed journal. The story appeared widely in the international media. Biotechnology firms published advertisements and activists used the Internet to make their case. Whilst scientific papers may have appeared neutral, in the other cases, the communication has been quite explicitly part of an ongoing political debate. Both sides of this debate were trying to affect the future prospects of GM crops as a whole. The supporters of GM crops see this case as useful evidence that genetic modification can have humanitarian benefits. The opponents dismiss Golden Rice as a 'Trojan horse', i.e. the introduction of an apparently benign GM product in order to ease the subsequent passage of more profitable crops. In their attempts to prove or disprove the usefulness of the rice, both sides of the debate have introduced quantification, in the form of Retinol Equivalents and Retinol Activity Equivalents, into their communications.

Activity 5.1

These answers were written by one of the authors in early 2006. Your answers may differ from ours, because you may have different values and experiences to ours, or because the global position of GM agriculture may have changed since the time of writing. These are contentious issues, and for many of the points made below, there are valid counter-arguments.

(a) The ethical judgement would be that the benefits should be directed to those for whom the practice will do most good. In reality this has not happened, within either developed or developing countries. The benefits of GM farming have accrued largely to the agrochemical multinationals, large-scale farmers and food producers. Few benefits to consumers have been apparent. From an ethical viewpoint, it is clearly unjust that the commercial development for GM has been largely devoted to the large-scale industrialised agriculture prevalent in developed countries, rather than to the small-scale peasant farmers of the developing world.

(b) Many people take the line that abandoning traditional agricultural practice would be unethical, partly because of the social disruption such a switch would cause. But what if the degree of gain for the producers and consumers in the developing world was significant? Any solution to this ethical dilemma might be influenced by the fact that many traditional farming practices are producing ever-declining yields, with the result that small-scale peasant farming is unsustainable in many parts of the world. Of course, if GM crops were found to be harmful to human health or to the environment in some way, the issue of fairness would be judged differently.

(c) Some people argue that if GM technology were confined to the developed world, agriculture in developing countries would be severely damaged, as their cash crops became uncompetitive. By this measure, encouraging developing countries to develop GM would be a just approach, a judgement influenced by the belief that enhancing traditional methods of farming could not improve quality or productivity sufficiently to render it internationally competitive.

Activity 5.2

Here are my thoughts about the articles; yours may differ in tone, but hopefully you may have picked up some of the errors in the *Guardian* article:

- The *New Scientist* article strikes me as fair, accurate and balanced. Pusztai's experiments are described, initially without adverse comments, together with the controversial circumstances surrounding publication. The *Guardian* article strikes me as less impressive; I find the word 'vindicating' inappropriate, perhaps indicating a bias towards Pusztai. Pusztai has certainly claimed the appearance of his work in *The Lancet* demonstrated his work's validity. But the circumstances of publication, plus the publicly expressed views of the editor, and a minority of the reviewers, incline me to the view that the work is not of the highest standard.
- There are minor errors in the *Guardian* article – it fails to make clear that the paper doesn't refer to 'stunted organ growth' or 'damage to their immune systems' – which were Pusztai's previous unpublished claims – though *New Scientist* does make this point. The *Guardian* article talks of experiments showing 'enlarged stomach linings' in those animals fed GM potatoes; *New Scientist* correctly refers to intestinal crypts.

Activity 5.3

Feedback on this activity is within the main text of the chapter.

Activity 5.4

The notes given here are far more detailed than I would expect you to make, so do not be concerned if you have not written this much. You should be aware that whilst I may differ with the authors over points of detail, I am broadly sympathetic with their arguments. You should keep that in mind when comparing your comments with my own.

1 I agree with the authors that substantial equivalence, as it was initially defined, was a vague concept. It is certainly true that the regulatory scientists did not initially offer precise ways in which equivalence could be measured. Many proponents of GM food, perhaps for good scientific

reasons, believe that GM food is always substantially equivalent to its traditional counterpart. They believe that if the products of the novel genes can themselves be proved to be safe, then the GM product will be safe. This strong belief has meant that in the USA, at least, there appeared to be very little safety testing before the initial GM products were released on to the market, or grown commercially.

2 I think that the authors claim that animal feeding experiments could easily be used to generate ADIs is problematic. As we have already discussed, in order to generate data equivalent to those generated in pharmaceutical or related tests, one would have to feed unnaturally large amounts of the product to laboratory animals. Given that many GM crops are staples, animals would also have to be fed supplementary foodstuffs in order to maintain a balanced diet. I think it unlikely that such a procedure could produce reliable results. That is not to say that the most obvious alternative, of feeding animals a normal diet but with elevated levels of the relevant proteins, DNA or other compounds characteristic of the GM material, would be without problems. The difficulty in designing and interpreting such tests should be apparent from our discussion of the Pusztai case (Section 5.2).

3 I think the authors have hit on a fair point here. There is a contradiction at the heart of the drive to commercialise GM products. They must be novel enough that they can be patentable, but not so novel that they can be seen to be in any way substantially different from their conventional counterparts.

4 Given the complexity of composition of any plant, a simple description of the components present in a plant is unlikely to give a clear indication of anything other than the presence of obviously high levels of toxins. I think the authors are right to point out this difficulty (but see the response quoted later in Section 5.3).

5 I think that in many respects the authors are right to identify the principle as a barrier to further research, certainly as it had been interpreted up to that time. I believe that there was a tendency to assume substantial equivalence without the necessary scientific experiments to support the assumption. However, in the broadest sense, I think that substantial equivalence is a reasonable starting point in a scientific risk assessment. Given that GM products are being developed, it is difficult to see how one could assess their safety without some sort of comparison with traditional products. Even if the term 'substantial equivalence' was abandoned, an experimental safety testing procedure would have to include some sort of control, which I would tend to assume would be the traditional product.

Activity 5.5

Comments on this activity are found on the S250 course website.

Activity 6.1 (Part 1)

What follows are, of course, my own views:

I support the use of embryos up to 14 days, on the grounds that prohibiting such research would more than likely slow down important medical advances. The types of medical conditions for which cures are being sought account for so much suffering that all reasonable avenues for research have to be kept open. I do not see the case for assuming that an embryo at this stage has an intrinsic right to life – any more than do the high proportion of embryos of this age that naturally fail to implant. Egg donation should be allowed, but because the commercialisation of the practice may well lead to abuse, donation should not involve financial reward.

Activity 6.1 (Part 2)

My own position on ES cell use has not changed in view of the appeal of adult stem cells. In many respects, adult stem cells offer less promising experimental material, which suggests that research progress would be slower if they were to be used exclusively. There is most to be gained from using both approaches, increasing the likelihood of soon discovering ways in which fully totipotent stem cells can be conveniently obtained from sources other than early embryos.

Activity 6.2

Each of these provides me with food for thought, but does not prompt a fundamental shift in my position. Some of the arguments appear directed towards animal use in more general terms. The more sharply defined question is whether, for example, using GM technology to bring about an animal cancer is less acceptable than other methods that are available to induce cancer. In relation to (1) and (2), I would not try to deny instances of animal suffering. Rather, I would be concerned with more carefully scrutiny of intended human benefit. With (3), imperfect though animal models may be for testing, denying researchers the opportunity to use such approaches may well prove detrimental to the safety and efficacy of pharmaceuticals for human use. The reasons why drugs tested on animals can kill humans is more complex that (3) implies.

Activity 7.1

In favour, I would argue that:

- It may prove the only effective treatment in some cases (recall the example of retinoblastoma).
- By some measures, it is more efficient (and perhaps cost-effective) than more conventional methods.
- It avoids putting future generations through time-consuming and taxing situations (e.g. those involving embryos screening) – remember the CF example.

A fourth argument that others have proposed is that medical researchers ought to be allowed the freedom to develop new modes of treating human disease.

The arguments against relate to the following:

- Concerns about safety and the possibility of unforeseen effects.
- Other methods are available to achieve the same ends.
- The genetic techniques that are used for medical treatment can be applied to other forms of genetic enhancement that may be of questionable benefit, i.e. the technique could be abused by the powerful and also increase the likelihood of designer babies.

References and further reading

Bauer, M. W. and Gaskell, G. (2002) *Biotechnology: The Making of a Global Controversy*, Cambridge University Press.

Bourgaize, D. J., Thomas, R. and Buiser, R. (2000) *Biotechnology: Demystifying the Concepts*, Addision/Wesley/Longman, San Francisco.

Bowring, F. (2003) *Science, Seeds and Cyborgs,* Verso, London.

British Medical Association (1992) *Our Genetic Future: The Science and Ethics of Genetic Technology*, Oxford University Press.

Campbell, S. (2004) A genetically modified survey, www.spiked-online.com/articles/0000000CA661.htm (accessed September 2005).

Clark, J. and Whitelaw, B. (2003) A future for transgenic livestock, *Nature Reviews Genetics*, **4**, pp. 825–833.

Clothier Committee (1992) *Report of the Committee on the Ethics of Gene Therapy*, London HMSO.

Economic and Social Research Council (1999) *The Politics of GM food: Risk, Science and Public Trust*, ESRC.

Glick, B. R. and Pasternak, J. (1998) *Molecular Biotechnology: Principles and Applications of Recombinant DNA,* American Society for Microbiology, Washington.

Harris, J. (1992) *Wonderwoman and Superman: The Ethics of Human Biotechnology*, Oxford University Press.

Harris, J. (1998) *Clones, Genes and Immortality*, Oxford University Press.

Irwin, A. (2004) Are we too risk averse? – no, *Risk and Biomedicine Debate: Fearing the Unknown*, sponsored by The Wellcome Trust, www.spiked-online.com/articles/0000000CA375.htm (accessed September 2005).

Jasonoff, S. (2005) *Designs on Nature: Science and Democracy in Europe and the United States*, Princeton University Press.

Klotzko, A. J. (2001) *The Cloning Sourcebook*, Oxford University Press.

Levinson, R. and Reiss, M. (eds) (2003) *Key Issues in Bioethics: A Guide for Teachers*, RoutledgeFalmer, London.

Levidow, L., Murphy, J. and Carr, S. (forthcoming 2006/7) *Recasting 'Substantial Equivalence': Transatlantic Governance of GM Food*, Science, Technology and Human Values.

Lewin, B. (2004) *Genes VIII*, Pearson Education International.

McHughen, A. (2000) *A Consumer's Guide to GM Food*, Oxford University Press, Oxford.

Millstone, E., Brunner, E. and Mayer, S. (1999) Beyond substantial equivalence, *Nature*, **401**, pp. 525–526.

Nicholl, D. S. T. (2002) *An Introduction to Genetic Engineering,* 2nd edn, Cambridge University Press.

NHS/Department of Health (2003) *Our Inheritance, Our Future: Realising the Potential of Genetics in the NHS,* Genetics White Paper, 24 June 2003, Available at: http://www.dh.gov.uk/PolicyAndGuidance/HealthAndSocialCareTopics/Genetics/fs/en/ (accessed December 2005).

Nuffield Council on Bioethics (1999) *Genetically Modified Crops: The Ethical and Social Issues*, Nuffield Council on Bioethics, London.

Pierce, Benjamin (2005) *Genetics: A Conceptual Approach*, W. H. Freeman and Company, New York.

Primrose, S. B., Twyman, R. M. and Old, R. W (2001) *Principles of Gene Manipulation,* 6th edn, Blackwell Science, Oxford.

Pringle, P. (2003) *Food Inc: Mendel to Monsanto – The Promises and Perils of the Biotech Harvest*, Simon and Schuster, New York.

Rollin, B. E. (1995) *The Frankenstein Syndrome*, Cambridge University Press.

Potrykus, I. (2000) *The Golden Rice Tale*, from: http://www.agbioworld.org/ at http://www.agbioworld.org/biotech-info/topics/goldenrice/tale.html (accessed September 2005).

Reiss, M. and Straughton, R. (2001) *Improving Nature: The Science and Ethics of Genetic Engineering,* Canto (digital) edition, Cambridge University Press.

Royal Society (2001) *The Use of Genetically Modified Animals*, The Royal Society, London.

Rowell, A. (2003) *Don't Worry (It's Safe to Eat): The True Story of GM Food, BSE, and Foot and Mouth*, Earthscan, London.

Reece, R. J. (2004) *Analysis of Genes and Genomes,* John Wiley and Sons.

Sherlock, R. and Morrey, J. D. (eds) (2004) *Ethical Issues in Biotechnology*, Rowman and Littlefield Publishers Inc., Oxford

Shiva, V. (2000) *The 'Golden Rice' Hoax – When Public Relations Replace Science*, Research Foundation for Science, Technology and Ecology, India.

Sudbery, P. (2002) *Human Molecular Genetics,* Pearson Prentice Hall, Essex.

Torr, J. D. (2001) *Genetic Engineering: Opposing Viewpoints*, Greenhaven Press, San Diego.

Tudge, C. (2000) *In Mendel's Footnotes*, Jonathan Cape, London.

Walters, L. and Palmer, J. G. (1997) *The Ethics of Human Gene Therapy*, Oxford University Press, Oxford.

Woolfson, A. (2004) *An Intelligent Person's Guide to Genetics*, Duckworth Overlook, London.

Ye, X., Al-Babili, S., Klöti, A. *et al.* (2000) Engineering the provitamin A (β-carotene) biosynthetic pathway into (carotenoid-free) rice endosperm, *Science*, **287**, pp. 303–305.

Acknowledgements

We are grateful to Mark Hirst for his helpful comments during the preparation of this topic. Grateful acknowledgement is made to the following sources for permission to reproduce material within this book:

Text

Extract 4.1: Shiva, V. (2000) 'The Golden Rice hoax: When public relations replaces science', Research Foundation for Science, Technology and Ecology, India; *Figure 5.2*: Sample, I., (2004) 'Medical crops coming soon, *The Guardian*, 13 July 2004, copyright © 2004, Guardian Newspapers Limited 1999. Reproduced by permission; *Figure 5.3*: Coghlan, A., MacKenzie, D. and Concar, D. (1999) 'It's that man again', *New Scientist*, 16 October, 1999, copyright © The New Scientist; *Figure 5.4*: Meikle, J. (1999) 'Journal to publish GM food hazards research', *The Guardian*, 5 October 1999, copyright © 1999, Guardian Newspapers Limited 1999. Reproduced by permission.

Figures

Figure 2.4: *Our Inheritance Our Future* (2003) Department of Health. Crown copyright material is reproduced under Class Licence Number C01W0000065 with the permission of the Controller of HMSO and the Queen's Printer for Scotland; *Figures 2.5, 3.8*: Pierce, B. A. (2005) *Genetics: A Conceptual Approach*, W. H. Freeman and Company, New York; *Figure 2.7*: Lewin, B. (2004) *Genes VIII*, Pearson Prentice Hall; *Figure 2.10*: Nicholl, D. S. T. (2002) *An Introduction to Genetic Engineering*, Cambridge University Press; *Figures 3.2, 3.3, 3.4*: Bourgaize, D., Jewell, T. and Buiser, R. (2000) *Biotechnology*, Addison–Wesley–Longman, Inc.; *Figure 4.1*: James, C. (2004) *Global Status of Commercialized Biotech/GM Crops*, International Service for the Acquisition of Agri-biotech Applications (ISAAA); *Figure 4.2*: Edward L. Barnard, Florida Department of Agriculture and Consumer Services, Forestry Images; *Figure 4.4*: Glick, B. R. (1998) *Molecular Biotechnology*, American Society for Microbiology; *Figure 4.7*: Photos used with permission of P. W. Simon, USDA, ARS; *Figure 4.8*: Time Life Pictures/Getty Images; *Figure 4.11*: Ye, X. *et al*. (2000) 'Engineering the provitamin A (β-carotene) biosynthetic pathway into (carotenoid-free) rice endosperm', *Science*, **287**, 14 January 2000, copyright © 2000 by the American Association for the Advancement of Science; *Figure 5.1a*: Copyright © Blackthorn Arable Ltd; *Figure 5.1b*: Courtesy of Nickerson UK Limited; *Figure 5.5*: Konig *et al*. (2004) 'Assessment of the safety of foods derived from genetically modified (GM) crops', *Food and Chemical Toxicology*, **42**, 2004, Pergamon; *Figure 5.6*: Greenpeace/Arbib; *Figure 6.2*: Courtesy of Professor P. R. Braude; *Figure 6.3*: Sample, I. (2004) 'Cloning debate: Human embryo research plan is first of its kind', *The Guardian*, 17 June, 2004, p. 4, copyright © Guardian Newspapers Limited 2004; *Figure 6.4*: Primrose, S., Twyman, R., and Old, B. (2001), *Principles of Gene Manipulation*, Blackwell Science Ltd; *Figure 6.5*: Nicholl, D. S. T. (2002) *An Introduction to Genetic Engineering*, Cambridge University Press; *Figure 7.1*: Adapted from Nicholl, D. S. T. (2002) *An Introduction to Genetic Engineering*, Cambridge University Press and Sudbury, P. (2002) *Human Molecular Genetics*, Pearson Education Limited; *Figure 7.2*: Sudbury, P. (2002) *Human Molecular Genetics*, copyright © Pearson Education Limited 1998, 2002; *Figure 7.3*: Pierce, B. A. (2005) *Genetics: A Conceptual Approach*, W. H. Freeman and Company.

Every effort has been made to contact copyright holders. If any have been inadvertently overlooked, the publishers will be pleased to make the necessary arrangements at the first opportunity.

Abbreviations

ADI	Acceptable Daily Intakes
ATP	adenosine triphosphate
AEBC	Agricultural and Environment Biotechnology Commission
cDNA	complementary deoxyribonucleic acid
CF	cystic fibrosis
CFTR	cystic fibrosis transmembrane conductance regulator
tRNA	transfer ribonucleic acid
ENTRANSFOOD	European network on safety assessment of genetically modified food crops
ESCs	embryonic stem cells
ETRs	expanding trinucleotide repeats
FAO	Food and Agriculture Organisation
FIX	human coagulation factor IX
FSE	Farm-Scale Evaluations
GMOs	genetically modified organisms
GNA	*Galanthus nivalis* agglutinin
GURT	genetic use restriction technology
HSCs	haemopoietic stem cells
IVF	*in vitro* fertilisation
mRNA	messenger ribonucleic acid
NGO	non-Governmental organisation
NOAEL	No Observable Adverse Effect Level
OECD	Organisation for Economic Cooperation and Development
ORI	origin of replication
OTC	ornithine transcarbamylase
RAE	Retinol Activity Equivalent
RE	Retinol Equivalent
SCID-X1	severe combined immunodeficiency-X1
SCNT	somatic cell nuclear transfer
siRNAs	short interfering RNAs
T-DNA	transfer DNA
UN	United Nations
VAD	vitamin A deficiency
WHO	World Health Organisation
WTO	World Trade Organisation

INDEX

Entries and page numbers in **bold** refer to glossary terms. Page numbers in *italics* refer to entries appearing mainly in tables or figures.

N

O

P